Speech Correction

in the Schools

Speech

Correction

in the

Schools

SECOND EDITION

JON EISENSON

Stanford University

MARDEL OGILVIE

Queens College

The Macmillan Company, New York
Collier-Macmillan Ltd., London

Fourth Printing 1965

Library of Congress catalog card number: 63-7215

The Macmillan Company, New York
Collier-Macmillan Canada Ltd., Toronto, Ontario

Printed in the United States of America

Introduction

SPEECH CORRECTION IN THE SCHOOLS is intended to introduce the readers to the problems and therapeutic needs of school age children whose speech requires remedial attention by persons professionally trained for this purpose. In the organization of the second edition of the book we have taken cognizance of the growth of speech correction as a professional field and of the increased influence of speech correctionists in school programs.

The classroom teacher is no longer likely to be called upon to do remedial speech work with children, but the ultimate goals and objectives for the child who is receiving remedial help have not changed. In an important sense, the teacher as well as the child is receiving professional help in the attainment of at least one of the goals—the improvement of the child's communicative ability.

Thus, the classroom teacher must have an understanding of the functions of the speech correctionists who are employed in our schools. It follows of course that the speech correctionist must also know and appreciate the function and role of the teacher in general and his more specific role as an inevitable adjunct member of the therapeutic team.

Speech correctionists may have one of several titles in our schools. The titles *speech correctionist* and *speech therapist* are the most frequent. Some are known as *speech clinicians;* a few have the designation of *speech consultants*. At least one large school system maintains the professional designation *teacher of speech improvement*. Whatever the title, the individuals we are talking about are professionally educated and trained in the diagnosis and treatment of persons with communicative impairments.

Some school systems employ professional personnel who are specialists in the assessment and speech training of children with hearing impairments. These professional workers are known as *audiologists*. Speech correctionists and audiologists are workers in related professions. Their educational backgrounds overlap to a considerable extent. Both the speech correctionist and the audiologist are likely to have had formal course work in psychology, particularly in the psychology of speech and problems of social adjustment; they are likely to share a common background in their course work in physiology, speech science, phonetics and general courses in speech correction and hearing impairments. Beyond this, the speech correctionist is likely to have additional specialized and advanced courses in areas such as stuttering, voice disorders, language disorders, or articulatory defects. The audiologist is likely to have specialized and advanced training in the measurement of hearing, in the physics and physiology of hearing, and in techniques for the education and habilitation of children with hearing impairments. The speech correctionist and the audiologist who work in school situations should be expected to know how the children whom they will be treating are educated. Both must necessarily understand the professional obligations and the multiple aspects of the classroom teacher.

The chapters in the first part of the book present the general considerations and the background of knowledge that are basic for the necessary common insights of the classroom teacher and the school speech correctionist relative to the child with defective speech. So, we begin with a chapter of the classification and incidence of speech defects and follow immediately with a chapter on speech correction services. The content and sequence of the chapters that immediately follow are based on the assumption that fundamentals of information about normal speech should precede discussion of defective speech. So, we included discussions of speech standards, the mechanism for speech, the productions of speech sounds, and the development of language in children.

Some of the problems involved in the stimulation of children to communicate appropriately are common to the classroom teacher and the speech correctionist. The specific techniques for stimulating speech may not be the same, but the objective of the improvement of the child's speech is shared. Often the task of the speech correctionist is to help the child overcome an initial impairment or defect. Unless this is accomplished, the child's effort at communicating may result in frustration and sometimes in a rejection of further effort at speaking in all but completely secure situations. For some children, the larger task and scope of the classroom teacher to help the child express himself orally through the language arts must be built on the remedial efforts of the speech correctionist.

To make the achievement of common objectives possible, the speech correctionist must have an appreciation of the language arts program in our schools. He must have an awareness of how his specialized educational and therapeutic efforts takes place in the classroom. On the other hand, the teacher must have an appreciation of the nature of speech therapy and the work of the speech clinician. The teacher should understand what is taking place in the speech correctionist's room. He must know what is happening to the child who leaves his classroom to correct his "cleft palate speech," or to overcome his stuttering, or to learn to produce a proficient *l* or *r*. In brief, mutual appreciation of the professional functions of the classroom teacher and the speech correctionist are in the best interests of the child.

The second part of the book deals with the specific speech problems that are found in five per cent or more of our school children. We have tried to present the problems as they affect the child in his over-all functioning. In each instance we have explained the nature and cause of the speech disturbance, its implications for therapy, and the therapeutic approaches and procedures of the speech correctionist. We have also indicated the role of the classroom teacher in regard to the speech problems of the child and the therapeutic efforts of the speech correctionist.

In this edition of SPEECH CORRECTION IN THE SCHOOLS we have endeavored to revise our materials in keeping with the comments and suggestions of some of our readers who were willing to act as constructive critics. We again called upon our colleagues for their evaluations based upon their experiences with the book as a required class text. We are grateful for the positive help we were able to get from these evaluations.

Contents

Speech Correction

in the Schools

1

Classification

and Incidence

of Speech Defects

[handwritten: Most Important]

SINCE every classroom teacher is teaching speech in the language arts program, he makes judgments about the adequacy of the speech of his students. A few of them are articulate boys and girls who speak clearly, fluently, and unusually effectively. These are the students whom their classmates are likely to choose to lead an important discussion or to play a leading role in an assembly program. A second group is made up of students who read and speak fairly acceptably and who, on the whole, communicate adequately although some aspects of their speech may be substandard. The students who make up both of these groups are normal speakers without speech defects.[1] At the other end of the

---

[1] Throughout this book we will use the terms "speech defect" and "speech difficulty" synonymously. These terms refer to the less serious speech problems. We will call the more serious problems, "speech disorders." They refer to those problems with a serious involvement, either psychological or organic. The more serious problems require the help of a specialist. Even though the classroom teacher has had some special training, he may not have the particular background or time to handle these problems.

continuum, however, is a small group of students who cannot communicate adequately; they are either unduly apprehensive about their speaking or their speech draws unfavorable attention to itself.

About these students, teachers and speech correctionists[2] often make identical judgments. For example, the teacher and speech correctionist agree that the five-year-old who still does not talk at all, the ten-year-old who says *wiwy* for *lily,* and the eight-year-old who starts, stops, repeats words, and whose classmates say, "Jackie can't get his words out," have speech defects. When Helen in kindergarten says *thay* for *say* and *thoap* for *soap,* no one notices, for the children are interested in what she has to say about her new truck. But when Nancy in eighth grade used the same substitution *th* for *s,* one of her classmates said of her, "She's cute. I love listening to her words with *s.* I wait for them." Since Nancy's lisp gets in the way of her communication, she has a speech defect. It draws attention to how she talks rather than to what she is saying.

Such difficulties as a lisp or stutter are barriers to successful communication. A child with a lisp does not communicate his ideas when his environment is favorable and he is feeling comfortable. His listeners are attracted to how he is talking rather than to what he is saying. Because of the child's failure to communicate successfully, a speech defect prevents the child from taking part effectively in his environment at home, in the playground, and at school.

Another aspect of a speech defect, a subjective one, may exist. When a speech difficulty, even though it is a small deviation and does not attract unfavorable attention, looms so large in the child's mind that he is unduly self-conscious or apprehensive, it is serious and needs attention. It is then a factor that will prevent his taking part easily in his environment at home, in the playground, and at school.

Less important barriers to completely successful communication are sometimes confused with speech defects. These barriers include: (1) substandard pronunciation and use of language; (2)

---

[2] The terms "correctionist," "speech correctionist," "speech specialist," "speech clinician," and "speech therapist" will be used synonymously.

poor oral reading; (3) a type of speech prevalent in a different section of the country; (4) incorrect articulation due to immaturity; and (5) a psychological disturbance which shows itself in speech. These barriers to completely successful communication are not speech defects that require the help of the correctionist. Rather they are difficulties that the classroom teacher will take care of through his speech improvement program or that other specialists will handle often cooperatively with the speech correctionist.

A ten-year-old child who says, "I din't reconize dat book," is not in need of help from a speech correctionist unless he is unable to produce the *th* sound in the word *that.* Half of his classmates may say *dat* rather than *that.* His parents probably use the same kind of speech. His classroom teacher, however, plans a program that will improve his level of speech and the level of all his pupils. Undoubtedly this child communicates effectively at home and with most of his classmates. But time and occasion may arrive when his substandard speech will call attention to itself. We have discussed acceptable levels and standards of speech in Chapter 3.

A child may have come from a section of the country where its inhabitants speak differently from where he is now living. The child's teacher and his classmates may be very conscious of the differences in his speech. In fact, at times they may be unable to understand what he is saying. As he lives in his new community, however, the differences will be ironed out because usually he will acquire the speech patterns of his playmates. The teacher can help his adjustment by accepting his speech and by explaining his differences to the members of his class. We have discussed regional differences in speech in Chapter 3.

Oral reading is difficult for some children because they have difficulty in understanding the meaning of the printed page. As a result, their oral reading is uncommunicative; it is hesitant, badly phrased, and hard to understand. The conversation of the same children, however, may be quite adequate. Their main problem in communication is one of oral reading although, as mentioned in the chapter on articulatory defects, reading and speech problems are often related. It has been our experience that as children improve in one ability, they frequently improve in another.

Kindergarten teachers often find that over half of their children do not articulate accurately. Physical maturity and environmental stimulation will take care of many of these articulatory difficulties, for the children's inaccurate speech often indicates a level in their development rather than a speech difficulty. The speech specialist can prognosticate with some success which children will need help. The development of this area of research will bring more accurate prognosis for these children. The chapter on language development includes norms for the development of sounds and the acquisition of speech.

In some instances, the major problem is not one of speech but of social adjustment. The child whose voice is consistently thin and weak and who speaks with little or no inflection surely exhibits a problem of voice. This problem, however, may be closely related to the child's concept of herself—she feels she cannot do anything very well. She says, "I feel like a big stupid lug most of the time." Her stooped posture, her halting walk, her untidy dress, her sloppy compositions, her lack of enthusiasm, and her dull, thin expressionless voice are all part of a syndrome. In such an instance, the voice is merely the symptom of a personality difficulty. The correctionist can help only in cooperation with other members of the school personnel.

Types of Speech Defects

Speech defects include: (1) articulatory defects; (2) stuttering; (3) voice defects; (4) cleft palate speech; (5) cerebral palsy speech; (6) retarded speech development; (7) language impairment, associated with brain damage; and (8) speech defects due to impaired hearing.

Articulatory Defects

Among articulatory defects are: (1) the omission of sounds. The nine-year-old boy who says *pay* for *play* and *banket* for *blanket* exemplifies omission of sounds. (2) The substitution of one sound for another. The ten-year-old who says *wabbit* for *rabbit* and *wun* for *run* illustrates the substituting of one sound for another. (3) The distortion of sounds. An example of a distortion of a sound is the twelve-year-old whose *s* has some of the characteristics of *sh*. A child with an articulatory defect may make any or all of these three errors. When the consonants which occur frequently, such as *s,* are involved and when some sounds are missing entirely, the child's speech may be unintelligible. The child may on occasion either include a sound he usually omits or make the sound acceptably. Frequently he makes a sound accurately in its initial position but makes the same sound inaccurately in its final position or in a blend with another sound such as *bl*. He may substitute an *f* for *th* but at the same time substitute a *p* for *f*. In other words, he is seemingly inconsistent in his articulatory errors. Ordinarily, however, a pattern exists even though the same individual uses several different substitutions or distortions for one sound. The substitution or distortion depends on the position of the sound in the word and its proximity to other sounds. A careful analysis of the child's articulatory errors will often point to a particular pattern for them.

Articulatory defects present one of the most important problems of the speech correction program, for most speech defects are of the articulatory type. About three-fourths of the speech defects in a school population are articulatory defects. Of this group, one-half have difficulty with *s*. But many parents do not feel that articulatory defects are serious, for they have become so accustomed to their children's articulatory errors that they do not even hear them. Other parents feel that their children will outgrow their articulatory difficulties. To the older child particularly, however, the difficulty often causes concern. His classmates think that he sounds like a baby and at times may treat him as one.

This category includes many terms. Perhaps the one parents use most frequently is "baby talk." Where the child omits, substitutes, or distorts his speech sounds like that of a younger child, this term is applicable. In fact, some writers now include articulatory defects under the term "delayed speech" or "retarded speech development."

They indicate that the child reaches a certain level of development but does not progress beyond that point.

Other terms commonly included in this category are lisping and lalling. Lisping refers to any defect of any or all of the four sibilant sounds: *s, sh, z,* and *zh.* For example, the *s* may be whistled, sound somewhat like an *l,* or have a *th* quality about it. Lalling means a person has difficulties with the *l* and *r* sounds. The child may substitute a *w* for the sounds or he may make them in such a weak manner that they are not readily distinguishable. We have suggested tests for the discovery of articulatory difficulties in Chapter 10.

Stuttering

The stutterer's speech interferes with the reception of his ideas by his listeners. No stutterer's speech is exactly like another's although a disturbance of rhythm is obvious in each case. Symptoms frequently include blocking on sounds, repetition or prolongation of sounds, repetition of syllables or words, and spasms of the speaking mechanism. One stutterer may speak abnormally slowly, another too quickly. The severity of stuttering varies for the individual stutterer. Almost always some situations exist where stutterers speak with comparative or complete fluency. Moments may exist, however, when the fluency is so badly interrupted that both the speaker and the listener are unduly aware of the interruptions.

Although many parents remain quite unconcerned about articulatory difficulties, most parents are too much aware of dysfluencies. Some parents diagnose the very young child's normal dysfluent speech as stuttering long before the child is aware of any difficulty. In the chapter on the development of language, we call attention to the number of times dysfluencies occur in the young child's speech. Adults' concern and anxiety about dysfluencies may be communicated to children who in turn may become concerned and anxious. All of us should think long and carefully before diagnosing dysfluent speech as stuttering. This idea will be discussed at greater length in the chapter on stuttering.

A type of rhythmic disorder sometimes confused with stuttering is cluttering. The child who clutters speaks at such a rapid rate that he omits and slurs syllables and pauses in the wrong places. He always sounds as if he is in a hurry.

Stuttering is not always easily discernible, since it is intermittent. If the children in the class are asked to read aloud, a stutterer may read aloud well. Furthermore, he may be able to speak easily to strangers but not to friends. The teacher who knows the child well frequently is the person who first notices a child's stuttering.

Vocal Defects

Vocal defects have to do with faults of pitch, quality, or intensity. A sixteen-year-old boy speaks at a pitch so inappropriate to his age and sex that it draws attention to itself. A sixteen-year-old girl speaks in a pitch so low that when she answers the telephone she is mistaken for her older brother. Both sixteen-year-olds have defects of pitch. A junior high school girl speaks through her nose and with a strident quality. Her voice quality needs improvement. A fourteen-year-old girl speaks so softly that she is almost inaudible to her listeners. She needs to be helped so that she will have enough intensity of voice to make herself heard. Sometimes rate of speaking is also included in this category. In this instance, children speak so quickly or slowly that they are difficult to understand.

These terms are not quite as completely whole in themselves as they may seem. For example, Mary pitches her voice too high, but the attribute of her voice that calls attention to itself is not so much the high pitch as the very light, thin quality of the voice. On the other hand, Joan pitches her voice too low, but the huskiness of her voice is what attracts attention. In both instances, the cause of the unpleasant quality is the wrong use of pitch. This wrong use, however, may not be too obvious to the listeners, since the pitches that the girls are using are similar to what most girls of their age use.

The pitch and quality of a voice are frequently related. In a later chapter on voice we shall discuss pitch of voice in more detail. Too high or too low pitches are evident through voices that are thin, strained, or hoarse.

Defects of intensity are easily recognizable, for voices are so light that they do not carry or so loud that they irritate the listeners. Here again, however, the lack of intensity may be connected with the wrong use of pitch. The girl or boy who speaks at a pitch higher than is natural often has trouble making himself heard.

Terms describing quality of voice tend to be more nebulous. Some persons will call a particular voice husky; others will call it hoarse; others will call it guttural; still others may call the voice a pleasant one though a bit throaty. But some of the adjectives describing vocal qualities are quite clear and well defined. Laymen may say that a person with a nasal voice talks through his nose. This term indicates excessive nasal resonance. Laymen portray a person with a denasal voice as always sounding as if he had a cold because his *m, n,* and *ng* lack sufficient nasal resonance. Some, however, label this an articulatory defect since it involves consonantal sounds. Furthermore, all of us recognize the breathy voice, the strident voice, and the falsetto voice.

Cleft Palate Speech

In cleft palate speech, the cleft, slight or extensive, may go through the teeth ridge, hard, and soft palates. It may go through any one of these or through the teeth ridge and hard palate or through both palates. Consequently, the air passes freely between the mouth and the nose. Thus, the speech has a very nasal quality and many of the consonant sounds are distorted. The child with the cleft palate often has difficulty with the plosive sounds *p, b, t, d, k,* and *g,* for the child cannot build up enough air to explode these sounds. In addition, the fricative sounds *f, v, s, z, th, th, sh,* and *zh* are often defective. The child may use a glottal stop or a nasal snort as substitutions. In severe cases the speech is unintelligible.

The combination of physical defect and the symptoms of speech make cleft-palate speech quite obvious.

Cerebral Palsy Speech

Cerebral palsy is a disturbance of the motor function resulting from damage to the brain before, during, or shortly after the birth of the child. The speech of the cerebral-palsied child may be normal when the muscles of the articulatory and respiratory organs are not affected. But, in about 75 percent of the cases, the speech is slow, jerky, and labored, and the rhythm is faulty with unnatural breaks. The consonants, particularly those which require precise articulation, are apt to be inaccurate. Language development may be retarded.

Delayed Speech

Delayed speech means a marked retardation in the child's use of language. He substitutes one sound for another and omits sounds. He uses decidedly shorter and simpler sentences than his contemporaries, many less sounds than friends his age, and few phrases and prepositions. His vocabulary is limited. His speech is like that of a youngster several years his junior.

Language Impairment

Language impairment associated with brain damage falls into two large categories. The first category includes the developmental failures and the unevenness of development in the child's ability to understand speech, to speak, and later to learn to read and write, etc. The second category includes the involvements in oral and written functions resulting from brain damage incurred after the individual had learned to use language. These are generally referred to as aphasic language disorders. Some persons would include the first of our categories under *delayed speech*. The second category is primarily a problem for those beyond school age. We will, therefore, not consider this category in our text.

Speech Defect Due to Impaired Hearing

A speech defect as a result of impaired hearing shows itself largely in articulatory errors and in voice aberrations. The child cannot pattern his own speech on others because he cannot hear well enough. Consequently, his sounds are not articulated accurately, and his voice reflects his lack of hearing by being too loud, too soft, or devoid of inflection. How his hearing is impaired influences his articulation and his voice. This is discussed in Chapter 14.

To help the classroom teacher decide whether his students have speech difficulties we have prepared the following questionnaire. When a preponderance of yes answers appear, the teacher should consult a speech correctionist.

ANALYSIS OF SPEECH DEFECTS

Articulatory Defects

Does the child substitute one sound for another?

Does he omit sounds?

Does he distort sounds?

Is he very hard to understand?

Stuttering

Is the child disturbed by his dysfluency?

Does he repeat sounds or syllables or words more than his classmates?

Is his speech decidedly arhythmical?

Does he block frequently?

Does he have difficulty in getting his words out?

Vocal Difficulties

Is the child's voice noticeably unpleasant in quality?

Is his pitch higher or lower than most of his classmates?

Is his voice monotonous?

Is his voice light and thin?

Is his voice husky?

Is his voice too loud?

Is his voice too weak?

Is his voice difficult to hear in class?

Cleft Palate Speech

Is there an obvious cleft of the teeth ridge or palate?

Is his voice excessively nasal?

Are his *p, b, t, d, k,* and *g* inaccurate?

Are some of his other consonants distorted?

Cerebral Palsy Speech

Does the child have obvious tremors of the musculature phonation and breathing?

Is his speech slow, jerky, and labored?

Is his rhythm of speech abnormal?

Delayed Speech

Is his speech markedly retarded in relation to his classmates?

Does he omit and substitute sounds substantially more than his classmates?

Does he use shorter and simpler sentences than his classmates?

Does he use fewer phrases and prepositions than his classmates?

Language Impairment

Is the child's comprehension of language markedly retarded?

Does he seem to be inconsistent in his ability to understand as well as to use language?

Is there a marked disparity between his ability to understand and his ability to use language?

Is the profile of his linguistic abilities uneven? (For example, can he read much better than he can spell? Is he surprisingly good in arithmetic and yet quite poor in either reading or writing?)

Speech Defect Due to Impaired Hearing

Does the child have frequent earaches and colds?

Does he have running ears?

Does he omit sounds or substitute one sound for another?

Does he distort sounds?

Does he speak too loudly?

Does he speak too softly?

Does he frequently ask you to repeat what you have said?

Does he turn his head to one side as you speak?

Does he watch you closely as you speak?

Does he make unusual mistakes in the spelling words you dictate?

Does he misinterpret your questions or instructions frequently?

Does he do better when given written instructions than when given oral instructions?

Does he seem more intelligent than his work indicates?

Incidence and Types of Speech Defects in A School in One Town

Teachers frequently find in their classrooms children with speech defects belonging to one of the categories mentioned above. To illustrate this point, we will describe briefly the number and type of speech defects found in the members of grades one through six in an elementary school in a rather average, typical town.

X is a rather typical town of 3,800 located in upper New York State. The parents of the children are shopkeepers, doctors, lawyers, carpenters, masons, laborers, bankers, and a few executives from a factory. The largest number of the parents are American born although a few are of Polish extraction. The school also includes some Indians from a nearby Indian reservation. The educational system is average; the teaching is neither ultraprogressive nor ultraconservative but rather middle-of-the-road. The teachers, mainly graduates of the teachers colleges of the area, are a definite part of the community. They know most of the parents of their children. On the whole, X is an average town with a rather typical teaching situation.

The first grade, which contains 28 students, includes: (1) A severe stutterer, a child who ceases speaking entirely, opens her mouth, gasps, and repeats the beginning sound or syllables of almost every word in a phrase. She often attempts to speak on inhalation. The rhythm of her speech is badly broken. (2) A slight stutterer, who blocks once in a while, whose rhythm is somewhat broken, and who sometimes repeats the first sounds of words. He is concerned about his speech. (3) A boy with retarded speech. He substitutes *t* and *d* for the *th* sounds, *w* for *r* and *l*, *p* for *f*, and *b* for *v*. Furthermore, he often omits sounds; for example, *goat* is *go*, *washing machine* often *wa ma*. His sentences normally consist of three or four words. He sounds much younger than he is; his speech development is retarded.

The second grade, made up of 24 students, has only one child with a speech defect, a child who substitutes *f* and *v* for the two *th's*. In the third grade, with 25 students, there is just one child who has a speech difficulty. She has no *sh, zh, ch,* and *j* sounds. Audiometric tests suggest that a hearing loss causes this difficulty. In the fourth and fifth grades with 29 and 32 students, respectively, there are no speech defectives. The sixth grade, which has 43 students, includes one severe stutterer, one severe case of nasality, where all the sounds come through the child's nose, two children who do not make the *s* sound correctly, and one child who substitutes *w* for *l* and *r*.

This illustration gives to some extent a picture of typical speech defects encountered in an ordinary classroom. The largest proportion of the defects are defects of articulation. The other defects include one serious vocal difficulty, one case of delayed speech, three cases of stuttering, and one articulatory disorder due to a hearing impairment. Those children with defective articulation were tested to make sure that hearing losses did not cause their speech difficulties. Other children had some hearing losses, but these losses had not hindered their ability to communicate. This situation is not ideally typical. For example, the school has no child with defective speech due to cleft palate or cerebral palsy.

As just illustrated, the teacher may have three children with speech defects in his class one year and none the next. But as an average he can expect at least one speech defective in his classroom almost every semester. Surveys afford somewhat different figures on the incidence. A 1959 report of the American Speech and Hearing Association Committee on Legislation (1)* notes that 5 percent of our school-age children and 1.3 percent of children under five years of age have speech problems. The Committee indicates that

*Numbers in parentheses refer to reading lists at the end of each chapter.

by 1960 more than 3 million children will have speech and hearing so seriously impaired that it can and frequently will interfere with their educational, social, and emotional adjustment. The breakdown is:

Estimated Number of School-Age Children Per 10,000 with Each Type of Speech or Hearing Problem

Type of Problem	Percentage of Children with Serious Problem	Number of Children with Serious Problem
Articulation	3.0	300
Stuttering	1.0	100
Voice	.1	10
Cleft Palate Speech	.1	10
Cerebral Palsy Speech	.1	10
Retarded Speech Development	.2	20
Speech Problem Due to Impaired Hearing	.5	50
Total	5.0	500

A study done by A. Mills and H. Streit (14) notes that of 4,685 children in the schools of Holyoke, Massachusetts 10.1 percent had speech defects. Of this group 44.8 percent were seriously defective. This estimate is similar to that found in the Midcentury White House Conference Report of 1952 (2). This report indicates that 5 percent of our population had serious speech defects. The authors of this report, however, emphasize that they do not account for an estimated additional 5 percent who have relatively minor speech and voice defects. These defects are unimportant for most practical purposes but are serious in their effect on personal and social adjustment in some cases and obviously significant for children destined for fields of work, such as teaching, requiring good speech (2, p. 129).

An examination of surveys of speech defects in school systems reveals that up to 10 percent of our school population are defective in speech. In most surveys the writers are counting those children with speech that is sufficiently different from normal speech to call undesirable attention to itself in conversation. We may arrive at various reasons for the differences in incidence found in publications. (1) The correctionist may have to examine too many children too rapidly so that he is not being thorough enough in his analysis. (2) Classroom teachers with little training in speech may be reporting. They may be inaccurate in their diagnosis. (3) The basis of judgment varies. What may be a decidedly unpleasant voice to one teacher or correctionist may be less so to another. One person may include a child with an articulatory defect, another may decide not to include such a child since he may feel that the difficulty is due to immaturity while the other person may consider it a serious defect.

Teacher's Role in Locating Speech Defects

A research study by the Subcommittee (on The Clinician: Professional Definition) of the Research Committee of the American Speech and Hearing Association indicates that in locating children who need speech training, 68 percent of the speech clinicians use the "referral" method and 64 percent frequently use the "survey" method. Only 12 percent use the "class visitation" method frequently (3, p. 16). In the survey method the speech correctionist carries major responsibility for finding the speech defective, but in the referral method the classroom teacher plays an important role. Since 55 percent of the clinicians regularly use reports of classroom teachers to determine the extent of children's disorders and another 40 percent occasionally use them (3, p. 16), the classroom teacher should be trained to hear symptoms representative of the various speech defects. The training may be accomplished by college courses, in-service courses, or a series of lectures by the speech correctionist.

In the light of a study by Diehl and Stinnett (7), this training seems absolutely essential. Diehl and Stinnett made their study in Kentucky where no public school speech correctionists had ever been to find out how efficient teachers are in discovering speech defects. The study concludes: (1) Elementary grade teachers with no orientation in speech disorders can be expected to locate speech defective children with less than 60 percent accuracy. They can be expected to fail to identify two out of every five who would be located by trained speech clinicians in routine screenings. (2) The same teachers can, however, be expected to locate severe types of articulation defects with slightly better than 80 percent accuracy. (3) Teachers appear to have least skill in recognizing a voice disorder in a second-grade child. This study emphasizes the need for the elementary school teachers to be trained in identifying speech defects particularly where the speech correctionist does not do a survey and where the classroom teacher is responsible for referring those children who need speech correction to the speech correctionist.

The classroom teacher does not ordinarily do audiological testing.[3] A research study by the Subcommittee (for Diagnosis and Measurement) of the Research Committee of the American Speech and Hearing Association indicates that audiological testing is accomplished by a variety of specialists. Diagnostic audiological testing is done in public school systems by the following persons in order of decreasing frequency: speech and hearing clinicians (24 percent), nurses (22 percent), physicians (15 percent), school audiologists (13 percent), health department personnel (4 percent), and other personnel (7 percent) (3, p. 54). Practically all public schools have provided for audiological screening, usually no less frequently than every fourth year of a child's school attendance, although in a small percentage only those children referred for the purpose are screened audiologically (3, p. 57).

Types of Speech Defects the Classroom Teacher Can Handle

The child with defective speech needs the help of each of his classroom teachers. The teacher knows the child well and is with

---

[3] See pages 341 to 346 for a more detailed discussion.

him for longer periods than any specialist. Frequently he is well acquainted with the child's parents. At times parents will understand the teacher and listen to him more effectively than they will to the specialist.

As mentioned previously, articulatory defects are most frequent. Most often no oral or dental malformation is associated with the difficulty; it is the result of faulty learning. In some of these cases the teacher with training can help the child to listen to the sound, make it accurately, and incorporate it into words. For example, some teachers can successfully manage Johnny's *tree* for *three*. He aids Johnny in hearing that he is substituting a *t* and *d* for the two *th*'s, teaches him to make the two *th* sounds accurately, and to incorporate them into words and conversational speech.

The teacher, however, must be careful in dealing with an articulatory defect. The teacher should be sure that his evaluation of the problem is accurate and that his chosen approaches are likely to produce the desired results. One of the authors once observed a college freshman who consistently used the two *th*'s for *s* and *z*. When her error was called to her attention, she said, "But I can do it right." Whereupon she made what was for her, because of her jaw formation, a very difficult coordination of *s,* almost touching the tip of her tongue to the teeth ridge behind her upper teeth. A teacher had taught her to place the tip of her tongue on the upper gum ridge. The teacher's suggestion for correction was so difficult for the girl that it was almost impossible to accomplish. If the jaw and teeth are so formed that the child needs to be taught compensatory movements, the teacher should refer the child to a speech specialist for help.

The teacher shows good judgment in refusing to accept primary responsibility for the correction of the speech of the stutterer or for serious voice problems. Children with such problems need the assistance of a speech correctionist. If the teacher has had no preparation in the correction of speech difficulties, he should refer even the less serious cases such as a lingual protrusion lisp (*th* for *s*) to the therapist. Frequently, in turn, the speech correctionist refers the student to another specialist in the field of medicine or psychology. The teacher, however, does have definite responsibilities when a speech correctionist is part of the school staff. Often, as noted, the teacher must be able to identify those children who need speech help. Furthermore, to work effectively with a correctionist, the teacher must understand the nature of speech correction and must know how and when he can reinforce the work of the correctionist. The teacher's role as a member of the speech correction team is discussed in the next chapter.

Suggested Readings*

1. American Speech and Hearing Association Committee on Legislation. "Need for Speech Pathologists," *ASHA,* **I** (December 1959), 138-139. (Gives statistics on prevalence of speech defects.)

2. American Speech and Hearing Association Committee on the Mid-century White House Conference. "Speech Disorders and Speech Correction." *Journal of Speech and Hearing Disorders,* **XVII** (June 1952), 130. (Gives the incidence of speech disorders in youth between the ages of five and 21.)

3. American Speech and Hearing Association Research Committee. "Public School Speech and Hearing Services." *The Journal of Speech and Hearing Disorders,* Monograph Supplement 8 (July 1961).

4. ANDERSON, V., *Improving the Child's Speech.* (Rev. ed.) New York: Oxford University Press, 1961, Chapter 3. (Tells how to recognize speech disabilities.)

5. BERRY, M., and J. EISENSON, *Speech Disorders: Principles and Practices of Therapy.* New York: Appleton-Century-Crofts, 1956, Chapter 3. (Describes the traits of the speech defective.)

6. BURDIN, L. G., "A Survey of Speech Defectives in the Indianapolis Primary Grades." *Journal of Speech Disorders,* **V** (September 1940), 247-258.

7. DIEHL, C. F., and C. D. STINNETT, "Efficiency of Teacher Referrals in a School Testing Program." *Journal of Speech and Hearing Disorders,* **XXIV** (February 1959), 35-36.

* Annotations after a bibliographic reference are made where the reference title does not clearly indicate the contents of the material.

8. IRWIN, R. B., *Speech and Hearing Therapy.* Englewood Cliffs, N.J.: Prentice-Hall, 1953, Chapter 3. (Tells how to find the children who need speech therapy. Gives the incidence of defects. Tells of the various survey methods.)

9. JOHNSON, W. *et al., Speech Handicapped School Children.* (Rev. ed.) New York: Harper and Brothers, 1956, Chapter 2. (Defines the various types of speech defects.)

10. JOHNSON, W., "Ten Children You Should Know." *National Parent Teacher,* **XXXVIII** (March 1944), 10-12. (Describes the types of speech defects and the influence of the classroom teacher on speech defective children.)

11. MAYFARTH, F. (ed.), *Learning to Speak Effectively.* Washington, D.C.: Association for Childhood Education, 1943. (Translates speech problems into a form and language suitable to others than speech specialists.)

12. MORRIS, D. W., "The Speech Survey." *Journal of Speech Disorders,* **IV** September 1939), 195-198.

13. ———, "A Survey of Speech Defects in Central High School, Kansas City, Missouri." *Quarterly Journal of Speech,* **XXV** (April 1939), 262-269.

14. MILLS, A., and H. STREIT, "Report of a Speech Survey, Holyoke, Massachusetts." *Journal of Speech Disorders,* **VII** (June 1942), 161-167.

15. SPRIESTERSBACH, D. C., "Speech—an Index of Maturity." *Childhood Education,* **XXVII** (February 1951), 260-263.

16. VAN RIPER, C., *"Speech Correction: Principles and Methods.* Englewood Cliffs, N.J.: Prentice-Hall, 1954, Chapter 2. (Describes the types of disorders of speech.)

17. WEST, R., "Rehabilitation of Speech." *Journal of Exceptional Children,* **XVI** (March 1950), 165-172. (Reviews the types of speech problems. Suggests how the school personnel can cooperate to help the child.)

Problems

1. Visit a lower grade classroom and try to screen the children into the following categories: (*a*) those who have acceptable speech; (*b*) those whose speech is faulty but likely to improve with maturation; (*c*) those who need speech improvement help; and (*d*) those who have more serious defects which require the attention of a speech correction specialist.

2. Visit one of the sessions held by a speech correctionist. Indicate the problem of one of the children and the kind of help he received.

3. Visit a kindergarten and a fifth-grade class. Indicate whether articulatory errors decrease or increase and whether dysfluences in the children decrease or increase in the two grades.

4. Answer the questions on pages 10-12 in reference to five particular children. Try to choose one child whom you suspect of having a speech difficulty.

5. Read one of the following references: 4, 5, 11, 15, or 16 and report on the reading to the group.

6. Visit a session held by a speech correctionist. Indicate in two specific ways how you could reinforce the work done in this session in the classroom.

2

Speech

Correction

Services

THE RESPONSIBILITY of the classroom teacher is as a member of the speech correction team, for the trend toward providing special help for the speech handicapped is continuing at an accelerating rate. Irwin states that before 1940 only nine states had legislation which permitted recognition of the special needs of the speech handicapped child by "promoting interest and financial support for the speech handicapped child in the public schools" (11, p. 127). In contrast, she notes that in 1959 39 states had special education laws which allowed the extension of services to children with speech problems (II, p. 142). The expansion is further shown in the requirements for state certification as a public school speech therapist. In 1955 Irwin (12) records that 15 states had certification requirements approaching those of basic certification in the American Speech and Hearing Association. She further indicates that in 1959 32 states seemed to have certification plans approximating those of the Basic Speech Certification in the American Speech and Hearing Association (11). Both the growth of permissive legislation concerning the speech handicapped and the up-ward trend in certification requirements augur well for the work of speech correction. As the needs of children for speech correction are being met by correctionists, the classroom teacher can turn his attention from correction to reinforcing the work of the speech correctionist and to speech improvement.

Organization of Speech Correction Services

Speech programs within schools differ in their administration and organization in many ways. Sometimes the teacher refers the speech-handicapped child to the correctionist; other times the principal, parents, school nurse, psychologist, or guidance director refer him; also, at times, the correctionist makes a clinical survey. Case loads of the correctionist vary from 50 in some cities to 450 in others. The correctionist meets the child for as short a period as 10 minutes or as long a period as 50 minutes. He may work with each child individually or in groups varying in size from three to 18. The groups are homogeneous or heterogeneous in terms of the speech difficulty and in terms of age.

Identification of Speech and Hearing Handicapped

Correctionists locate children with speech problems primarily by means of survey and through teacher referrals. However the problem is handled, it takes time. Speech screening usually takes from one to three weeks of the clinician's time each year. Although teachers often do give a kind of preliminary speech test, they do not give hearing tests. Although audiological screening is provided in almost all schools, it is under the supervision of nurses most frequently and of speech and hearing clinicians next most frequently (1, p. 57).

Case Load

A recent survey of the American Speech and Hearing Association (1) gives norms as to numbers in case load, kinds of defects within it, and grade level of the participants. A mean current case load of 130 children was reported by 1,462 clinicians. The average number of children seen weekly is 111, while the average number of children worked with in the course of a year is 130. One-fourth of the clinicians, when asked to specify what factor seemed to limit their case load, reported that the state law established this limitation; 23 percent indicated that the number of children with speech problems established their case load; and 45 percent stated that the size of their case load is left to their own discretion (1, p. 34). Of the case load, 81 percent is comprised of children with articulatory problems; 6.5 percent of children who stutter; and 4.5 percent of children with delayed speech. The remainder, including children with organic and voice disorders, make up only a small percentage of the case load (1, p. 38). About three-fourths of correctionists work primarily with children in kindergarten, grade 1, and grade 2. Only 2 percent work strictly at the high school level (1, p. 35).

Individual and Group Therapy

Approximately nine-tenths of the children who are subjects of speech therapy receive the therapy in groups. National averages indicate that clinicians each week see about 10 children individually and 101 children in groups of four or five (1, p. 38). Most of the clinicians meet both individuals and groups twice a week although a substantial percentage meet them only once a week. Of those responding in this study, 57 percent indicate that their group sessions last from 25 to 34 minutes while 29 percent indicate that their sessions last from 15 to 24 minutes. The periods of individual therapy are shorter; 40 percent devote 14 to 24 minutes to individual sessions; 36 percent, 25 to 34 minutes (1, p. 38-39).

Work of Correctionist   No

The largest part of the working week of the correctionist is spent in therapy; the mean number of hours spent in therapy as reported by 705 clinicians is 23.09 hours. The distribution of the rest of the working time of the clinician is: traveling, 2.68 hours; conference, 2.53 hours; writing reports, 2.12 hours; preparing lessons, 3.23 hours; and other duties, 1.55 hours (1, p. 15).

Limiting Case Load

A frequent problem in schools is a case load that is too large for the correctionist's program. To the correctionist's dismay he may find that, although his therapy schedule should surely not be more than 100, he has 182 cases. The situation provides a variety of possible approaches:

1. He can give a little help in large groups to all 182.
2. He can train the classroom teachers to take care of the less severely handicapped.
3. He can limit his case load to 100.

The first alternative, to give some therapy to all the handicapped, does not seem feasible, since a small amount of training usually results in a small amount of improvement, and marked success requires effectively treated students. Feasibility of the second alternative depends on many factors: the speech background of the classroom teachers; the availability and ability of the correctionist to train the teachers; the class size of the teachers; their schedule and that of the correctionist; and the attitudes of the administration and the teachers to the problems of the speech handicapped. In a few instances, the correctionist may be able to give the necessary training to some of the teachers.

Usually, however, the correctionist will choose the third alternative of giving training to approximately 100 students. But he must make his selection of the 100 students on the basis of valid principles. Disgruntled parents whose children have been deprived of speech therapy or those parents whose children have been asked to take it may demand an explanation. The reasons for selection should be arrived at thoughtfully and carefully and in consultation with the administrative officers of the school. Such factors as grade and school placement, severity of handicap, and ability to benefit from training are all important. When classroom teachers have not participated in the discussion, the principles should be carefully explained to them. They are better able to explain the principles to disgruntled parents when they have been part of the discussion which led to the formulation of the principles.

Although the administration and organization of speech correction programs may differ, the correctionist always keeps the classroom teacher informed of what he is doing. The teacher, in turn, reinforces the learning acquired in speech correction sessions. Almost always the correctionist and the teacher confer with the parents. Both the teacher and the correctionist often consult with the school health authorities. In other words, a team approach is appropriate. The personnel of the team may vary somewhat, but typically the classroom teacher, the correctionist, the school health personnel, and the school psychologist make up the team. Its members meet to discuss the problems of the handicapped children and to work out programs for particular children. At times they invite other specialists such as an otologist, orthodontist, neurologist, or psychiatrist to be members of their team.

Roles of the Members of the Team

The Classroom Teacher

Surely the classroom teacher knows the child better than any member of the team, since he is with him all day. Because he is interested in all of the child's development, he sees the child's speech as part of his total development. Of the members of the team, he in all likelihood has the most opportunity to understand the child: He knows how the child acts on the playground and in class. He recognizes the child's ability to lead, to be a good student, to build bird houses, or to throw a baseball. Furthermore, he usually has more contact with the parents than any of the other members of the team. Consequently, he is most intimately acquainted with the child.

The ideal classroom teacher for the speech-handicapped child is a good teacher for both the child with normal speech and the one with defective speech. He accepts the child with a handicap, whether it be speech or physical, and helps his classmates accept him. When the teacher controls his feeling of sympathy and accepts the handicapped child with his difficulty, the child and his classmates are more likely to adopt the same attitude. Second, the teacher makes sure his classroom invites oral communication. When the children plan their work together, when they like to play with each other, they talk and listen. As they go on purposeful trips, as they act in a play, or as they build a bookcase, they have worthwhile discussions. Their classroom, with its interesting bulletin board, with its busy work corner, invites conversation. Chapter 8 contains suggestions on how to stimulate speech activities. Third, the teacher fosters good human relationships among the children. When a warm friendly feeling exists in the classroom, when youngsters like each other and their teacher, when the teacher helps to build a constructive concept of self in the child, when activity is stimulating, speaking is necessary and enjoyable. As children participate in decisions, as they realize that they are the most important part of the school program, they have a feeling of belonging to their school group. Last, the good teacher is a cooperative person. He reinforces the learning taught by other teachers. He contributes factual information about the child to other colleagues when it will prove useful.

In addition, the classroom teacher who is to be successful in helping the child with handicapped speech must have certain other qualifications more directly related to speech: (1) His own speech and voice must be worthy of imitation. These factors will be discussed in the chapter on the teacher's speech. (2) He must have a discerning ear so that he can hear the articulatory and vocal errors his children are making. (3) He must have an accurate knowledge of how the American-English vowels and consonants are made. The chapter on the production of speech sounds covers this area. (4) He must be able to plan a program of speech improvement for all his children. Whereas only 5 percent have need of speech correction, almost all students have need of speech improvement. This need is explained in Chapter 8. (5) He should have enough knowledge of speech correction to reinforce the teaching of the correctionist. He must, therefore, be able to understand the aims, objectives, and procedures of the correctionist. In this book the chapters on the various speech defects contain this material. (6) He should be able to pick out those students in his class who need speech help. The chapter on the definition of speech defects includes some of this information.

The teacher can cooperate in other ways. For example, classroom teachers can help students above the first grade to carry the responsibility of watching the clock for the time when they are to go for speech help. Frequently, the teachers write the time on the blackboard on the day the child is to go for help. Through some means, the teacher should help the child to get to the correctionist at the scheduled time.

The Correctionist

The correctionist must appreciate that he is a working member of an educational team. As such, he must have a professional awareness and attitude and get along with his students, their parents, and the school personnel. In addition, he must be able to gain the help of other school personnel, set up his program effectively and cooperatively, and report on its progress capably and efficiently.

PROFESSIONAL STATUS AND ATTITUDES. Part of being a good teacher is maintaining professional status and attitudes. Now that speech correction has attained a professional status, the correctionist should be aware of it. The first factor in awareness is gaining the necessary training. The American Speech and Hearing Association lists the requirements for basic certification. If the speech correctionist is working in the schools, he should preferably meet the requirements upon his employment. If he does not, he should take work in summer school to meet them as quickly as possible. A second factor is the correctionist's relationship to other professions. He must recognize the delimitations of his field from that of the doctor, psychologist, psychiatrist, dentist, and physical therapist. He neither criticizes these workers nor makes even a hint of a diagnosis in a field other than his own. The third factor is the knowledge of his own limitations. When he does not understand a voice case or when he has difficulty with a parent, he seeks help from someone who knows more than he. Professors in universities, experienced workers in the field, and administrative officials of a school are all glad to help the young correctionist.

Since the correctionist is working with individuals and with small groups, he must be particularly careful to maintain a professional and workmanlike attitude and to allow no undue familiarity between him and his students. He should be friendly but at the same time keep the necessary professional distance. He should not respond emotionally to the child's problem, for his attitude must remain objective. He undoubtedly wants a permissive atmosphere for his speech correction work; however, he should set limits and hold strictly to these limits. His permissive attitude should not mean a laissez-faire attitude. The failure of the correctionist to establish limits and to hold to them may cause the classroom teacher to be justly critical. Some language and some activities should be discouraged. A cartoon in a recent *New Yorker* (August 19, 1961) points to such a situation. A mother, very erect and very proud, is walking with a six-year-old in hand who is nonchalantly puffing a cigarette. Two long-nosed females say, "I think there's such a thing as being *too* permissive."

HUMAN RELATIONSHIPS. Another part of the correctionist's being a good teacher is in his ability to get along well with others. He will need to have good personal relationships with members of the community, with teachers, and with the parents of his children. In other words, he must be able to work with people effectively. The success of his program depends to an extent on how well the members of the community receive it. He must be able to explain his program to the men of the Rotary Club or the Lions Club. Such persons are already sympathetic to the handicapped child, but the correctionist must be able to make them understand that the speech-handicapped child can receive help. Furthermore, he must motivate them to think that their community must offer such help. One specialist talked about the kind of help three children with different difficulties were getting to a club in the town. His presentation was persuasive.

The specialist needs the cooperation and help of the classroom teachers. In turn, the correctionist must appreciate the work of the teachers. One correctionist made it his duty to visit a classroom when one of his children who came for help was absent. His few warm words of appreciation to the teacher at the end of the visit aided in building a good relationship between the two.

The support of the parents of the handicapped children is as important as the classroom teacher's. One father remarked recently, "I'll only live in this town three years, but I'll always be thankful for Davy's speech help. Suppose I'd happened to be in a place where there was no help." Sincere appreciation of parents is an asset in firmly establishing and maintaining a speech correction program. The conferences with parents and the home visits are important. The specialist must be able to gain the confidence of the parents so that they will cooperate for the good of the child and the success of the program.

IN-SERVICE COURSES. In some schools, the correctionist will not only treat the children but will also lead discussions and give lectures or in-service courses so that the teacher can reinforce the work given in correction sessions: He will give the teachers the necessary training to diagnose the speech difficulties of the children in their classrooms. He will send out mimeographed bulletins to help them understand the various speech handicaps of their children. He will explain to them the relationship of speech difficulties to academic achievement, such as reading, and to behavior problems. He will report to them research which relates speech correction to classroom teaching.

As he talks to teachers and parents, he will use non-technical terms. He will not say that Mary has dysphonia and that Johnny has a lall; rather he will explain that Mary's voice is hoarse and that Johnny substitutes *w* for *r* and *l*. Parents particularly are wary of specialists' terms; therefore, both the classroom teacher and the correctionist will not talk about "cases," "correctionists," or "clinics."

In-service courses, lectures, and discussions are but one avenue of cooperation between the specialist and the classroom teacher. The specialist will explain to the teacher the kind of difficulty a particular child has, what he and the child are doing about it, and what the child's chances of success in controlling the difficulty are. In short conferences or notes, the correctionist tells the teacher what words and phrases the child has learned to say or what kind of behavior he exhibited during speech help. For example, one specialist aided a child in preparing to read aloud a report he was to give before a meeting of the parents of his class. Another noted that William could now say his own name correctly and that he could also pronounce the street he lived on: Maple Street. The teacher commended William's accomplishment.

PREPARING SCHEDULE. Last, the correctionist must serve as a team member in preparing his schedule of correction classes and in making his reports. Many variables make the preparation of a correction schedule difficult. The correctionist may want to place students homogeneously in terms of defect and age, to work with certain cases in the morning, or to cut across several classes and age levels for stuttering groups. In addition, he usually has to work around the schedules of the classroom teachers and other specialists; for example, the classroom teacher may not wish a child to lose certain fundamental work usually given at a particular time. Since so many of the school personnel are involved, their cooperation and that of the administration is essential in working out a schedule. Consultation with the teachers and the administration helps to insure prompt and regular attendance of the speech-handicapped children. The resulting schedule should be placed in the hands of the administrator and the teachers involved. All the members of the team should adhere to the schedule except for necessary absences.

When assigning students to the speech correction classes, the correctionist should notify the parents. In this activity, the advice of classroom teachers is important, for most teachers meet with the parents at least once a semester. With the advice and consent of the supervisor or principal, the correctionist or director of speech and hearing services sends a letter such as the following to the parents of children to be enrolled in speech correction classes:

Dear Mrs_____:

    A recent test shows that your son can profit from work in speech. I have, therefore, scheduled him to work with me twice a week during which time I shall try to teach him to speak more clearly.

    I shall be glad to have your help. You can, I am sure, give me information and advice which will make my work with your son more effective. Won't you come to see me next week when I have planned conferences with parents? Would Tuesday at 3:00 be a possible time? If it is not, please call me between three and five on Friday at Forest 6-7000, extension 7, and I shall arrange another time.

Sincerely yours,

Before enrolling a child in speech correction class, the correctionist should make sure that the child is not receiving help from a speech and hearing center or a private individual. Speech instruction from both a school and another source usually are not advantageous to the child, although overanxious parents often believe the more help received the better it is and, consequently, enroll a child for private help without informing the school. Local centers and school personnel should cooperate to do what is best for the youngster. In some instances the child is better treated at a center; in other instances, he is better treated at school. A school administrator may coordinate the work by approving the child's taking therapy from an outside source and by excusing him from school therapy. A signed slip is then sent to the outside source. The superintendent or another official should also request information on the amount and kind of therapy being given the child by outsiders. The work between the agency and the school should be related.

    RECORDS. Correctionists keep records for several reasons: (1)

The correctionist wants to know as much as he can about each child. From interviews with the child, teachers, and parents, the correctionist acquires information about the child's interests, personality, medical history, and intellectual attainments which can be helpful in handling the child. When such information is recorded, the next correctionist has a basis for understanding the child. (2) The correctionist needs to know what has been done with a child before his arrival and how effective the therapy has been. (3) Teachers, administrators, and other school personnel need to find out what has taken place in the speech correction program. (4) Administrators frequently want reports for justification of the program. (5) State departments of education often require reports to serve as a basis for financial aid to the local community.

According to the American Speech and Hearing Association, clinicians maintain the following kind of reports for individual students. Numbers indicate the percentage of 705 clinicians who stated that they keep records for each student:

Record	Percentage
Case history	73
Record of phonetic improvement	71
Reports of conferences	69
Daily log	33
Weekly or monthly progress reports	41
Semester or annual reports	21 (1, p. 42)

The school case history is much simpler than the case history kept in a speech and hearing center. The form on page 33 suggests the kind of case history that might well be kept in a school.

Other reports frequently made by correctionists include results of speech testing, results of hearing testing, schedules of schools and classes, therapy progress reports, and final reports (1, p. 42). Geraldine Garrison suggests the following reports for her staff: a case history when the speech difficulty is the result of a physical, psychological, social, or educational condition, and a short record

CENTRAL VALLEY ELEMENTARY SCHOOL

Speech History

Date_____

Name of Student_____Address_____

Name of Guardian_____Address_____

Telephone Number_____

Date of Birth_____Sex___Homeroom___Homeroom Teacher_____

Speech Difficulty_____

_____

Father: Age_____Education_____

        Occupation _____Speech defect, if any_____

        Health_____

Mother: Age_____Education_____

        Occupation _____Speech defect, if any_____

        Health_____

Brothers and Sisters:

Names	Ages	Speech defect, if any

Physical Condition: Weight_____Height_____

    Abnormality in mouth, throat, nose, or teeth structure_____

_____

    Motor Impairment_____

    Defect in Hearing_____

    Defect in Vision_____

    Serious Illnesses_____

Mental and Educational Development:

    I. Q._____ Test_____

    Scholastic Achievement_____

    Scholastic Interests _____

    School Attendance_____

when the speech difficulty is minor; a brief report including nature of difficulty, progress, attitudes, attendance, and cooperation of parents for the child's cumulative record; a report to the principal indicating the progress of each child; a report to the classroom teacher as to his students' progress; a report to parents; and a report to superintendents (8, p. 23).

The report to the superintendent may well include:

1. Number of students who have received correction during the term, including breakdown for each type of speech or hearing problem.
2. Number of students receiving correction at the end of the term.
3. Number of students dismissed during the term with reasons for their dismissals.
4. Number of students added during the term.
5. Number of conferences with parents.
6. Number of conferences with students.
7. Number of home calls.
8. Number of referrals—broken down specifically.
9. Number of meetings with parent group—broken down specifically.

COMPETENCIES OF SPEECH CORRECTIONISTS. All of these duties point to the need for a certain level of competence of the speech correctionist. A bulletin published by the United States Government (18, p. 48-50) suggests the following requisites for competence of speech correctionists in the public schools:

1. The speech correctionist must understand the various types and causes of speech defects and be able to apply specific diagnostic and remedial procedures to individual children.
2. The speech correctionist must have a broad understanding of human development and specific knowledge of how speech disorders affect such development in children. He must understand the needs of both typical and atypical children.
3. The speech correctionist must be able to establish rapport with the

child and to help him deal with social and emotional problems which he may have as a result of his speech condition or which may be slowing down therapy. Closely related to this competency, is the one that he will be able to develop a teaching atmosphere free from pressure and conducive to good mental health.

4. The speech correctionist must understand the general principles of education—curriculum, methods, philosophy, and organization—and should be able to integrate and correlate his speech correction work with the total program of the school.

5. The correctionist should be able to apply survey and referral systems and to develop, plan, and coordinate an effective schedule for a speech correction program in several schools acceptable to pupils, teachers and parents.

6. The correctionist should be skillful in working as a team member and should be able to coordinate the resources of the school and community for the good of the child.

7. The speech correctionist should have a knowledge of the facilities for obtaining information and evaluations concerning the child's physical, social, emotional, and intellectual status, be able to interpret the information obtained so as to further the speech correction program, and have skill in reviewing and writing reports and case histories.

8. The speech correctionist should have the ability to help parents understand their child's speech problems and personal attitudes.

9. The speech correctionist should have a knowledge of professional literature and research studies.

Psychologist

The psychologist helps the teacher, the correctionist, and the parents in understanding the child. The results of his testing program may help all three in handling the child. For example, in one case a psychometric test showed a child to be far brighter than the teacher, correctionist, or parents thought. In another case, the administration of the Children's Thematic Apperception Test revealed a definite adjustment difficulty for the child. Because of the information and advice given by the psychologist, both the teacher and the correctionist treated these children more wisely.

In still another case, the counseling services of the psychologist were of inestimable value. A stutterer was determined to become a lawyer. The choice definitely appeared to be his own. But the psychologist discovered in talking with him that the choice was really his grandfather's. The boy was deeply interested in science and mathematics. As a result of conferences with the psychologist and the boy's parents, the boy changed his high school major from social science to science and mathematics. The pressure to major and do well in social studies, about which he was not enthusiastic, was removed.

A mother and father, both college graduates, set high academic standards for their boy—who was struggling through an academic high school course. The psychologist helped the parents to understand their son and his academic problems—and incidentally to better understand themselves. The boy is now doing very well in a general course. He spent some of his free time selling Christmas cards, which until recently was a forbidden activity. The suggestions and advice of the psychologist are particularly helpful in the adjustment of children such as these.

Medical Personnel

When a speech defect is the result of an organic or psychological difficulty, the health authorities contribute to solving the speech problem by arranging for appropriate medical treatment. They talk the health problem over with the parents and frequently refer the child to medical specialists. For instance, the nurse's home visits may be the beginning of a sound health program for the child. At times the need for the help of other specialists is obvious. For example, when the results of the audiometric examination reveal a hearing loss, the child is referred to an otologist. The child with a cleft palate will be under the care of an oral or a plastic surgeon and an orthodontist. A stutterer with a serious adjustment difficulty may require psychiatric help. The situation where many specialists work together for the benefit of the child is ideal.

As the specialists work together, an appreciation for and an understanding of the work of the others comes about. Inevitably, some overlapping takes place. The speech correctionist, for example, surmises that certain problems of the speech-handicapped child need investigation by the psychiatrist, psychologist, or doctor. The pediatrician, on the other hand, is concerned that a child has developed a stutter and recognizes that the child's speech difficulty needs treatment. The psychologist, in examining the speech handicapped child, may uncover a deep-seated personality problem that the psychiatrist must handle. Each specialist is learning from those in other fields, and each is primarily interested in helping the child to develop into an effective and well-functioning human being.

References and Suggested Readings

1. American Speech and Hearing Association. "Public School Speech and Hearing Services." *The Journal of Speech and Hearing Disorders,* Monograph Supplement 8, July 1961.

2. ANDERSON, V. A., *Improving the Child's Speech.* (Rev. ed.) New York: Oxford University Press, 1961. (Contains material on integrating speech training with the school curriculum.)

3. BREINHOLT, B. A., "New Look in Speech Education: Goals and Techniques for Programming." *Exceptional Child,* **XXII** (February 1956), 194-196. (Explains the importance of the community in developing a successful speech program.)

4. CHAPMAN, M. E., "The Speech Clinician and the Classroom Teacher." *Journal of Speech Disorders,* **VII** (March 1949), 53-61. (Describes bulletins used by the correctionist to get cooperation from the teacher. Explains the duties of the correctionist.)

5. CHIPMAN, S., "On Receiving Your First Appointment as a Speech Correction Teacher." *The Speech Teacher,* **IV** (September 1955), 173-175. (Gives advice about human relationships with teachers and supervisors.)

6. EDNEY, C. W., "The Public School Remedial Program." In W. JOHNSON *et al., Speech Handicapped School Children.* (Rev. ed.) New York: Harper and Brothers, 1956, 406-519. (States the problems of the school speech therapist and makes sound suggestions for their solution.)

7. FOSSUM, E. C., "Cooperating with the Speech Correctionist." *Journal of Education,* **CXXXVI** (March 1954), 182-184. (Explains the services of the correctionist including surveys and in-service insti-

tutes for classroom teachers. Talks about the counseling of parents and the cooperation with physicians.)

8. GARRISON, G., *Speech and Hearing Services ... A Design for Program Development*. Hartford, Conn.: State Department of Education, Bulletin 92, June 1960. (Suggests policies and procedures which will help in (1) determining need for such a program; (2) organizing, conducting, and improving services; and (3) clarifying procedures to be followed in securing state funds for speech and hearing services in Connecticut. Contains samples of many forms needed in providing speech and hearing services.)

9. HOUCHIN, T. D., "Notes on Organizing a Speech Correction Program in the Public Schools." *Journal of Speech and Hearing Disorders,* **XIV** (March 1949), 53-62. (Tells how to organize a new speech correction program in a public school system. Gives procedures on beginning a program. Contains speech correction forms, samples of letters to parents and teachers, and articulatory testing materials.)

10. IRWIN, R. B., *Speech and Hearing Therapy*. Englewood Cliffs, N.J.: Prentice-Hall, 1953. (Comprehensively treats speech therapy in the public schools.)

11. ————, "Speech Therapy in the Public Schools: State Legislation and Certification." *Journal of Speech and Hearing Disorders,* **XXIV** (May 1959), 127-143. (Reviews state legislation and certification requirements for speech therapists in each of the states.)

12. ————, "State Programs in Speech and Hearing Therapy: Certification." *The Speech Teacher,* **IV** (November 1955), 253-258.

13. ————, "State Programs in Speech and Hearing Therapy: Legislation." *The Speech Teacher,* **IV** (March 1955), 101-109.

14. ————, "State Programs in Speech and Hearing Therapy: Organization and Administration." *The Speech Teacher,* **V** (March 1956), 125-131. (Studies case loads, patterns of organization, and the cost of therapy.)

15. LILLYWHITE, H. S., and R. L. SLEETER, "Some Problems of Relationships between Speech and Hearing Specialists and Those in the Medical Profession." *ASHA,* **I** (December 1959), 127-131. (Suggests sound, specific ways in which the speech specialist may cooperate with the medical profession.)

16. LUPER, H. L., and S. H. AINSWORTH, "Speech Correction Rooms in the Public Schools." *Exceptional Child,* **XXII** (October 1955), 24-26. (Indicates space, acoustic treatment, and special furnishings needed for the speech correction room.)

17. MacLearie, E. C., "Evaluation and the Effectiveness of the Speech and Hearing Teacher in Public Schools." *The Speech Teacher,* **II** (September 1953), 209-211. (Discusses briefly personal relationships, physical facilities, rapport with children, lesson planning, follow-up, and records and reports.)

18. Mackie, R. P., and W. Johnson, *Speech Correctionists: The Competencies They Need for the Work They Do.* Washington, D.C.: U.S. Govt. Printing Office, Bulletin No. 19, 1957.

19. Matis, E. E., "Psychotherapeutic Tools for Parents." *Journal of Speech and Hearing Disorders,* **XXVI** (May 1961), 164-170. (Suggests help for parents of speech-handicapped children.)

20. Powers, M. H., "What Makes an Effective Public School Speech Therapist." *Journal of Speech and Hearing Disorders,* **XXI** (December 1956), 461-467. (Includes material on professional relationtionships, personal characteristics, and professional attitudes and ethics.)

21. Stern, J., "Speech Correctionist, Classroom Teacher, Parents, and the Child With a Speech Defect." *ASHA,* **I** (November 1959), 84. (Discusses cooperation among speech correctionists, parents, and classroom teacher.)

22. Van Riper, C., *Speech Correction: Principles and Methods.* (3rd ed.) Englewood Cliffs, N.J.: Prentice-Hall, 1954, Chapter 13. (Deals with the speech therapist and discusses his role in the public schools.)

Problems

1. Outline the kind of program for speech-handicapped children that your state provides. How does this program compare with that of one of your neighboring states?

2. Read and report on one of the following references: 2, 4, 5, 6, 8, 15, or 17.

3. Indicate how the speech correction services in your town are organized. What do you think can be done to improve this program?

4. What are the professional requirements for a school speech therapist in your state? How do these compare with the requirements in one of your neighboring states?

5. Does your state provide additional financial help to schools which have speech correction programs? Does your school superintendent consider the financial assistance sufficient?

6. Compare the requisites for competence needed by the speech correctionist with those you believe the classroom teacher needs.

3

Standards

of Speech

IN THE first chapter we indicated that some students communicate with their fellow students and their teacher adequately but that the speech patterns of some of these students are substandard. We noted there that the correction of substandard speech lies within the realm of the classroom teacher and not of the speech correctionist. This chapter deals with the concept of speech standards and the role of the teacher in helping students attain acceptable speech in terms of these standards.

In discussions of pronunciations, neighbors, friends, storekeepers look to the teacher as an authority. Rarely a week passes that a teacher is not asked to arbitrate an argument about the pronunciation of a word. Comments heard during these discussions include:

"Jane's affected. She says *tomahto*. Why doesn't she also say *potahto?*"

"One of my students criticized me for saying *ketch* for *catch*."

"That conductor always says *krik*. I wish somebody would tell him it's *creek*."

"You pronounce *orange* funny. You say *ahrange*."

"I distinguish between the verb and the noun when I use *rise*. I say the *rice* of civilization."

All these queries and complaints are trivial. Even though a person does say *tomahto,* his speech is not necessarily affected. Those who live in the North Central section of America usually do say *ketch.* In the United States as a whole *krik* is used almost as commonly as *creek. Awrange* is common in some areas; *ahrange* in others. If you live in Eastern New England, the New York City area, the Middle Atlantic area, or the South, you likely do say *ahrange.* If you live in the Southern Mountain area, you are more likely to say *ahrange* than *awrange.* But if you live in the rest of the country, you probably say *awrange.* Few of us and few dictionaries distinguish between the noun and the verb form for *rise.*

Interest in pronunciation arises because pronouncing words acceptably is essentially a social skill. The true test of a social skill is whether the act is performed without apparent effort and in a manner that commands no attention to its execution—that is, the act is completely habitual. Because of this social skill, cultivated persons tend to sound alike. Their speech is characterized neither by substandard pronunciations nor by usage suggesting self-consciousness or affectation. Such skill is not learned overnight. Since the high school senior about to go for a college interview cannot acquire the veneer of acceptable speech in two months, he must acquire acceptable speech gradually throughout his school years. During his school years, his teachers should motivate him to follow the speech conventions of the educated persons in his community.

No single "correct" standard of pronunciation, but rather many acceptable pronunciations, exist. The section of the country from which we come, the particular pronunciations we happen to prefer, and the pronunciations we have heard most frequently influence our choice. To talk about acceptable pronunciations rather than correct pronunciations or a single standard of pronunciation makes sense. The educated, cultured members of the community provide a reliable standard of the acceptability of pronunciation. G. P. Krapp says, "A sufficient definition of the term *standard* will perhaps be found in the statement that speech is standard when it passes current in actual use among persons who must be counted as among the conservors and representative of the approved social traditions of a community" (14, p. 7). Bronstein emphasizes the same concept. He notes that the students of our language must be careful to distinguish between the pattern commonly used in a community and that which is considered standard or acceptable. He points out that "standard" speech is not the "average speech" of all members of the community—halfway between the illiterate and the literate—but rather the habitual speech used by cultivated members of our society (3, p. 8).

Styles of pronunciation change. Many of these changes are obvious. We do not pronounce the *k* in *know, knight,* and *knee.* These words began to lose their *k* sound in the seventeeth century and completed the loss in the eighteenth century. *K* does remain in the pronunciation of such proper names as *Knag* or *Knode,* however. The seventeenth-century poet, Pope, rhymed *join* with *thine.* We know that *join* was then pronounced *jine.* Furthermore, he rhymed *obey* with *tea. Tea* was then pronounced *tay.* Changes may occur in the pronunciations within families from one generation to the next. A father and mother may say *erster* for *oyster* and *boin* for *burn.* Their daughter pronounces *oyster* and *burn* the way most of the rest of us do. Here some influence, perhaps that of the child's playmates or her teachers, brought about the change.

Assimilation

Language is always changing. Words, meanings, and pronunciations are added or discarded. Part of the change in pronunciation is the result of the influence of adjacent sounds. *Assimilation,* the modification of pronunciation, has usually occurred throughout the decades in the direction of simplicity and economy of effort. For instance, the past tense of *flip* is *flipped.* The final sound is not a *d* but a *t. P* is an unvoiced sound that influences the unvoicing of the sound *d* that follows. *T* is made in the same way as *d* but it is unvoiced. In other verbs where the final sound of the verb in its present tense is voiced, the *d* of the past tense is preserved. For instance, the final sound in *begged* is *d* because *g* is a voiced sound; the same is true of plurals. The final sound in *taps* is *s* but in *tabs* it is *z*. The *b* which is voiced influences the *s* to become *z*. *Captain* sometimes becomes *capm*. The *p* sound is made with both lips and this position influences the *n* to become *m*. But the nasal characteristic of the *n* is maintained. The *t*, however, is dropped entirely. In *horseshoe* the *s*, too, is completely lost; the *sh* sound takes over the *s*. Dissimilation, a special form of assimilation, is an assimilative change where a sound is changed to make it less like its neighbor; the loss of the first *r* in *surprise* is an example.

Some assimilations are acceptable; others are not. No dependable rules apply. Nor are we consistent in what we accept. *Nature* and *picture* are commonly pronounced *natcher* and *pikcher*. Almost all of us take these assimilated pronunciations for granted. Few of us attempt to say *natyer* or *pictyer*. The same kind of change occurs when we say *wonchu* for *won't you*. Many persons, however, do not accept the assimilation of *woncha* although they themselves use the same kind of assimilation in the word *nature*. Many teachers of education struggle to encourage their students not to accept *edzhikation* for *education*, although this pronunciation is widely used.

Levels of Usage

Since the child learns his speech patterns from those persons in his environment, he may use predominantly acceptable assimilations or he may use many unacceptable assimilations. Pronunciations vary according to the occupations and to the social backgrounds of the individuals using them. When a child lives in a low socioeconomic neighborhood, he is likely to hear substandard pronunciations which are typical of the speech of persons with limited educational opportunity. Substandard speech sounds careless, uncultured, and excessively slurred. Phrases like "jawannago?" for "do you want to go?" are part of the pattern. Education tends to influence the individual to drop these pronunciations which are social hindrances.

Formal pronunciation lies at the other extreme. It is used mainly in lectures and addresses by ministers, statesmen, and public speakers. Those using it tend to speak precisely, quite slowly, carefully, and deliberately. They do not say *haven't* but rather *have not*. Although the educated speaker does use formal speech before a large audience, he has tended in recent years to be less formal even in a formal situation.

Informal pronunciation, lying between the two extremes, is the pronunciation employed in the conversational speech of educated persons. Informal pronunciation shows more regional flavor than formal speech. Its vowels are less distinct. It is uttered at a faster rate. Many consonants, difficult to say in their particular positions, are dropped or assimilated with other sounds. For example, "I want to go" may become "I wanta go" or "Joe and Mary" becomes "Joe 'n Mary." It is used in the classrooms, at social gatherings, and at council meetings. Informal speech is the conversation of our normal, everyday life; it is sometimes called colloquial speech.

Obviously, these three levels are not completely discrete; overlapping does exist. Some words, patterns of speech, and grammatical structures are used in all three areas; others in two areas. Since, however, these levels are part of our speech conventions, students do well to understand them.

Many teachers, therefore, teach these three levels to their students. High school teachers may teach them by asking students to play roles (as accepting the honor of being chosen "Miss America" at Atlantic City, being a lumberjack in the North Country, and talking with members of the student council) or by discussing the characteristics of the three levels. One elementary teacher uses creative dramatics—with the "President" addressing the nation, with two "lumbermen" telling tall tales, and with a "doctor" talking to his patient. The students adopt the necessary vocabulary and speech patterns. After the performance, the students analyze the differences among the three levels.

Regional Differences

We have spoken about a "standard" pronunciation and indicated that pronunciation varies with levels of usage. Another difference exists—that of region. Again in any one community the accepted speech is that spoken by the cultured, educated members of the community regardless of whether the community is in the North, South, East, or West. The educated person from Boston has little difficulty understanding the educated person from Atlanta. The backwoodsman from Minnesota with little education may, however, have difficulty understanding the mountaineer from Tennessee with little education. Differences in speech among the educated are not as wide as those among the uneducated, even though admittedly there are discernible differences in the speech patterns of educated persons of different areas.

Early texts dealing with phonetics list three main regional zones: Southern, Eastern, and General American, with General American being spoken by about four-fifths of the population. The work of linguistic scholars, however, now defines geographical divisions more precisely. Thomas (20, p. 216) reports that the geographical divisions in American speech are most clearly defined along the Atlantic Coast. There he notes Eastern New England, the Middle Atlantic area, and the South. He adds to these areas the New York City area which he says is anomalous because its speech resembles both the Middle Atlantic and Southern types and because this type was never reflected further west. He further includes the North Central area, Western Pennsylvania, with Pittsburgh as its cultural and economic center, the Southern Mountain area, including most of the mountain settlements of some Southern states, Central Midland, the Northwest, and the Southwest coastal area.[1]

The differences among the areas are, however, not too numerous. A New Englander and a Southerner may say *bahn* for *barn*,

---

[1] See map in C. K. Thomas, *Phonetics of American English* (New York: Ronald Press, 1958), p. 232 or in A. J. Bronstein, *The Pronunciation of American English* (New York: Appleton-Century-Crofts, 1960), p. 46.

whereas an Ohioan is likely to pronounce the *r* in the same word. A New Englander approaches *pahth* for *path*. The Ohioan is likely to use the same vowel in *path* that he uses in *cat*. In the South the *o* in *glory* is usually the same *o* as in *tote;* whereas in some other regions, it may be the *aw* sound in *law*. The vowel in the word *scarce* in the North Central and Eastern areas may be either the vowel found in *hate* or the one in *let;* in the South, for the word *scarce* the vowel in *hat* is heard frequently. In *greasy* and the verb *grease,* the New Englander uses the *s* sound whereas the Southerner uses the *z* sound.

Influence of Spelling on Pronunciation

Until the fifteenth or sixteenth century spelling, changing frequently, kept pace with changes in pronunciation. As we look at the following extract from the Prologue to *The Canterbury Tales,* we realize how different our spelling is today. This excerpt is representative of Middle English.

The Prioresse:

Ther was also a nonne, a Prioresse,
That of hir smylyng was ful symple and coy;
Hir gretteste ooth was but by Seint Loy;
And she was cleped Madame Eglentyne.
Ful wel she soong the servyce dyvyne,
Entuned in hir nose ful semely, ...

For the last four or five hundred years spelling has remained relatively constant while pronunciations have changed. Spelling today, therefore, does not closely approximate the pronunciation of words. For example, the *t* sound in *castle* and *whistle,* the *b* sound in *limb* and *comb,* the *w* sound in *write,* the *s* sound in *island,* and the *l* sound in *calm* are not pronounced. The ĭ [I] sound is variously spelled as *o* in women, *y* in *myth,* and *i* in linen.

The discrepancy between sound and spelling has caused some

persons to ask that the writing conform to the sounds. Thus, over the years, many attempts have been made to change spelling to reflect the spoken word. Before George Bernard Shaw died, he specified in his will that a considerable sum of money be used for spelling reform. Such systems are frequently proposed, then abandoned. The same discrepancy has caused others to try to make the sound conform to the spelling. Some persons today try to pronounce both *p* and *b* in *cupboard* and all the sounds in *indict*. Although the *t* in *often* was dropped, it is creeping back. The same is true of the *l* in *almond*. Some of our American pronunciations as distinguished from British pronunciations show that we have placed some value on spelling. For example the name *Anthony* in Britain is pronounced with a *t* for the *th* and *secretary* in British English usually has three syllables as compared to our four syllables.

Influence of Dictionaries on Pronunciation

Long before dictionaries existed, people understood the words that others pronounced. Today, however, lexicographers record pronunciations. One of the dictionary's functions is to describe the pronunciation of a word, not to dictate or prescribe it. The early lexicographers based their recording of pronunciations not only on the pronunciations of the cultured people of the time, such as statesmen and actors, but also on their own idiosyncrasies. Daniel Webster, however, realized that pronunciations must be based on the pronunciations of the people. Mencken says of Webster:

He was always at great pains to ascertain actual usages and in the course of his journeys from State to State to perfect his copyright on his first spelling book he accumulated a large amount of interesting and valuable material, especially in the field of pronunciation ... He proposed therefore that an American standard be set up, independent of the English standard, and that it be inculcated in the schools throughout the country. He argued that it should be determined not by "the practice of any particular class of people," but by "the general practice of the nation ..." (17, p. 9).

Today lexicographers do try to record accurately the pronunciations of the educated, cultured members of our country and to keep the recordings current.

A pronunciation given in a dictionary is a generalization of the way many persons say a word. The recording of this generalization differs from dictionary to dictionary. Dictionaries frequently record more than one pronunciation. In some instances, the first pronunciation is the one held to be more widely used; in others, the editor makes no attempt to show which pronunciation is the more prevalent. At least one dictionary indicates pronunciations current in regional areas. Most do not. Some dictionaries record the pronunciations using diacritic markings; others record them with phonetic symbols. Some adopt for representation the style of formal platform speech, others include informal pronunciations. The teacher should read the introduction to a dictionary to learn what its levels and procedures are. He should also note its date to determine whether the pronunciations recorded are current.

For example, Webster's, *New International Dictionary* (2nd ed.), is a dictionary that bases its pronunciations on formal platform speech. On the other hand, Kenyon and Knott's, *A Pronouncing Dictionary of American English,* is "a dictionary of colloquial English, of the everyday unconscious speech of cultivated people— of those in every community who carry on the affairs and set the social and education standards of those communities" (5, p. vii). Webster's *New International Dictionary* (3rd ed.) uses diacritic markings, based on spelling, to indicate pronunciation. For example, the sounds represented by the letters italicized in the following words: sof*a*, slack*e*n, penc*i*l, butt*o*n, circ*u*s, mart*y*r, and the sound that occurs between the *k* and *l* in *tinkle* are all represented by different symbols in Webster's *New International Dictionary*. Kenyon and Knott, on the contrary, represent the sound in these listed words by the same phonetic symbol, a schwa/ə/. Kenyon and Knott base the pronunciations in their dictionary on the International Phonetic Alphabet.

Dictionaries are useful in assisting us to pronounce unfamiliar words. When students come across a word like *esophageal,* the dictionary is an excellent source of information for pronunciation. But for the usual, everyday words, students do better to train their ears to listen rather than to find the pronunciations in the dictionary, for we learn pronunciation largely through imitation. The person desiring to improve his pronunciation must listen to the speech of the educated, cultivated members of his community who have had certain social advantages. In addition, he must listen to himself (often with a recorder) so that he knows how his speech differs from theirs. If a student looks up *duty* in the dictionary, he may find the *y* sound before the *u;* however, careful reading of the introduction of the dictionary usually indicates that the word is pronounced both with and without the *y* sound. Surely to listen and to perceive the differences is more helpful than to use the dictionary. Furthermore, dictionaries give pronunciations of a word as it is used individually. When we speak, however, we rarely speak in single words, but rather in phrases or sentences. The same words in different phrases with different rhythm, tempo, intonation, and meaning intended by the speaker do not sound alike. For instance, dictionaries usually include the strong forms (stressed ones), not the weak forms (unstressed). The student, whether in elementary or in secondary school, should learn to use the weak forms both in speaking and in reading aloud.

Strong and Weak Forms

We frequently change the sounds in conversation from strong to weak forms. The following are examples: When a child reads the word *to* in a list of words, he pronounces it as he does *two* or *too.* But when he reads *to* in the sentence "I want to do it," the vowel in *to* is no longer a long o͞o but a short o͝o or even the schwa/ə/, the sound in the last syllable of *sofa.* The *to* pronounced like *two* is the strong form while the *to* pronounced like *to͝o* is the weak form. When we say we live in apartment 2A, we pronounce the *a* to rhyme with *day*. But when we say "We live in a house," the *a* is the same sound as we use in the last syllable of *sofa*, the schwa. The *a* that rhymes with *day* is the strong form; the one that is the schwa is the weak form. The *a* in *and* in a list of words is pronounced with a short *a* but the *a* of *and* in the phrase *Mary and John* is likely to be the schwa. The first *a* is the strong form; the second *a* the weak form. Ordinarily we use the weak forms of pronouns, prepositions, articles, auxiliaries, and conjunctions in conversation, except where we want to stress a particular word. For example, if we want to stress that *both* Mary *and* John are going, we may use the strong form of *and*. In strong forms, the vowel is stressed; in weak forms, it is weakened or unstressed.

Unacceptable Diction

Teachers are particularly concerned with those pronunciations which are substandard, which make a student's speech unacceptable, or which indicate that the student is not following accepted speech conventions. These unacceptable pronunciations are different from articulatory defects which are definitely speech difficulties. The correctionist works with those articulatory defects which are definitely speech difficulties. The ten-year-old boy who substitutes *f* and *v* for the two *th's* or the twelve-year-old who still says *w* for *r* is in need of speech correction help. The child, however, who carelessly substitutes *t* and *d* for the two *th's*, who says *acrost* for *across* needs the help of the classroom teacher to improve his speech.

Children's unacceptable diction usually involves: (1) the substitution of one sound for another; (2) omission of sounds; (3) addition of sounds; (4) transposition of sounds; and (5) distortion of sounds.

Substitution of Sounds

The substitution of one sound for another is frequently associated with substandard speech. One consonant may be substituted

for another. A common unacceptable substitution of consonants is
the substitution of *d* for *th,* as in *dem* and *dose* for *these* and *those.*
Some substitutions are, however, acceptable. For example, educated
speakers pronounce *when, where,* and *what* either with an initial
wh or *w.* Other acceptable substitutions are represented by *ingcome
tax* for *income tax, grampa* for *grandpa,* and *pangcake* for *pancake.*
One vowel is frequently substituted for another. The substitution
of the *oy* sound for the *er* sound, as in *boyd* for *bird,* is an instance
of the unacceptable substitution of one diphthong for a vowel. In
some areas, this substitution is fast disappearing. One cause may
be the humor associated with it. Stories such as the following give
a social impetus to drop the substitution:

The child said to the teacher, "Look at the boid on the window
sill." The teacher remonstrated, "You mean bird."

To which the child replied, "He choips like a boid."
Some vowel substitutions as *merry* for *Mary* are acceptable. Common vowel substitutions which are not acceptable are:

short *i* for *e,* as *git* for *get*

short *i* or *e* for short *u,* as *sich* or *sech* for *such, jist* or *jest*
for *just*

short *e* for short *i,* as *ben* for *been*

short *oo* for short *i,* as *mulkman* for *milkman*

er for *oy,* as *berl* for *boil*

Voicing and unvoicing errors are errors of substitution, for they
are the substitution of a voiced sound for an unvoiced sound or of
an unvoiced sound for a voiced sound. *S* and *z* are often substituted
for each other. They are made in the same place (tip of tongue
behind upper teeth ridge or lower teeth ridge), but *z* has voice
whereas *s* does not. The other sounds commonly confused are *t* and
d and *ch* and *j.*

A child may substitute a voiced *th* for the voiceless *th* in the word
truth. This error in which a voiced sound has replaced an unvoiced
sound is unacceptable.

On the other hand, an unvoiced sound may replace a voiced

sound. The child may substitute *s* for *z*, *ch* for *j*, *sh* for *zh*. He may use *s* in the word *rose* rather than a *z*, a *ch* in the word *orange*, rather than a *j*, or an *sh* in the word *pleasure* rather than a *zh*. Or he may use an *s* in *because* rather than a *z*. Again these are all unacceptable.

In some instances, the changes are acceptable. For example, the *American College Dictionary* and the Kenyon and Knott dictionary list both *absorb* and *abzorb* for *absorb*.

Omission of Sounds

Frequently sounds included in the orthographic representation are omitted. Most dictionaries agree that the first *r* in *February* is pronounced. Kenyon and Knott, however, indicate that the pronunciations with or without *r* are acceptable. The word *clothes* is frequently pronounced *cloz*, omitting the *th* sound completely. Both the *American College Dictionary* and Webster's *New Collegiate Dictionary* accept these variants. Before a teacher insists on the inclusion of a sound, we recommend that a good recent dictionary be consulted.

The following, however, are examples of unacceptable diction characterized by omission of sounds.

> *Libarian* for *librarian*
> *reconize* for *recognize*
> *probly* for *probably*
> *stronger* without the *g* sound after the *ng* sound
> *finger* for *fingger*
> *uge* for *huge*
> *simily* for *similarly*

Addition of Sounds

Again throughout the years we have added sounds that are now acceptable. *Against* was once *agens*. The sound *t* was added. Dictionaries for years did not recognize the *t* in *often* or the *h* in *forehead*. Some dictionaries now include both pronunciations of

these words. Many additions, however, exist which are not acceptable. Examples of them are:

> *wisht* for *wish*
> *acrosst* for *across*
> *efen* for *if*
> *ringging* for *ringing*
> *fillum* for *film*
> *umberella* for *umbrella*
> *onct* for *once*
> *drownded* for *drowned*
> *plumber* (with the b) for *plumber*
> *athalete* for *athlete*

Transposition of Sounds

Children frequently, and adults sometimes, transpose sounds.
Here again dictionaries record that educated persons use some of
these transpositions. Kenyon and Knott list both *children* and
childern and *hunderd* and *hundred*. Cultured persons, however,
clearly do not use some of these transpositions. Examples of these
unacceptable transpositions are: *prespire* for *perspire, plubicity* for
publicity, modren for *modern, revelant* for *relevant, I akst him* for
I asked him, pernounce for *pronounce,* and *tradegy* for *tragedy.*

Distortion of Sounds

Sometimes a child approximates a given sound but distorts it.
He may make an *s* so that it cannot be clearly distinguished from
an *sh,* or a *t* so that it is almost like a *d.* The problem arises as to
how liberal to be in the acceptance of distortions. The first part of
the diphthong of *now* is normally a back sound. Many Americans,
however, raise the tongue on this diphthong so that it is in the same
position as the *a* in *cat.* Furthermore, many Americans raise the
tongue on the *a* sound in *hat* nearly to the position of the *e* sound
as found in *met.*

Correcting Children's Unacceptable Diction

The first step in correcting a child's errors in diction is his acceptance of the fact that to speak well is a social advantage. The teacher frequently can help children come to this realization through a discussion of speech standards. The discussion might well include: What is acceptable speech? Who uses acceptable speech? Why do we need acceptable speech? When do we need acceptable speech? Where do we need acceptable speech? How can we help one another to have acceptable speech?

As children talk about what acceptable speech is, they will not only list correct pronunciation, pleasant voices, and saying the sounds correctly, but they will also frequently include such other factors as sounding friendly, making one's self clear to others, and having others respond favorably. One child said that acceptable speech was really a way of getting along well with others. This idea, which the children at first rejected, provided the impetus for the children's speech work. A teacher can help children to realize that our speech today is a living, changing medium of communication. Children are interested in the fact that pronunciations have changed, that meanings of words have changed, and that even grammar has changed over the centuries.

When children talk about who uses acceptable speech, they are really setting up their standard. They include among those who habitually use acceptable speech some of the educated members of the community. Often they cite the names of broadcasters. Analyzing why the children like the voice and diction of certain broadcasters is helpful. Such talk encourages children to listen to the articulation and pronunciations of the broadcasters and, as a result, to be critical of their own speech. Many times they imitate some of the pronunciations of broadcasters. One teacher employs a very interesting device to teach the levels of pronunciation. She uses puppets dressed in various ways—as a king, as a queen, as a bedraggled beggar. As the children manipulate the puppets, they speak as they think the characters would. This device serves as a basis for discussion of how people in the various walks of life speak differently.

The question, "why do we need acceptable speech?" is always provocative. Some students quite frankly feel little need of acceptable speech. They say that most persons have little difficulty in understanding them. They do not see that their present uncultured speech makes any difference in their relationships with people. On the other hand, acceptable speech to some seems a valuable asset. One youngster, interestingly enough, said that when he collected for his newspapers, he talked very carefully. He said that he thought his customers might not consider him a good salesman if he spoke carelessly. He also made the point that his attempts at good speech and good manners paid dividends in terms of tips. He ended by saying that he enjoyed speaking well and being courteous to his customers.

From such a point the talk may well turn to the times when we need acceptable speech. Obviously the child selling papers profited from his use of acceptable speech. But another youngster made the point that the older boys on the block think him a sissy when he speaks well. He felt that he ought to have several sets of speech patterns: one for school, one for home, and one for his playmates. He indicated that when he spoke well at home, his brother accused him of showing off. But he also insisted that he had to speak better at home than when he was playing with his friends. He thought his solution of several patterns a good one.

This topic leads naturally into the places where we need acceptable speech. Children usually agree that whatever their jobs are going to be, they will have to speak well. This objective is not immediate. Therefore, children must think of present situations where they need good speech. One child said that while he worked in his father's shoe repair shop, he must wait on customers courteously and speak to them so that they understand him easily.

In all this discussion, the teacher's voice and diction are important. Unconsciously the child thinks of how his teacher sounds as he speaks. Children imitate teachers, particularly teachers they like.

They wear clothes similar to their teachers', walk as the teachers walk, and speak in the same way.

Many times the child wants to speak better than he does but he does not know what to do about it. The teacher gives him individual help. First, the child must hear what he is saying that is unacceptable. Then he must be able to make the sounds correctly and to incorporate them into words. Finally, the new way of speaking must become part of his habitual speech pattern. One boy's attitude indirectly showed the result of his teacher's leadership. He said *dese* and *dose* for *these* and *those*. The child never realized that he said these sounds incorrectly. When the teacher told him, he was not convinced. Whereupon the teacher recorded some of his conversation. As he heard the inaccuracies, his remark was revealing: "It's like *I done*. I got rid of the bad grammar. I'll get rid of *dese* and *dose* too." Quite obviously he classed both the grammatical error and the diction errors as social hindrances.

After the teacher has motivated the child to want to improve his speech, he must then help the child hear what he is saying that is unacceptable. Consequently, the child must be trained to listen to those who are the cultured leaders of the community and to himself. The child's ever-present source of imitation is his own teacher, whose speech must be worthy of imitation. Sometimes the teacher believes that she must first teach children to listen to sounds in general before attempting any improvement work. The activity described in Chapter 8 where children listen and write about sounds in the house, in the street, and at various seasons of the year gives this kind of auditory training. Other activities include listening to poems that are alliterative, to sounds of names of classmates—enjoying the sounds of the names, making up rhymes about them, giving names to the various consonantal sounds—then proceeding to build a story around these sounds. After the general training comes the more specific training in listening.

The next step is to teach the child to make the sound accurately or pronounce the word acceptably. One teacher had a large number of students in her class who substituted *n* for *ng*. She read them part of "The Cataract of Lodore" by Robert Southey. While the youngsters did not completely understand the meaning of the poem, they were aware of the repetition of the *ing* sound. They liked the poem just for its sounds and finally repeated some of the *ing* words themselves. At this point the teacher explained that many of the children made an *ng* error—that they substituted the sound of *n* for *ng*. She told them *n* was made with the tip of the tongue and *ng* with the back of the tongue. She asked them to imitate her saying: *goin, going.* The children then made up sentences using many words with *ing.* From then on they helped one another to say the *ing* accurately. They were proud that they knew that they were not dropping a *g* but were substituting *n* for *ng.* The final step is practice in making the sound, using the words, and incorporating the corrected sound or pronunciation in conversation. The teacher may use material for reading aloud that contains the sound and words. But if he does, he must make sure that the children readily understand the meaning of the material and that its content and style are stimulating to the child and his audience. The teacher may also promote conversation or telephone situations involving the words or sounds. Or he may create creative drama situations which will involve the desired words and sounds. The student must learn to use the sound or pronunciation consistently. When he forgets, the teacher should remind him.

Children use the dictionary to find the pronunciation of unfamiliar words. Children like to use the dictionary if it is serving a real need of the group. In one class the children bring in news reports. When a word that is new appears, one of the children looks it up and gives its pronunciation and its meaning. In addition, as the children study a new area and find unfamiliar words, they look them up and learn their meaning and pronunciation. They file this information. At the end of each month, copies of the words with their meanings and pronunciations are distributed to each student.

Unacceptable Vocal Qualities

The teacher is concerned that a student's voice serve his communicative purposes as well as it can. The student's voice problem may be serious. We will discuss the more serious difficulties of voice in Chapter 12. When a child has a consistently hoarse voice, the teacher may assume that the difficulty calls for specialized help. Many times, however, children's voices are adequate for communicative purposes but they would be more effective if improved. In such instances the teacher works for improvement. He takes into consideration four aspects of voice: volume, pitch, quality, and rate of speaking. (See Chapter 12 for correcting significant vocal difficulties.)

Loudness

The child's voice should not be too loud or too soft. He should be able to adjust the loudness of his voice to the demands of the room in which he is speaking. Florence always spoke rather quietly. In the classroom children heard her fairly well although sometimes they had to listen carefully. But when she was to act as mistress of ceremonies in the auditorium, she discovered that the children in the back of the room could not hear her. She had to learn to adjust the volume of her voice to the size of the larger room. She further learned that speaking more slowly and articulating more clearly helped her to be heard. Harry, a ten-year-old, seemed to be yelling. He rarely spoke quietly. He seemed afraid that his classmates would not heed him and to feel that when he spoke loudly, they listened more attentively. He came from a family where he who spoke loudest received the most attention. With the teacher's direction he came to realize that he was more effective as a personality and easier to listen to when he spoke more softly.

Pitch

The child's voice should be appropriate to his age, sex, and physical maturity. It should express the meaning and emotion of what he desires to communicate. The material on pitch, pages 277-279, is important in consideration of children's pitch. No child's habitual pitch should be changed without careful diagnosis of his pitch difficulty. Many changes are safely made, however. Mark's voice tended to be monotonous, for he spoke on one pitch level. Although he was a lively youngster, he had acquired the habit of speaking with little inflection. The school psychologist felt that his monotonous speech was a carry-over from a time when he had had many adjustment problems. These problems were no longer evident, but the monotonous voice was. The teacher helped him to make his voice more lively.

Quality of Voice

Quality of voice refers to the tone that distinguishes one voice from another. The tone differs because of the way the resonating system acts to modify it and because of the particular way in which vocal cords vibrate. The quality may be clear, pleasant, resonant; or it may be breathy, muffled, or nasal. The changing of a consistent quality of voice is discussed in the chapter on voice. Quality, however, is also used to help express a person's feelings and emotions. The teacher can help the child to use a quality of voice that does express his feeling. One child, partly because of personality difficulties, always spoke as if he were angry. With the teacher's help, the child began to realize that his attitude toward life tended to be negative rather than positive. With the guidance of the school psychologist and with such classroom work as creative dramatics, the boy changed his tone from one of almost consistent anger to one of friendliness.

Rate of Speaking

Few children speak too slowly. A large number of them speak at too fast a rate. Some are in a hurry to get their words into the conversation. Others tend to run fast, to work fast, and to talk fast. They need to realize that their listeners miss part of what they are saying because of their speed. One fourteen-year-old boy sang very well. In fact, he was the best boy vocalist in his school. But when he spoke, he ran his words together and overassimilated sounds so that his listeners missed at least half of what he was saying. The speed with which he spoke affected even the quality of his speaking voice. It became muffled. Yet when he sang, he articulated very clearly and the quality of his voice was excellent. As he heard the contrast between his singing and speaking voices on a recording, he diagnosed his own difficulty and proceeded to do something about it.

Teaching the Improvement of Voice

Discussing voice and its part in communication makes children aware of their own voices. Children talk about the kinds of voices they like. Almost inevitably the discussion goes on to how voice reflects personality. They ask themselves whether certain voices suggest friendliness and kindness or whether they indicate that the person is bored and irritated. They talk about the control of pitch, volume, and speed. The next step is for the individual child to use a voice that expresses the meaning and feeling he intends to express. A recording of voice is an excellent motivation for children to change their voices.

Loudness

Almost all children have to be reminded to speak loudly enough to be heard in a classroom. Inability to hear a child justifies interrupting him. One teacher said that he did not like to interrupt Jimmy to ask him to speak louder, because Jimmy was so interested in what he was telling. Jimmy was interested, but at least sixteen children in the room were squirming and at least six were talking with one another. They resented the teacher's admonition to them to listen. An early interruption, casually asking Jimmy to speak so that all could hear, might well have avoided the discourtesy on the part of his audience. Children need to know that rate of speaking and clear articulation are related to ability to be heard. When the teacher insists on each child's speaking loudly enough to be heard, communication is easier. In some instances the child's speaking too softly may be related to his feeling of insecurity in the room or of general insecurity. The teacher must do what he can to make sure the social atmosphere of the room is conducive to speaking and being heard. If the child is generally insecure, help should be given to modify this situation.

Pitch, Quality, and Rate

Children learn that the rate of speaking and the pitch and quality of their voices show how they feel about what they are reading or saying. Some teachers use puppets or creative dramatics very effectively for this purpose. One child holds the angry puppet who tells the others off. Another holds the sad puppet who speaks slowly of the misfortunes of others. Another holds the gay puppet whose speech is merry. The teacher helps the child to use the pitch, quality, and rate that are most expressive for his particular puppet. The teacher can use creative dramatics for the same purpose. Through setting up particular situations, children realize the importance of pitch, quality, and rate of speaking in their interpersonal relationships. They learn that the expression of different moods and of different meanings requires differences in pitch, quality, and rate.

One teacher uses a single phrase, asking that the children think of as many ways as possible of conveying different meanings with it. One of her phrases is, "Why, Joe and Jill were half an hour late." Children express happiness, sorrow, anger, sarcasm, or sympathy at Joe and Jill's being late. Sometimes they build a story around a particular child's rendition of the phrase.

References and Suggested Readings

1. AKIN, J., *And So We Speak: Voice and Articulation.* Englewood Cliffs, N.J.: Prentice-Hall, 1958. (Contains chapters on the linguistic environment, the structure of American-English sounds, the anatomy of the speech mechanism, and voice.)

2. ALLEN, H. B., *Readings in Applied English Linguistics.* New York: Appleton-Century-Crofts, 1958. (Contains an excellent discussion of the standards of pronunciation and grammar.)

3. BRONSTEIN, A., *The Pronunciation of American English*. New York: Appleton-Century-Crofts, 1958. (Contains a particularly good section on the standards of American English. Includes a complete and thorough analysis of all the sounds of American English.)

4. BRONSTEIN, A. ,"Trends in American Pronunciation." *Quarterly Journal of Speech,* **XXVIII** (December 1942), 452-456.

5. CROCKER, L., "The Linguist, The Freshman, and the Purist." *The Speech Teacher,* **III** (March 1954), 129-130. (Points out that the constantly changing usage is difficult to teach. Depicts the struggle between the linguists and the purists.)

6. EISENSON, J., *Basic Speech*. New York: Macmillan, 1950, Chapters 2, 5, 6, and 7. (Includes suggestions for improving the speech sounds and voice.)

7. FAIRBANKS, G., *Voice and Articulation Drillbook*. New York: Harper and Brothers, 1959.

8. FRANCIS, W. N., *The Structure of American English*. New York: Ronald Press, 1958. (Includes chapters on language and linguistic science, phonetics, phonemics, morphemics, grammar, the dialects of American English, and linguistics and the teacher of English.)

9. HAHN, E., and C. S. LOMAS, D. E. HARGIS, and D. VANDRAEGEN, *Basic Voice Training for Speech*. New York: McGraw-Hill, 1958. (Contains material on critical listening, articulation, and integrating the vocal skills.)

10. KENYON, J. S., *American Pronunciation*. (9th ed.) Ann Arbor, Mich.: George Wahr, 1944.

11. ———, "Levels of Speech and Colloquial English." *English Journal,* **XXXVII** (January 1948), 25-31. (Distinguishes between "cultural level of English" and "functional varieties of standard English." Points out that it is impossible to draw a strict dividing line between the colloquial and the literary or formal diction.)

12. ———, and T. A. KNOTT, *A Pronouncing Dictionary of American English*. Springfield, Mass.: G. and C. Merriam, 1944. (Provides the best source for the pronunciation of American-English words.)

13. KONIGSBERG, E., "Making Drill Functional." *The Speech Teacher,* **I** (March 1952), 128-130. (Suggests ways of making drill on articulation and voice interesting to the students. Shows the need for teaching voice and articulation.)

14. KRAPP, G. P., *The English Language in America*. New York: Appleton-Century-Crofts, 1925.

15. LANGE, P., "Pronunciation and the Dictionaries." *Quarterly Journal of Speech*, **XXXII** (April 1946), 190-193. (Describes a study of six dictionaries. Indicates the need for standardizing symbols of pronunciation. Gives suggestions for improving dictionaries.)

16. MAYNARD, N., "Poor Reading, Handmaiden of Poor Speech." *The Speech Teacher,* **V** (January 1956), 40-46. (Reviews the relationship between reading and speaking difficulties. Shows that poor reading can be caused by poor speech on three reading levels: the readiness level, the primary or beginning level, and the intermediate reading level.)

17. MENCKEN, H. L., The American Language. (4th ed.) New York: Alfred A. Knopf, 1946.

18. NICHOLS, R. G., "How Shall We Teach Pronunciation?" *Quarterly Journal of Speech,* **XXVII** (February 1941), 60-67. (Explains the nature of pronunciation, the use of the dictionary, and the influence of mass media on pronunciation. Discusses acceptable pronunciation.)

19. SNOOK, M. J., "Speech and the Language Arts Program." *The Elementary English Review,* **XXII** (April 1945), 139 ff. (Discusses a project for speech improvement in the elementary school.)

20. THOMAS, C. K., *Phonetics of American English.* (2nd ed.) New York: Ronald Press, 1958. (Deals with the pronunciation of English in the United States. Includes chapters on the mechanism of speech, the vowels, the consonants, stress, length of sounds, assimilation, regional variations, and standards of pronunciation.)

21. WEAVER, C. H., "Don't Look It Up—Listen!" *The Speech Teacher,* **VI** (September 1957), 240-246. (Points out the constant shift in the pronunciation of words. Discusses the use of the term "cultured speech." Indicates that the dictionary is a guide, not a refuge, in matters of pronunciation.)

Problems

1. Visit a classroom. Either (*a*) list the articulatory errors you hear or (*b*) the characteristics of the voices which are ineffective in the classroom situation.

2. Indicate the ways in which the teacher of a classroom you have visited helped the children to speak with more pleasant and effective voices.

3. Find a list of frequently mispronounced words. Look up ten of

them in three different recent dictionaries. Note the agreement or disagreement on how to pronounce these words in the dictionaries you consulted.

4. Read the introductions to two unabridged dictionaries. Tell how the information might prove helpful in your use of the dictionary in the classroom.

5. Listen to your favorite newscaster. What are the characteristics of his voice which made you think him effective?

6. Using the word "insane," indicate synonyms that might be used in formal, informal, and substandard speech.

7. As far as possible, list the influences of parents, school, community, and education upon your own speech.

8. List five sentences, phrases, or words in which assimilation occurs. Indicate the assimilation that may occur.

9. List the voicing and unvoicing errors, if any, made by one child.

10. Would you accept the following omissions or transpositions in the pronunciation of the following words:

goverment for government
childern for children
liberry for library
English (without the *g*) for English (with the *g* sound)
Support your "decision."

4

The Teacher

as a Speaker

No

IN THIS chapter we will talk about the teacher's own diction, voice, and way of communicating ideas and listening to the ideas of others. Because children tend to imitate the diction, voice, and manner of communication of their teacher, he is a powerful force influencing his children's speech. The teacher, especially if he is admired, serves as a model for his students. For most impressionable school children, the respected teacher is the embodiment of standard. Children who cannot otherwise identify with a teacher are likely to do so in manner of speech.

The following incident illustrates one way in which a child may copy his teacher. Joan, a kindergartner, was playing school with her playmates. She was sweet and patient, and she kept her voice quiet and pleasant as she worked with "her children." The next year she was again playing school, but quite a different school. She shouted, "Get in line, Jimmy. Don't talk so loud." When Janey did not spell a word accurately, she remonstrated crossly, "Janey, you know better than that." Joan's voice, usually pleasant, was loud, shrill, and scolding as she played school. One day when a neighbor asked her how she liked her teacher, she said, "Oh, she's nice only she hollers a lot. I liked my kindergarten teacher better. She was always kind." Although Joan did not point out the differences in the speech of the two teachers, she revealed them in her playing of the roles.

Studies show that a relationship does exist between a teacher's speaking ability and his professional success. Wagner (11) draws the conclusion from a study of 283 senior students that estimates of teaching success correlate quite highly with the index of achievement in speech making. Fessenden (4) found that the better student teachers were the better student speakers. For example, those students who received A as a grade in practice teaching, received a modal speech grade of A. Those who received B in practice teaching, received a modal speech grade of B. Those who received C in practice teaching, received a modal speech grade of D. His study also indicates that the principals of schools in which 400 high school teachers taught judged those teachers with the most college speech courses to be the best teachers. Lillywhite (8) reports that 61 percent of the administrators he questioned note that some teachers fail to secure positions because of inadequate speech. Of the administrators questioned, 72 percent placed the percentage of failure between 1 to 10 percent; 23 percent between 10 and 30 percent; and the rest between 30 and 50 percent. A study by Bond reported in the *Journal of Education Research* (1) gives evidence that effective speech, interpreted broadly, contributes markedly to successful teaching. He indicates that teachers use speech to ask questions, make suggestions, aid students in formulating ideas, summarize, conduct drills, give directions, explain, and lecture. He selected from a total of 855 those students who had been rated high in speech; this group comprised 31 percent of the whole. He found that the mean ratings of this group were higher than the ratings of the unselected group in every one of 32 items important in teaching and that the ratings of this group were particularly high in traits pertaining directly to pupil-teacher contact.

These studies do not prove that more speech training makes a better teacher. It may well be that students who naturally are superior in oral communication are more successful teachers. It may also mean that students who elect more speech courses have the kind of personalities and interests that make them more successful teachers. These studies do indicate, however, that speaking abilities are important in teaching success. They also suggest that teacher training institutions should find out what speech factors in the teaching situation are important and learn how a teacher can be prepared to deal with these factors effectively. This section will analyze the speaking factors that seem to be part of the teaching situation.

Speaking Factors in the Teaching Situation

Let us assume for this purpose that in the teacher's speaking the following factors are involved: the teacher himself, his ideas, the organization and presentation of these ideas, his listening to the ideas of his students, the social climate of his classroom, and its physical environment. These are very similar to the factors in any speaking situation. In other words, teaching is merely a specialized kind of speaking situation wherein the teacher has a greater degree of control than usual over ideas, their presentation and organization, over his listeners, over the social climate, and over the physical environment.

Teacher's Personality

First, the teacher himself is a factor in the speaking situation. Surely his personal traits and characteristics influence the reactions of his students. Probably an individual is no better a teacher than he is a person. Similarly a speaker is no better a speaker than he is a person. In his *Institutes of Oratory,* Quintilian stresses that the good orator is a good man speaking well. Whately in the nineteenth century, like Aristotle, said the character to be established must be one of good principles, good sense, and good will. Similarly each of us think of certain positive traits that we like in both teachers and speakers. We like the teacher who respects and accepts himself and others, who is intellectually honest, who is unaffected, and who is enthusiastic. The enthusiasm does not need to be vociferous; it may well be quiet. Furthermore, most of us want him to have a sense of humor. Last, most of us want both the teacher and the speaker to be sincerely interested in other human beings.

The Teacher's Voice and Articulation

The voice of the teacher is one of his most important attributes. One teacher reported, "As my voice has become less strident and more mellow, my students are less troublesome and more relaxed." Another said, "As my hoarseness has disappeared and as I have spoken more slowly, my relationships with students are better. One child even remarked that I seemed less angry. And I never really was very angry."

The teacher's voice should be appropriate in loudness, pitch, quality, and rate of speaking. Its level should be loud enough so that students can hear readily, but not loud enough to call attention to itself. He should adjust his voice to the size of the room in which he is speaking. His pitch should be appropriate to the specific occasion. His quality should be pleasant. His rate should be that which the children can understand.

Effective voice is a term that carries different concepts to different people. Hendrickson (7) shows that the correlation between the supervising critic's rating of teachers' voices and the rating of the same teachers' voices by public school supervisors, though positive, is rather low (.20± .03). It may well be that other factors such as personality or ability to teach influence the rating of voice. In a discussion by adults of the voices of television commentators, the personality of the commentators obviously affected the judgment of voices. Several adults, admirers of Ed Murrow, were vociferous in praising his voice. One, however, obviously influenced by dislike of Murrow's personality, declared his voice unpleasant. Most administrators of schools consider voice as part of the whole picture of the teaching applicant. A good proportion of them would not hire a teacher with a nasal, hoarse, weak, or monotonous voice (2).

The teacher should listen carefully to his own voice by means of a high fidelity recording device, preferably after speaking, reading, and participating in discussion in the classroom. After listening, he should analyze to find out what he believes is pleasant and effective and what is unpleasant and ineffective in his voice. At times he should ask help from the school's correctionist. The correctionist can sometimes make a fairly simple suggestion so that when the teacher follows it, he sounds better. For example, one teacher spoke much too rapidly. As she held on to vowels, gave more time for pauses, her voice quality seemed to change. It seemingly became less nasal, less staccato, and much more pleasant.

Just as the voice may attract attention to itself and detract from the communicative ability of a teacher, so may the teacher's articulation. Acceptable articulation allows the children to concentrate on what the teacher is saying. In addition, the teacher's articulation should not be careless or substandard. Even though the teacher may have come from a region where the patterns of pronunciation and usage are different from where he is teaching, his own speech should be representative of the educated speech of his own region. If it is, he will be readily understood. In a study made of attitudes of school administrators toward teachers' speech (2), it was found that the candidate whose speech possesses patterns commonly recognized as "careless" or "substandard" will not be appointed unless other factors are strongly in his favor.

Again listening is important. The teacher should listen to the pronunciations of educated, cultured members of the community and to his own pronunciations. Where he hears differences, he should listen again more intently and more extensively. He should listen to commentators he admires. Where he feels it wise, he should make subtle changes in his articulation.

Ideas

Second, the ideas of the teacher are important. When he has read widely, thought deeply, inquired judiciously, observed keenly, listened carefully, and appraised completely, he has extensive knowledge and, consequently, a fund of ideas from which to draw. But the ideas need not all be derived from books, travel, or learned individuals. Some ideas are creative, original. For instance, the teacher may find a picture in a magazine from which an exciting bit of theater can grow, or may discover a cartoon that motivates discussion, or may invent a game that furthers auditory discrimination. Or, perhaps, he may make up a story that is sheer nonsense, but well suited to his particular group. The good teacher is a person with wide knowledge and understanding and a creative urge who will continue to acquire a liberal education throughout his life.

Speaking Activities Involving the Organization and Presentation of Ideas

The teacher frequently just chats. His friendly "good morning" may make the day start right for Johnny. His truly sympathetic "I'm sorry" may give Helen encouragement to try again after her bit of ceramics blew up in the kiln. His chuckle and his "That's a good story" may make Jay feel a worthwhile member of the class.

A fairly large amount of a teacher's time is spent in explaining. Normally the students want to listen and to understand explanations. Much of the explaining in the classroom is like giving an informative speech. The teacher selects the subject and then gathers his materials by thinking, reading, observing, inquiring, and listening, and these are the materials he uses in planning his presentations. His materials should have a main idea (aim of the lesson) which he must make clear. The teacher should employ such devices as illustration, testimony, audio-visual aids, analogy, just as the speaker, to develop his ideas. Furthermore, the teacher should use the factor of interest to hold the attention of his students and adapt his material to his listeners. In addition, he should introduce his explanation and develop a conclusion. As in a speech, his conclusion may list the main points or may contain a comparison or illustration to summarize. While giving the explanation, the teacher's delivery should be much like that used in an extemporaneous speech, and his language and delivery should suit both his subject and his students. The teacher should plan the presentation carefully and organize it effectively, usually with an outline (a lesson plan).

After he has explained the material and the students have read other materials, the teacher should frequently question them to reinforce their understanding or to clear up confusing points. The questions should be so worded that they stimulate all students to think actively of the answers and to listen intently. As a particular child responds, the teacher should not rephrase the response of a child to get the terminology he prefers, for children grow in language through experimentation and practice. Similarly, to make sure that the child does practice language, he should seldom ask the kind of question which brings forth single words as answers.

Sometimes the teacher persuades. He may want to persuade his students to listen to a particular television program, to investigate the principles of jet propulsion, to find how the city council works, to keep their work corner neat, efficient, and well organized, or to plan an assembly program. In such cases the teacher works hard at persuading. Furthermore, in persuasion he should arrive at his own opinions intelligently and objectively and encourage his students to do the same.

What other speech activities does the teacher engage in? He leads and participates in discussion, reads aloud, and tells stories.

In discussion the teacher and students should share ideas objectively and evaluate them to find answers to a problem. Such sharing fosters understanding and, consequently, a willingness to accept a decision. It constitutes an essential means by which individuals participate in the democratic process. The students, under the guidance of the teacher or one of their classmates, should take part in the formulation of the problem, in setting discussion goals, and in reflective thinking. The teacher should stimulate careful analysis and evaluation, promote clear definitions and explanations, and help the discussion to move forward. Such discussion, however, should be not teacher-centered, but rather student-centered. The teacher should demonstrate by voice and action that he welcomes each contribution, and he should motivate each person to participate by fostering a democratic, permissive atmosphere. Although he may use discussion as problem solving to obtain new knowledge and to find the best solution to a problem, he should recognize that discussion is not feasible when learning has already established knowledge. Furthermore, he is aware that in problem solving, students must have adequate experience to provide bases for understanding the problem.

In reading aloud the teacher must have a thorough understanding of what he is reading and must be able to communicate this understanding to his students. He has selected his material purposefully for learning goals and for the interests, needs, and abilities of his students. As he reads, he is conversational. Similarly in telling a story the teacher recreates the ideas of the story and its characters for his listeners. He does not enact the story but rather suggests the characterizations.

Listening

Just as the teacher sets an example by his speaking, he sets one by listening. Whereas the teacher is important when he gives forth ideas, he is equally important when he receives, interprets, and evaluates the ideas of his students. The teacher almost immediately communicates to his students whether he is listening carefully or whether he is attending to his own affairs or to some other distraction in the room. When the student is chatting, the teacher should listen graciously. When he is reporting, the teacher should listen carefully and thoughtfully. The teacher should show that he is listening by questioning a source, a reason, or a statistic; he should not show disapproval or skepticism, but rather thoughtful interest. As the child persuades, the teacher should listen critically. When the child uses the technique of the half-truth or becomes overly emotional, the teacher should question. His own critical listening sets an example for the student. When the child is playing a part, sad or gay, or when he is recreating a poem, the teacher should listen sympathetically and appreciatively. His listening throughout should be active and should be reflected in both his oral and visual responses to the child.

Social Climate

Some classrooms approach a democratic society whereas others approach an autocratic one. The classroom should approach the democratic society in which we believe. This society promotes respect for the individual and for the group, responsibility of the individual for himself and for the group, and the use of discussion in problem solving. The teacher should foster these attitudes and habits through his acceptance of the individuals within the group, through his feeling of group responsibility, and through his use of group discussion. In addition, many teachers encourage students to participate in planning the work of the classroom. Here children have a chance to assume their share of responsibility for direction of an area of learning. In this process, they are using a tool of democracy, setting up their goals, their rules and limits, and making significant choices. Such processes make them feel free and valued as individuals.

Physical Environment

The teacher should make sure that the physical environment is as conducive to communication as possible. As indicated earlier, the bulletin board, the magazines, and the seating arrangement can stimulate talk. When possible, the teacher should group chairs so that conversation is made easy. He should promote as far as he can a physical environment which fosters speaking and listening.

In summary, the successful classroom teacher strives to develop effective personality traits and characteristics, to increase his fund of ideas, and to present them efficiently and capably. In addition, he tries to listen accurately and perceptively, to develop the kind of social climate that furthers democratic participation and acceptance of self and others, and to make the classroom a comfortable and inviting place in which to live.

References and Suggested Readings

1. BOND, J. A., "Analysis of Observed Traits of Teachers Rated Superior in Using Speech as a Teaching Instrument." *Journal of Education Research,* LI (May 1958), 669-677.

2. BRONSTEIN, A. J., and M. OGILVIE, "Administrators Attitudes Toward the Oral Examination of Teacher Candidates." *The Speech Teacher,* I (September 1952), 174-180.

3. ECROYD, D. H., *Speech in the Classroom.* Englewood Cliffs, N.J.: Prentice-Hall, 1960. (Deals with the relationship of speaking to teaching. Shows how to apply the fundamental principles of speaking, reading, and listening to teaching.)

4. FESSENDEN, S. A., "The Classroom Teacher Is not a Public Speaker." *Quarterly Journal of Speech,* XXIX (February 1943), 92-93. (Reports a survey of 400 high school teachers to show the relationship of courses taken in speech to teaching success. Indicates the relationship between grades in practice teaching and speech courses.)

5. ———, "Speech for the Classroom Teacher." *Speech for All American Youth, Bulletin of the National Association of Secondary School Principals,* XXXII (January 1948), 202-207. (Explains the needs of the teacher in terms of voice and diction.)

6. ———, R. I. JOHNSON, and P. M. LARSON, *The Teacher Speaks.* Englewood Cliffs, N. J.: Prentice-Hall, 1954.

7. HENDRICKSON, E. H., "Comparison and Rating of Voice and Teaching Ability." *Journal of Educational Psychology,* XXXIV (February 1943), 121-123.

8. LILLYWHITE, H., *Speech Needs of Elementary and Secondary Teachers in Minnesota with Special Reference to Teachers College Graduates.* Ph.D. thesis (New York University, 1943).

9. ———, "Speech Needs for Teachers." *Quarterly Journal of Speech,* XXXII (December 1946), 496-501.

10. THOMAS, O., "Discussion: Let's Have More of It." *School Executive,* LXIX (August 1950), 51-53.

11. WAGNER, L. A., *A Diagnosis of the Speech Needs and Abilities of*

Prospective Teachers. Iowa City: Ph.D. thesis (State University of Iowa, August 1937).

Problems

1. Visit three classrooms. Indicate what you consider to be the effect of the voices of the three teachers upon the children.

2. Indicate how you as a teacher can use group discussion methods in your teaching.

3. Read aloud a story or poem that you might use in your classroom.

4. Report on one of the following references: 1, 2, 3, 6 or 10.

5

The Mechanism

for Speech

Voice Production

THE HUMAN voice-producing mechanism functions in a manner roughly comparable to that of a musical wind instrument. The wind or horn instruments employ (1) reeds or the lips of the blower as vibrators or noise makers; (2) air blown over or through the reeds as the source of energy to set the reeds in vibration; and (3) an elongated tube to reinforce the sound produced by the "vibrating" reeds. The human voice-producing mechanism employs laryngeal folds (vocal bands) for "vibrators," air that might otherwise have served only normal respiratory purposes for a source of energy, and the cavities of larynx, pharynx (throat), mouth, and nose as reinforcers or resonators. These cavities, if we include the trachea or windpipe, may be directly compared to a curved, elongated tube of a wind instrument. The human "elongated tube" is considerably more modifiable than any wind instrument, and so is capable of producing a wide variety of sounds that may be modified in respect to pitch, quality, loudness, and duration. The arrangement of the parts of the voice mechanism is indicated in Figure 1.

The Larynx

The larynx, commonly referred to as the voice box, is located in the neck between the root of the tongue and the trachea. The outer and largest part of the larynx consists of two shield-shaped cartilages fused together along an anterior line. Together, these fused shields are known as the thyroid cartilage. The reader may locate the larynx at this point by running his index finger down from the middle of his chin toward his neck. His finger should be stopped by the notch at the point of fusion of the cartilages.

From each side of the larynx, folds of muscle tissue lined by

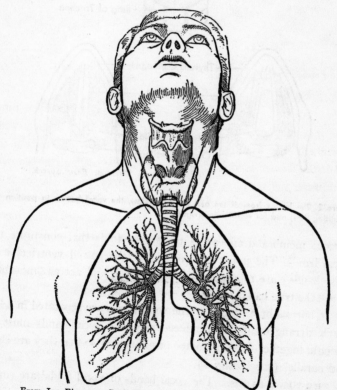

From Jon Eisenson: *Basic Speech.* New York: The Macmillan Co., 1950.

Figure 1. The larynx, trachea, and lungs.

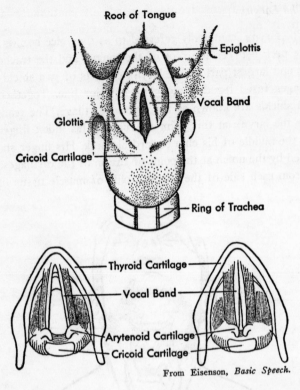

Figure 2. The larynx from above and behind. Below, the vocal bands, in position for breathing (left) and for vocalization (right).

mucous membrane appear as transverse folds that constitute the vocal bands. The upper pair of folds (the paired ventricular or false bands) are relatively soft and flaccid, and not as "movable" as are the true bands below.

In normal breathing, the true vocal bands are separated in a letter V arrangement. To produce voice, the vocal bands must be brought together (approximated or adducted) so that they are close and parallel (see Figure 2).

THE VOCAL BANDS. The vocal bands or vocal folds[1] are small,

---

[1] Unless otherwise specified, all references are to the true vocal bands. These may also be referred to as the vocal folds or vocal cords.

tough strips of connective tissue, which are continuous with comparatively thick strips of voluntary muscle tissue. Viewed from above, the vocal bands appear to be flat folds of muscle with inner edges of connective tissue. In male adults the vocal bands range from about ⅞ inch to 1¼ inches; in adult females they range from ½ inch or less to about ⅞ inch.

The opening between the vocal bands is called the *glottis*. In normal phonation (vocalization) the breath under pressure meets the approximated vocal bands and forces them to move apart. As a result, a stream of air flowing with relatively high velocity escapes between the vocal bands which continue to be held together (approximated) at both ends. The reduction in pressure beneath the bands, together with the reduced air pressure along the sides of the high-velocity air stream, aided by the elasticity of the bands themselves brings about recurrent closures after successive outward movements of the bands. Thus vocalization is maintained. If the action or position of the vocal bands fails to produce a "complete" though momentary interruption in the flow of air, the result is a kind of noise or voice quality we identify as breathiness or hoarseness. Figure 2 indicates the position of the bands as they are approximated and ready to be set into motion by the pressure of the air beneath them.

LOUDNESS. The loudness of the voice is directly related to the vigor with which air is forced from the lungs through the larynx, though not to the total amount of air which is expended. Pressure and velocity depend, in part, upon the size of the glottal opening and the length of time the glottis is open. Loudness is, in effect, a result of the pressure of the released pulsations produced by the movements of the bands. Vocal tones are reinforced in the larynx, in the tracheal cavity immediately below the larynx, in the cavities of the throat and mouth, and in the nasal cavities.

PITCH. The fundamental pitch of a vibrating body varies directly with its frequency of vibration. Thus, the greater the frequency, the higher the resultant pitch. Vocal pitch is a product of factors related to the condition of the vocal bands. The primary factors are the mass or thickness of the bands, their length, and the elasticity (tension) in relationship to mass and length. In the process of phonation the vocal bands elongate as they increase in tension. By the same process, the bands also are reduced in mass per unit area. The overall effect of the modification of mass-tension factors is to produce a higher rather than a lower pitch when the bands are set into motion. In general, the greater the tension, the higher the pitch. If tension is held constant, with greater length or mass, the pitch is lower. If length and mass are held constant, the greater the tension of the vocal bands, the higher the pitch.

Women tend to have higher pitched voices than men because usually they have shorter and thinner vocal bands than men. Our voices become lower in pitch as we mature because maturation is accompanied by an increase in the length and thickness of the vocal folds.

The changes in pitch that we are able to produce under voluntary control take place, as we have indicated, largely by modifications in the degree of tension of the vocal folds. Through these modifications, we are capable of producing voices with ranges of pitch. The ranges may vary somewhat for singing and speaking. Good speakers may have a range of about two octaves. Poor speakers may have narrower ranges. For most nonprofessional speakers it is probably more important to have good control of a one-octave range than poor control of a wider range. For each individual speaker it is important that voice be produced within the pitch range easiest and most effective for him. The range will include the optimum pitch level—the level of pitch at which the individual is able to produce the best quality of tone with least expenditure of effort. This will be considered later on in our discussion of optimum pitch.

THE ARYTENOID CARTILAGES. The vocal bands are attached at their sides to the wall of the thyroid cartilage. At the front, the bands are attached to the angle formed by the fusion of the two shields of the thyroid cartilage. At the back, each of the bands is attached to a pyramidal-shaped cartilage known as the arytenoid.

The shape and muscular connections of the arytenoid cartilages enable them to move in ways that make it possible for the vocal bands to be brought together for vocalization, partly separated for whispering, or more widely separated for normal respiration. The arytenoids can pivot or rotate, tilt backward, or slide backward and sidewise.

THE CRICOID CARTILAGE. The arytenoid cartilages rest on the top of the first tracheal ring. This ring, which has an enlarged and widened back, is known as the cricoid cartilage.

The movement of the vocal bands is brought about by the muscular connections of the bands to cartilages, and by the interconnections of the cartilages. Two types of action are important for vocalization. One is for the closing and opening of the bands (adduction and abduction) and the other is for changing the length and tension of the approximated bands to bring about changes in pitch.

The Chest Cavity

The larynx, with its intricate structure of cartilages and muscles, provides the vibrator for phonation. The source of energy which sets the vibrators into motion is found in the chest cavity.

The chest (thoracic) cavity comprises a framework of bones and cartilages that includes the collar bone, the shoulder blades, the ribs, the breastbone or sternum, and the backbone. The diaphragm, as may be noted in Figure 3, constitutes both the floor of the thoracic cavity and the ceiling of the abdominal cavity. The lungs and the trachea are within the chest cavity. In the abdominal cavity directly below are the digestive organs, which include the stomach, the intestines, and the liver.

THE LUNGS. The lungs consist of a mass of air sacs that contain a considerable amount of elastic tissue. The lungs expand or contract, and so are partly filled or partly emptied of air as a result of differences in pressure brought about by actions of the muscles of the ribs and abdomen, which expand and contract the thoracic

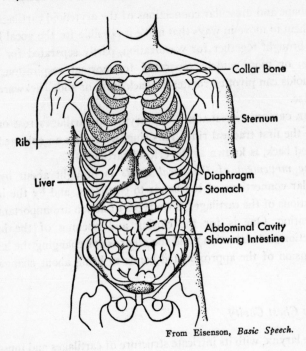

From Eisenson, *Basic Speech.*

Figure 3. The chest and abdominal cavities.

cavity. When the muscles of the ribs and abdomen and the downward action of the diaphragm expand the chest cavity, air is forced into the lungs by the outside air pressure. When the ribs and the upward movement of the diaphragm and abdominal muscles act to contract the chest cavity, air is forced out of the lungs. Through these actions, inhalation and exhalation take place.

THE DIAPHRAGM. The diaphragm is a double-domed muscular organ that separates the thoracic and abdominal cavities. The right half of the diaphragm rises somewhat higher—is more dome shaped —than the left. When the capacity of the chest cavity is increased, air enters the lungs by way of the mouth, nose, throat, and trachea. In this part of the respiratory cycle—inhalation—the diaphragm is actively involved. The contraction of the diaphragm and its down-

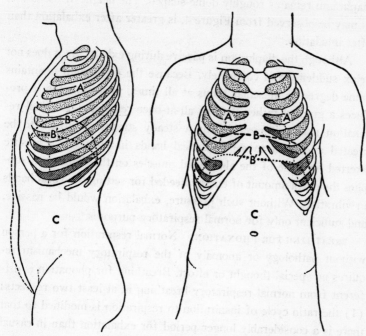

From Eisenson, *Basic Speech*.

Figure 4. Action of the diaphragm and abdomen in breathing.
A. The chest cavity or thorax.
B. The diaphragm "relaxed" when exhalation is completed.
B'. The diaphragm contracted as in deep inhalation.
C. The abdominal cavity. The abdominal wall is displaced forward as the diaphragm moves downward during inhalation.

ward action serve to increase the volume of the chest cavity. In exhalation the diaphragm is passive. It relaxes and returns to its former position because of the upward pressure of the abdominal organs. In the modified and controlled respiration necessary for phonation and speech, the muscles of the front and sides of the abdominal wall contract and press inward on the liver, stomach, and intestines. These organs in turn exert an upward pressure on the diaphragm, which transmits the pressure to the lungs and so forces air out of the lungs. Throughout the respiratory cycle, the diaphragm remains roughly dome-shaped. The height of the dome, as may be observed from Figure 4, is greater after exhalation than after inhalation.

Although the diaphragm is passive during exhalation, it does not relax suddenly and completely. Because the diaphragm maintains some degree of muscular tonus at all times, pressure upon it produces a gradual rather than an all-at-once relaxation. Gradual relaxation makes it possible for a steady stream of breath to be created and used to set the vocal bands in vibration. Pressure exerted by some of the abdominal muscles on the diaphragm supplies the extra amount of energy needed for setting the vocal bands in vibration. Without such pressure, exhalation would be passive, and sufficient only for normal respiratory purposes.

BREATHING FOR PHONATION. Normal respiration for a person without pathology or anomaly of the respiratory mechanism requires no special thought or effort. Breathing for phonation is different from normal respiratory breathing in at least two respects: (1) the ratio cycle of inspiration to respiration is modified so that there is a considerably longer period for exhalation than in casual breathing; (2) a steady stream of air must be created and controlled at the will of the speaker to insure the initiation and maintenance of good tone. This type of air flow is usually most easily accomplished by controlling the abdominal musculature and by using small amounts of air rather than by inhaling large amounts of air. Attempts at deep inhalation tend to be accompanied by exaggerated activity of the upper part of the chest. This type of breathing (clavicular), which Gray and Wise (3, p. 154) observe, frequently promotes unsteadiness. The result may be a wavering tone and a strained voice quality. Clavicular breathing tends to produce excessive neck and throat tensions, and so prevents free and appropriate reinforcement of vocal tones in the cavities of the larynx and throat. Adequate breath supply is difficult to maintain, and the speaker needs to inhale more frequently than in abdominally controlled breathing.

The Resonating Cavities

The important resonating cavities for the human speech mechanism are those of the larynx, throat (pharynx), mouth (oral or buccal cavity), and nose (nasal cavity). To a lesser but not insignificant degree, the part of the windpipe below the larynx also serves as a resonating cavity. The principal cavities may be located by an examination of Figure 5.

The resonating cavities serve two functions in voice production: (1) they permit us to reinforce or build up the loudness of tones without resorting to constant energetic use of air pressure; and (2) through modification in the tension and shape of the cavities of the mouth, the nasopharynx, and the nasal cavity we produce changes

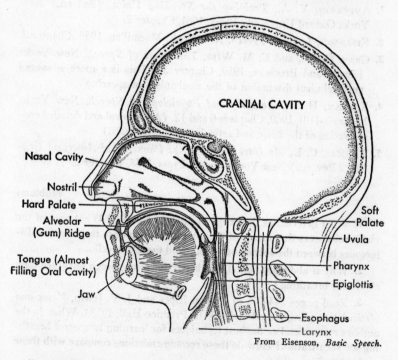

CRANIAL CAVITY

Nasal Cavity

Nostril

Hard Palate

Alveolar (Gum) Ridge

Tongue (Almost Filling Oral Cavity)

Jaw

Soft Palate

Uvula

Pharynx

Epiglottis

Esophagus

Larynx

From Eisenson, *Basic Speech.*

Figure 5. Head section showing principal resonators and organs of articulation.

Sound is A VARBRATION of molecules in the AIR.

in the quality of vocal tones. For example, nasality as a voice quality takes place when sound is permitted to enter and be emitted through the nasal chambers.

We have little control over the larynx as a resonating chamber. We have most control over the oral cavity and considerable control over the pharynx. The speech sounds we identify as vowels are produced by modifications in the size and shape of the oral cavity. Those we recognize as consonants are produced as a result of changes of the organs of articulation, the lips included, within the oral cavity.

References and Suggested Readings

1. ANDERSON, V. A., *Training the Speaking Voice*. (2nd ed.) New York: Oxford University Press, 1961, Chapter 2.
2. EISENSON, J., *Basic Speech*. New York: Macmillan, 1950, Chapter 2.
3. GRAY, G. W., and C. M. WISE, *The Bases of Speech*. New York: Harper and Brothers, 1959, Chapter 3. (This is a more advanced and technical discussion of the mechanism of speech.)
4. KAPLAN, H. M., *Anatomy and Physiology of Speech*. New York: McGraw-Hill, 1960, Chapters 6 and 12. (A technical and detailed consideration of the voice and articulatory mechanisms.)
5. THOMAS, C. K., *An Introduction to the Phonetics of American English*. (Rev. ed.) New York: Ronald Press, 1958, Chapter 2.

Problems

1. What determines the range of pitch in a violin? What part of the violin reinforces the sounds of the vibrators? What are the essential differences between the sounds of a violin and those of a cello.

2. Why is abdominal breathing better for most speech purposes than clavicular breathing?

3. Read pages 344-346 of C. Van Riper and J. V. Irwin, *Voice and Articulation* (Englewood Cliffs, N.J.: Prentice-Hall, 1958). What do the authors recommend as the best techniques for learning to control breathing for vocalization? How do these recommendations compare with those of this text?

4. What are the functions of the resonating cavities in phonation?

5. Over which resonating cavity do we have most control? Over which do we have least control?

6. What cavities does the diaphragm separate? What is the shape of the diaphragm during exhalation? How does the shape change during the inhalation?

7. Blow up a toy balloon and then gently squeeze out the air while holding the neck of the balloon between thumb and index finger. How does this action compare with the activity of the lungs and the vocal bands during vocalization?

8. How do birds make sounds? What are the essential differences in the mechanism for sound making in birds and in most mammals?

9. Male and female vocal bands overlap in range of length, yet it is usually easy to distinguish the voices of high pitched males and low pitched females. Why?

6

The Production

of Speech Sounds

Iɴ ᴛʜɪs section, we will try to make clear the usual positions of American speech sounds and to show how the consonant, vowel, and diphthong sounds are produced. We recognize that the positions described are merely the conventional ones and that, since our mechanism is adaptable, sounds can be produced in a number of other ways. This observation is more applicable to vowels than to consonants. This information is needed both by the classroom teacher and the correctionist. The teacher needs it to understand more completely his students' speech patterns and to be able to reinforce the work done by the correctionist. The correctionist needs the information in his work with children with articulatory difficulties.

Production of Speech Sounds

Articulation

From a purely motor point of view, speech consists of modified sound. Modifications of sounds take place as a result of articulatory action. When modifications result in the production of conventional sound patterns, with which meanings are associated, we have words. When the sound patterns are arranged in conventional units, we have phrases or sentences, provided, of course, that the patterns and the units refer to objects, situations, or relationships known to both speaker and listener. The discussion immediately following will be concerned with how sounds are produced and a description of the parts of the speech mechanism employed in articulation.

Speech sounds are produced when the breath stream that comes from the lungs by way of the trachea and larynx is modified in the mouth before leaving the body. Breath may be modified by movements of the lips, teeth, jaws, tongue, and the soft palate (roof of the mouth). Most American-English sounds are produced as a result of lip and tongue activity and resulting contacts with other organs of articulation. The front part of the tongue (tip and blade) and the part of the mouth at or near the upper gum ridge is the "favored" area for articulatory contact for American-English speech sounds. The sounds *t, d, l, n, s, z, sh*[ʃ], *zh* [ʒ], *ch* [tʃ], and *j* [dʒ] all produced by action of the anterior tongue and contact at or close to the upper gum ridge.

If we examine Figure 6 we will note that the upper gum ridge or alveolar process is the area directly behind the upper teeth. Immediately behind the alveolar process is the hard palate. Posterior to it is the soft palate or velum. The uvula is the most posterior part of the "roof of the mouth."

The tongue lies within and almost completely fills the oral or mouth cavity. The tongue, from the point of view of articulatory action, may be considered as being divided into tongue tip, blade, front (mid), and back as indicated in Figure 6.

The lips act as articulators for the production of the sounds *p* and *b*. The sound *m* is produced with closed lips. The sounds *f* and *v* are usually produced as a result of action involving the lower lip and upper teeth. The various vowel and diphthong sounds are produced with characteristic lip and jaw movement though the lips do not make any articulatory contacts for these sounds. The production of American-English sounds will soon be considered in somewhat greater detail.

Speech sounds may be emitted either through the mouth or through the nasal cavity. In the absence of specific pathology, the speaker is able to determine the avenue of sound emission. Most American-English sounds are emitted through the mouth. The sounds *m, n,* and the consonant that is usually represented in spelling by the letters *ng* are emitted through the nasal cavity.

The Sounds of American English

It is hardly necessary to impress the readers of this text with the realization that American English, or British English for that matter, does not consistently represent the same sound with the

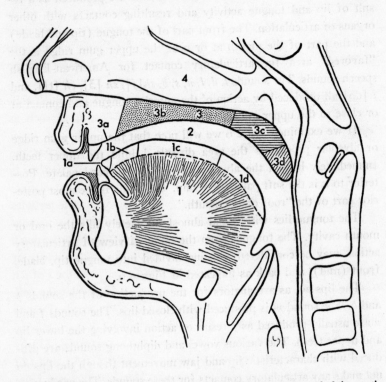

Figure 6. Diagram showing parts of the tongue in relationship to the roof of the mouth.

1. Tongue
1a. Tongue tip
2. Mouth (oral) cavity
3. Palate
4. Nasal cavity
1b. Blade of tongue
1c. Front or mid of tongue
1d. Back of tongue
3a. Gum or alveolar ridge
3b. Hard palate
3c. Soft palate
3d. Uvula

same alphabet letter. The teacher who has had any concern with teaching children to read has on numerous occasions had to explain that many words are pronounced in a manner only remotely suggested by their spellings. Perhaps the teacher has been aware that we have forty or more sound families in our spoken language. If not, the teacher has surely known that we have twenty-six letters, many of which represent more than one sound, and some of which, according to given words, represent the same sound. So, the child has been instructed to memorize the pronunciation and spelling of such words as *though, enough, through, and cough* as well as the varied ways in which the sound *sh* is represented in the words *attention, delicious, ocean,* and *shall.* Vowel sounds too have their inconsistencies so that before the child at school is too far along in his career he becomes aware that the sound of *ee* in *see* may be represented differently in words such as *eat, believe, receive, species,* and *even.* Later, he may be able to accept without too much consternation the spellings of words of foreign derivation such as *subpoena* and *esprit.*

PHONEMES. If the teacher has had a course in phonetics, the concept of the *phoneme* may have been established. A *phoneme* is a distinctive phonetic element of a word. It is the smallest distinctive group or class of sounds in a language. Each phoneme includes a variety of closely related sounds which differ somewhat in manner of production and in acoustic end results, but do not differ so much that the listener is more aware of difference than of similarity or sameness. So, for example, the *t* of *tin* is different from the *t* of *its, spotted, button,* and *metal,* and of the *t* in the phrase *hit the ball,* but an essential quality of *t* is common in all these words. Despite differences we have a phoneme *t.*

In this text, phonemes will be represented in two ways: (1) by the symbol of the International Phonetic Alphabet (IPA), and (2) by the diacritic symbols employed in the Merriam-Webster Unabridged Dictionary (2nd ed.). For purposes of ready reference, the following table is included with key words and symbols from the International Phonetic Alphabet (IPA) and from the Merriam-Webster Dictionary (1955 edition).

this will be required to know.

The Common Phonemes of American-English

Key Word	Dictionary Symbol	IPA Symbol

Consonants

Key Word	Dictionary Symbol	IPA Symbol
1. *p*at	p	[p]
2. *b*ee	b	[b]
3. *t*in	t	[t]
4. *d*en	d	[d]
5. *c*ook	k	[k]
6. *g*et	g	[g]
7. *f*ast	f	[f]
8. *v*an	v	[v]
9. *th*in	th	[θ]
10. *th*is	th	[ð]
11. *s*ea	s	[s]
12. *z*oo	z	[z]
13. *sh*e	sh	[ʃ]
14. trea*s*ure	zh	[ʒ]
15. *ch*ick	ch	[tʃ]
16. *j*ump	j	[dʒ]
17. *m*e	m	[m]
18. *n*o	n	[n]
19. si*ng*	ng	[ŋ]
20. *l*et	l	[l]
21. *r*un	r	[r]
22. *y*ell	y	[j]
23. *h*at	h	[h]
24. *w*on	w	[w]
25. *wh*at*	hw	[ʌ] or [hw]

Vowels

Key Word	Dictionary Symbol	IPA Symbol
26. f*ee*	ē	[i]

* If distinction is made in pronunciation of words such as what and watt; when and wen.

Key Word	Dictionary Symbol	IPA Symbol
27. sit	ĭ	[ɪ]
28. take	ā	[e]
29. met	ĕ	[ɛ]
30. calm	ä	[ɑ]
31. task	ă or à	[æ] or [a] depending upon regional or individual variations
32. cat	ă	[æ]
33. hot	ŏ or ä	[ɒ] or [ɑ] depending upon regional or individual variations
34. saw	ô	[ɔ]
35. obey, sew	ō	[o] or [ou]
36. bull	ŏŏ	[ʊ]
37. boon	ōō	[u]
38. hut	ŭ	[ʌ]
39. about	ă,ĕ,ĭ,ŏ,ŭ,à,ē	[ə]
40. upper	ēr	[ɚ] [ə] by most Americans and [ə] by many others
41. bird	ûr	[ɝ] by most Americans and [ɜ] by many others

Diphthongs

42. sigh	ī	[aɪ]
43. noise	oi	[ɔɪ]
44. cow	ou	[aʊ] or [ɑʊ] depending upon individual variations
45. may	ā	[eɪ]
46. go	ō	[ou]
47. refuse	ū	[ɪu] or [ju]

Key Word	Dictionary Symbol	IPA Symbol
		depending upon individual variations
48. *u*se	ū	[ju]

It will be noted that phonetic symbols represent pronunciations as they are made. The same sound and its phonemic variants are represented by a single symbol. This is not the case with diacritic symbols which, for some vowels and diphthongs, require several representations for the same phoneme.

If the reader wishes to memorize the phonetic symbols, it may be encouraging for him to know that sixteen of the consonant symbols are taken from the English alphabet. They are: p, b, t, d, k, g, f, v, s, z, m, n, l, r, h, and w. IPA symbols for vowels, however, vary considerably from alphabetic representations.

Sounds Classified as to Manner of Production

Thus far, speech sounds have been classified into large categories of consonants, vowels, and diphthongs. Now we will attempt a further classification of speech sounds according to the manner in which they are made. Information as to the manner of articulation should enable the teacher interested in correcting sounds to analyze what the child is doing that produced an incorrect result, and what needs to be done to correct the articulatory product.

CONSONANT PRODUCTION. Consonants, we recall, are sounds produced as a result of some degree of modification of the breath stream by the organs of articulation. The types of modification may be the following:

1. A *stopping* of the breath stream followed by release of the breath. This would produce stop consonants such as [p], [t], and [k], and their vocalized counterparts [b], [d], and [g].

2. A *continuous fricative* release of sound through a narrow opening between the organs of articulation. A stream of breath

is maintained with some pressure to make the sound continuous. The degree of friction varies according to the sounds produced. Considerable fricative quality may be discerned for [f], [v], *th,* (voiceless and voiced), less for [s]; [z], *sh* [ʃ], *zh* [3]; and probably the least for [hw] and [h]. The sound [r] in some contexts also suggests fricative value.

3. *Nasal direction. Nasal* sounds are directed from the mouth through the nasal cavity and are emitted nasally. Nasal sounds, unless intentionally whispered, are voiced. The nasal consonants of American-English are [m], [n], and the sound usually represented in spelling by the letters *ng* and phonetically by the symbol [ŋ].

4. *Continuous movement* of the articulators during the act of the articulation. Sounds so produced are referred to as glides. Because they are relatively unobstructed sounds, they suggest vowel quality almost as much as they do consonant quality. The glide consonants include *y*[j] and [w]. The sound [hw] is also considered a glide. The sound [r] in some contexts is also produced as a glide consonant. In others, as we have noted, [r] is produced as a fricative rather than a glide. The reader might check his own articulation for the words *real, cry,* and *three* and decide which of the [r] sounds is more like a fricative consonant and which is more like a glide.

5. *Lateral emission.* One American-English sound is produced with the sound emerging from two sides of the mouth rather than in a single breath or voice stream. This sound is [l], which is made with openings between the sides of the tongue and the upper teeth. The consonant [l], because of its manner of production, is characterized as a lateral consonant.

PLACE OF ARTICULATION. The classification of consonants just given was according to manner of articulation. Consonants may also be classified as to which articulators are used and the position they are in during the act of sound production. The following is a classification of consonants as to position of articulators:

1. *Bilabial.* Sounds are produced as a result of the activity of the lips. The sounds [p], [b], [m], [hw], and [w] are bilabials.

2. *Lip-teeth* (*labiodental*). Contact is made between the upper teeth and lower lip for the production of labiodental sounds. The sounds so produced are [f] and [v].

3. *Tongue-teeth* (*linguadental*). Contact is made between the point of the tongue and the upper teeth or between the point of the tongue in a position between the teeth. The *th* sounds [θ] and [ð] may be made either postdentally or interdentally. Most mature speakers are likely to produce these sounds postdentally.

4. *Tongue-tip gums* (*Lingua-alveolar*). The region of the mouth at or near the gum ridge, as previously indicated, is the "favored place" for the articulation of American-English sounds. The sounds [t], [d], [n], and [l] are produced with the tip of the tongue in contact with the upper gum ridge. The sound [r] is most frequently produced with the tongue tip turned back slightly away from the gum ridge. The sounds [s], [z], *sh* [ʃ], *zh* [ʒ], *ch* [tʃ], and j [dʒ], are produced with the blade of the tongue making articulatory contact a fraction of an inch behind the gum ridge.

5. *Palatal*. The sound *y* [j] is produced with the middle of the tongue initially raised toward the hard palate. The sounds [k] and [g] are usually produced with the back of the tongue in contact with the soft palate. In some contexts [k] and [g] may be produced with the middle of the tongue in contact with the hard palate. The reader may check his place of articulation for the [k] in *car* compared with [k] in *keel*. He may also wish to compare the [g] of *get* with the [g] of *got*.

The sound of *ng* [ŋ] is most likely to be produced with the back of the tongue in contact with the soft palate.

In some contexts, the sound [r] is produced with the middle of the tongue raised toward the palate. Some persons produce the [r] of *rose* and *around* in this manner.

6. *Glottal*. One American-English sound, [h], is produced with the breath coming through the opening between the vocal folds and without modification by the other articulators. The [h] is referred to as a glottal sound.

VOCAL COMPONENT. A third classification of sounds is accord-

Production of Consonants in American-English Speech

	Articulators Used					
Manner of Articulation	Lips (Bilabial)	Lip-Teeth (Labio-dental)	Tongue-Teeth (Lingua-dental)	Tongue Point Gum (Lingua-alveolar)	Tongue and Hard or Soft Palate (Palatal)	Vocal Folds (Glottal)
Voiceless stops	p			t	k	
Voiced stops	b			d	g	
Voiceless fricatives		f	θ (th)	s, ʃ (sh)		h
Voiced fricatives		v	ð (th̵)	z, [ʒ] (zh)		
Nasals (all voiced)	m			n	[ŋ] (ng)	
Glides (vowel-like consonants)	hw [ʍ], w			r*	j (y), rʈ†	
Lateral				l		

* The tongue tip in many instances is curled away from the gum ridge toward the center of the hard palate.

† In combinations such as k or g followed by r, the r sound may be produced in this position.

ing to the presence or absence of voice. Consonants produced without accompanying vocal fold vibration are referred to as *voiceless* or *unvoiced;* those produced with accompanying vocal fold vibration are called *voiced*. The voiceless consonants of American-English speech are: [p], [t], [k], [hw], [f], *th* of *th*ink [θ], [s], *sh* [ʃ], and [h]. The voiced consonants are: [b], [d], [g], [m], [n], *ng* [ŋ], [v], *th of th*is [ð], [z], *zh,* [ʒ], [w], [r], y[j], and [l].

A resume of the multiple classification of American-English consonant sounds is presented in the chart on page 97.

Production of Vowels and Diphthongs

Vowels

Vowel sounds share the following characteristics in their manner of production: (1) All vowels are voiced, unless for special purposes the entire speech content is intentionally whispered; (2) all vowels are continuant sounds in that they are produced without interruption or restriction of the breath stream; (3) changes in tongue and jaw position are primarily responsible for the distinctive differences in vowel phonemes. To a lesser degree, lip activity accounts for some of the difference in articulatory activity and in acoustic end result.

All vowel sounds require activity of the tongue as a whole. It will be noticed, however, that each of the American-English vowels is produced with one part of the tongue more actively involved than the remainder of the tongue. For example, in the production of the vowel of the word *me,* the tip of the tongue remains relatively inactive behind the lower teeth, while the front of the tongue is tensed and raised toward the hard palate. In changing from *me* to *moo,* we may note that the front of the tongue is relatively relaxed, while the back is tensed and elevated toward the roof of the mouth. The vowel of *me,* because of its characteristic tongue activity, is considered to be a *front vowel;* similarly, the vowel of *moo,* because of the back of the tongue activity, is considered to be a *back vowel.*

Now, let us contrast the production of the vowels of *me* and *man.* Both of these are produced with front of the tongue activity, but the tongue is higher for the vowel of *me* than it is for the vowel of *man.* Similarly, the tongue is higher for the back vowel of *moon* than it is for the vowel of *mock.* In the words *mirth* and *mud,* where middle of the tongue activity is characteristic, we may also note that the vowel of *mirth* is produced with the tongue higher in position than it is in *mud.* The difference in height of tongue position, however, is not as great as for the other pairs of words.

Thus far, we have seen that vowels differ somewhat in individual production according to the part of the tongue which is most actively involved and the height of the tongue. We may also have noted that the change in the height of the tongue is likely to be accompanied by a change in the position of the lower jaw. That is, the jaw drops as the tongue drops, in going from a "high" to a "low" vowel. A third aspect of vowel production will now be considered.

If we compare the vowels of *meek* and *man,* we should be able to sense that the tongue is more tense for the vowel of *meek* than it is for the vowel of *man.* Similarly, the vowel of *moot* is produced with more tongue tension than the vowel of *mock.* Further analysis will show that the differences in tension are not confined to the muscles of the tongue. The muscles of the chin also differ in degree of tension. A third muscle difference may be felt by observing the changes in the position of the apex of the larynx—the "Adam's apple." When the tongue and under part of the chin are tense, the apex of the larynx is elevated and moves toward the front of the chin as it does in the act of swallowing. When the tongue and the under part of the chin are relatively relaxed, the larynx drops back to its normal position of rest as in quiet breathing.

On the basis of our discussion thus far, we may arrive at a threefold classification for vowel sounds.

1. Vowels differ as to place of production. They may be pro-

duced either in the front of the mouth, with the front or blade of the tongue most active; in the middle of the mouth, with the mid-tongue most active; or in the back of the mouth, with the back of the tongue most active.

Front Vowels

	Phonetic Symbol	Phonetic Dictionary Symbol
meet	[i]	ē
milk	[ɪ]	ĭ
may	[e]	ā
men	[ε]	ĕ
mat	[æ]	ă
ask*	[a]	à

Mid Vowels

	Phonetic Symbol	Phonetic Dictionary Symbol
mirth	[ɜ] or [ɝ]	ûr
about	[ə]	{ ȧ,ĕ,ĭ,ŏ / ŭ,ȧ,ĕ }
upper	[ɚ]	ĕr
mud	[ʌ]	ŭ

Back Vowels

	Phonetic Symbol	Phonetic Dictionary Symbol
boon	[u]	ōō
book	[ʊ]	ŏŏ
boat	[o]	ō
ball	[ɔ]	ô
bog	[ɒ]	ŏ
balm	[ɑ]	ä

* When the speaker compromises between the vowels of mat and of balm.

2. Vowels differ as to height of tongue position.
3. Vowels differ as to degree of muscle tension.

A fourth feature which distinguishes some vowels from others, especially when the vowels are produced as isolated sounds, is

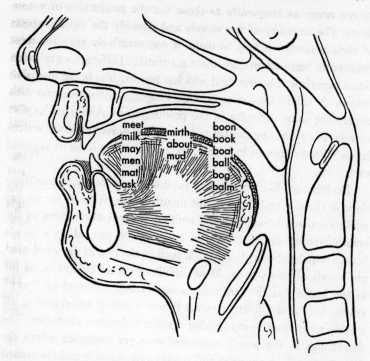

meet
milk
may
men
mat
ask

mirth
about
mud

boon
book
boat
ball
bog
balm

Figure 7. Representative tongue positions for American-English vowels. In actual speech, there is considerable individual variation from these positions according to speech context.

lip-rounding. Back vowels, with the exception of the *a* of *calm,* are produced with the lips somewhat rounded. The vowel of the word *pool* is most rounded. There is lesser rounding for the vowels in *pull, boat, ball,* and *cot.* For persons who do not distinguish between the vowels of *cot* and *calm,* there will be no lip-rounding for either.

In the lists of words on page 100, the first column contains front vowels, arranged in order of highest to lowest tongue position. The second column contains mid vowels, and the third back vowels, arranged in the same order.

The tongue position for the vowels of these words are shown in Figure 7. The dots represent the high points of the tongue.

DEFECTIVE VOWEL PRODUCTION. Defects of vowel production

do not occur as frequently as those for the production of consonants. The intensity of the vowels and possibly the visible aspects of their articulation help to make it comparatively easy for most children to learn to produce them accurately. Difficulties are sometimes experienced by the child who has hearing loss in the low-pitch ranges. A child exposed to foreign language influences may also experience some difficulty in the production of American-English vowels. We should be careful not to confuse defective vowel articulation with differences in vowel production on the basis of regional variations.

Diphthongs, like vowels, are produced as a result of modifications in the size and shape of the mouth and position of the tongue while vocalized breath is being emitted without obstruction of the breath stream. Diphthongs are voice glides uttered in a single breath impulse. Some diphthongs, such as the one in the word *how*, are blends of two vowels. Most diphthongs were originally, as far as the history of the language is concerned, produced as "pure" vowels but "broke down" to what is now a strong vowel gliding off weakly to another vowel lacking distinct individual character. The diphthongs in the words *name* and *row* are examples where the first element is emphasized and readily recognizable and the second element is "weak" and somewhat difficult to discern.

The following list of words includes the most frequently recognized diphthongs in American-English speech. Most phoneticians would limit the *distinctive* diphthongs to those in the words *aisle*, *plough*, *toil*, and *use*.

aisle	*bay*
plough	*hoe*
toil	*dear*
fair	*sure*
fort	*use*

7

Development

of Language

in Children

very important

SINCE speech is a learned activity and not natural or instinctive as is eating or crying, both the teacher and the correctionist should know what factors influence how well and how soon it is learned. Characteristics of both the child and of his environment contribute to language development. The child's intellectual ability, his rate of maturation, and the functioning efficiency of his organs of speech and hearing all play important roles. In the environment, the child's family constellation, the specific languages he speaks and hears, his family's socioeconomic status, the emotional climate of his home, and the kind of stimulation which he receives at home, in the playground, and at school have decided bearing. To a limited extent whether the child is a boy or a girl plays a part in the extent of language acquisition.

Factors That Influence Language Development

Intelligence

In society today, ability to verbalize is considered an index of intellectual ability. If a child is slow to talk, if his vocabulary seems limited, or if he does not articulate clearly, his parents tend to show concern about his intellectual ability. Studies do show a relationship between intelligence and vocabulary. For example, for six-year-olds Templin (35, p. 117) reports a .50 correlation and Schneiderman (28) a .48 correlation between intelligence and vocabulary.[1] Other studies report other relationships among language factors. A study of Williams (39) does not show that the amount of vocabulary is closely related to accuracy of articulation, correct usage of words, and length of sentences but that these three last items do seem to go along together. Smith's study (31) gives a .69 correlation between sentence length and size of vocabulary. Studies are not in agreement on the relationship of articulation to intelligence. Templin and Schneiderman indicate a relationship between intelligence and articulation while Templin (35, p. 128) notes a correlation of .39 between intelligence and a measure of correct articulation for six-year-olds and Schneiderman (28) notes that when she matched children on mental age, differences in articulation tended to disappear. On the other hand, Reid's study (24) does not find a significant relationship between intelligence and articulatory ability when the intelligence quotient is over 70. Yedinack's study (44) supports this finding.

Much of the strength of the relationship of intelligence to linguistic skills may be due to the highly verbal nature of most intelligence testing. Usually intelligence tests which have a high degree of validity depend on language. Vineyard (38) notes that such linguistic skills as vocabulary, paragraph comprehension, and spelling relate with one another and with intelligence. The high degree of relationship among linguistic skills may be due to the saturation of intelligence in all of the items involving language.

Neuromuscular Coordination and Physical Condition

Ability to articulate and perform some of the finer motor tasks unquestionably increases as children become older, for the produc-

---

[1] A positive correlation indicates that a relationship exists but does not imply causality. The higher the correlation, the stronger the relationship.

tion of speech is a neuromuscular process that depends on motor skills. Although a child may not run easily and may falter and stumble on occasion, he can still get around adequately. The manipulation of his speech organs, however, requires a greater degree of motor skill, since they involve the smaller muscles and a finer coordination. Two studies point to this relationship: Bilto (1) found that those children who are defective in speech are generally inferior in motor development and skill to children of the same age with normal speech. Shirley (29) discovered a moderate positive correlation between fine motor coordinations and language development after the age of 45 weeks.

The child must have a neuromuscular system that enables him to receive auditory cues and to comprehend the meaning of the person speaking to him as well as an efficient articulatory mechanism in order to produce sounds and words accurately. When the neuromuscular system is damaged, marked speech retardation is often present. For example, children with brain damage and cerebral palsy showed marked retardation in the development of speech sounds. Irwin (12) indicates that cerebral-palsied children are 5½ years old before they reach the proficiency in articulation of most 2½-year-old children. At 5½ cerebral-palsied children show a marked deficiency in making consonant sounds, a decrement of back vowels, and a preponderance of front and middle vowels. When the teeth, tongue, lips, throat, or larynx are defective, a child is likely to have a speech difficulty. Many children, however, who have short tongues, abnormally high palates, or cleft lips do speak clearly and distinctly.

The part of the child's physical condition and development that is most important for the acquisition of language is his ability to hear, for children learn to speak by hearing others speak. When they cannot hear part of or all that is spoken, they are handicapped. Obviously the child who is almost completely deaf is most seriously handicapped. The child's ability to see how and where a sound is made is important, but to make most of the sounds accurately the child must hear them. Even though his hearing is defective, the child may often hear enough of speech patterns to comprehend what is said because facial expression, gesture, melody patterns, quality of voice, and the general context of words help him understand. But such a child's speech may possess distorted consonant and vowel sounds, since he is not able to produce them correctly because of his lack of hearing acuity.

The hearing acuity necessary for speech is much keener than for many other purposes. A kindergartner may hear the door being closed, but he may not hear the sounds necessary for speech. In some children of this age, the development of the nerves related to hearing is delayed. The result is a reduction of the efficiency of the hearing mechanism. The sounds of speech may not be sharply enough discriminated to be reproduced by the child. When the development is complete, children then hear. Sometimes a child does not hear well enough to distinguish between sounds until he is eight, nine, or ten years of age.

An intact speech mechanism that operates efficiently is in all likelihood a factor in speech development. An organic difficulty such as a tongue-tie may hinder the child's ability to articulate. This difficulty is very rare—occurring only infrequently. Structural abnormalities of the mouth may also produce late articulatory development. Most writers, however, in the field of speech correction are cautious in regarding organic defects as causal factors in articulatory difficulties, although admittedly, in some instances, malocclusion, malformed arches, absence of teeth, and faulty dentures are factors in delayed articulatory development.

Maturation

Both an increase in intellectual ability and ability in neuromuscular coordination go along with an improvement in ability to use language. These factors together with the increased environmental stimulation and growing concern for good human relationships bring about maturity. Children's rates of maturation differ. Some tend to develop more rapidly than others. But obviously as children grow older, their linguistic skills increase. Templin (35) notes that, on the whole, children's abilities to articulate sounds, to use and understand words, to discriminate between sounds, and to use longer and more complex responses increase as children grow older. M. E. Smith (31) indicates that the steady increase in the size of vocabulary goes along with the increase in age. Several studies such as Reid's (24) show a positive correlation between chronological age and articulatory ability. Sayler (27) establishes that the number of articulatory errors decrease with maturation in the early grades in the elementary school. Schneiderman (28) demonstrates that vocabulary and sentence length, as measured by teachers' estimates, increase in growth with chronological age and mental age. Growth in vocabulary, sentence length, and the decreasing number of articulatory errors are clearly related to the maturation of the child.

Family Environment

The kind of family in which a child is reared makes a difference in his language development. Whether he is an only child or a twin, whether he grows up in a bilingual home, whether he belongs to a family of high socioeconomic status, or whether he lives in the kind of home atmosphere which fosters communication affect the child's language development.

The child who associates chiefly with adults and who has the undivided attention of his mother is apt to speak more quickly and in longer sentences and, in general, to show more rapid language growth. McCarthy (17) reports that the median percentile rank on length of response in her experimental group, the members of which associated mainly with adults, was significantly higher than her comparison group, the members of which associated mainly with other children. The only child who likely spends more time with adults and who does have all of his mother's attention is clearly superior in language development to other children (4). On the other hand, twins are usually retarded in language development:

Davis (4), comparing twins, singletons with siblings and only children, notes that twins are retarded in language as compared with other groups but the difference diminishes as twins enter and proceed in school. The school experiences probably bring greater demand for communication with other children and broaden the socialization process. Other studies involving triplets and the Dionne quintuplets point to linguistic retardation among children of multiple births. McCarthy, in noting the importance of the child's being able to identify with the mother, points out that the child who has to share his mother and never has her completely to himself during the formative period is frequently among those children who tend to develop speech more slowly. She further notes that girls, who usually spend more time with their mothers, are more advanced in language than boys (22, p. 10).

If a child is born into a bilingual environment, his vocabulary may be below average for his age for either language or for a combination of both languages. M. E. Smith (32), in a study of the vocabularies of 30 bilingual children (approximately 3 to 6 years of age) of Chinese ancestry in Hawaii, found, in both English and Chinese, the children had below average-sized vocabularies for children of their ages and, even when the vocabularies of the two languages were added, only two-fifths of the children exceeded the norm. When words of the same meaning were subtracted, only one-sixth of the children exceeded the norm. On the basis of her study, Smith believes that it is probably wiser for young bilingual children to receive their two languages from separate sources; and she, therefore, recommends that each adult in the home consistently use one language. Research studies on bilingualism may not be too meaningful, for as McCarthy (16, p. 593) points out most of these studies are based on families from the upper social level who deem preserving language important because of cultural reasons or families from lower socioeconomic levels where parents are not sufficiently intellectual or interested in learning to acquire the second language. Since more schools are now teaching a foreign language early and since more families are now in government service in foreign countries, the problem of bilingual experiences at different age levels should be further studied.

Teachers are usually familiar with children who come from bilingual homes, many of whom must learn to talk with others by a new system of communication. The child of foreign parents may be entering a classroom where he hears a strange language and where the customs are quite different from those in his own home. Furthermore, the ability to handle two languages may require a certain degree of maturity. These factors may hinder the child's development of his oral communicative skills.

Children born of families in a higher socioeconomic status tend to develop speech earlier than those born in lower socioeconomic families. Templin (35, p. 147) points out that there are consistent language differences in children from upper socioeconomic groups and lower socioeconomic groups. The children from the upper socioeconomic group receive higher scores on all language measures at each level. These language measures include ability to articulate sounds, discriminate between sounds, recognize words, and utter longer and more complex remarks. The particular socioeconomic background brings with it many factors influential in language development; these may include intellectual level, amount of education of parents, cultural opportunities offered to children, and certain home attitudes. Furthermore, parents in upper socioeconomic classes tend to give their children more attention and to share more stimulating and interesting experiences with them.

Irwin (11) did an interesting and provocative study on providing language stimulation to children. Previously he had found that children born of fathers in the business and professions acquired sounds more quickly than children born of fathers of semiskilled or unskilled workers. Consequently, he wished to test the hypothesis that in the homes of working families systematic reading of stories to infants during the year and one-half period between 13 and 30 months would increase the amount of their phonetic production. As a result, mothers of 24 infants in the experimental group were instructed to spend 15 to 20 minutes each day reading stories to their children from illustrated children's books, talking about the books, making up original simple tales about them, and, in general, furnishing an enriched speech sound environment. The results of the study suggest that systematically increasing speech sound stimulation of children under 2½ years in homes of lower educational status by reading and by talking about stories will lead to an increase in phonetic production of these children over what might be expected without such enrichment.

A somewhat similar study by Dawe (6) tells of an educational program designed to develop language in children who were living in an orphanage. The program provided for approximately 50 hours of individual and group training in understanding words, looking at and talking about pictures, listening to selections from children's literature, and taking short trips. Eleven pairs of children were matched on chronological age, mental age, sex, school group, and vocabulary. The experimental group, who received the training, made considerably more progress on sentence length and vocabulary scores than the control group who received no such training. Even the average intelligence quotient score of the experimental group reflected an increase of about fourteen points.

Part of the increase in language scores may be due to the new warm relationship with adults or to an improved mother-child relationship. Mykelbust (21) emphasizes the need of the child to relate to his mother. He makes the point that an infant must "feel that he wants to be like a talking human being if he is to learn the complex symbols known as language." The importance of the influence of home atmosphere on the development of language is patently clear.

A study of home background influences, including permissiveness of parents and parental demands and techniques to implement these demands on the development of speech skills in preadolescent children of normal socioeconomic status and intelligence, was done by Marge (18) and reported in *ASHA*. It presents three conclusions:

1. The more permissive parents tend to have children with higher scores in speaking ability.

2. Parents who demand achievement in the development of better oral expression have children who achieve higher levels of speech skills.

3. The more techniques of speech training employed during the early years, the greater the tendency for children to achieve higher scores in general speaking ability.

It should be remembered, however, that parents who tend to be perfectionists and who insist on high standards all around sometimes demand more in speech than the child can give. Although parents may be quite sympathetic with the child's difficulty in managing his zipper, they may be adamant that he speak clearly and fluently. As the child revolts, he says little. When adults remember the obstacles to learning to speak—the complexity of our grammatical structure, the need to find the right words and to use them in the right order, and the number of words that the child must learn—they realize that they must not set too high standards for speaking.

Surely, however, a secure mother-child relationship and a healthy, warm home atmosphere, which stimulates communication, are important. A study by Wood (43) which compared a group of children who had speech correction work with another matched group who not only had the same speech lessons but whose mothers also had psychotherapy points to the secure mother-child relationship. The progress in articulation for the children whose mothers received help through psychotherapy was more noticeable than for the other group. A study by Milner (20) indicates the qualitative differences in the home atmosphere of children who are advanced or retarded in language development. This investigation found that children in the lowest third of their class did not talk with adults in a two-way conversation before school. They did not eat breakfast with their parents. They did respond to orders, but they did not engage actively in conversation before school, at supper, or at other times when most families talk together. Their families gave these children little outward sign of affection. In contrast, the children whose language scores were in the upper third of their class did eat breakfast with their families and did engage actively in conversation before school and at supper. They did receive considerable outward show of affection.

Stimulation to Speak

As just indicated, stimulation to speak may come partly from the atmosphere of the home and partly from experiences which provoke linguistic activity. Some social environments provide more stimulation to speak and more good models to imitate than others. When a mother talks to her child frequently and simply and when her own speech is clear and intelligible, the child is likely to speak earlier. If, as he grows older, he lives with parents who share and enjoy interesting experiences with him, such as going to the seashore and talking about books, he tends to speak more fully and with longer sentences than the child who has fewer experiences. Talk cannot thrive in a vacuum; it needs the stimulation of common experiences and adventures. An example of a child who had little stimulation to speak is that of a five-year-old boy who has a seven-year-old sister who is a chatterbox and who almost constantly interprets for him. "He doesn't like his cheese sandwich toasted; he likes it plain." When an adult suggested that he'd like to hear what the little boy thought of toasted sandwiches, the little sister replied, "He's too shy. He don't talk much." The poor lad never gets much chance to talk with a loquacious sister at his elbow.

Admittedly some children are overstimulated. A seven-year-old boy lived with very verbal and alert parents, overly interested in bringing up their child with "broad horizons." From the time the child was two, they talked at him. As he grew older, they provided him with a wealth of sensory experiences such as listening to classical records and watching the ballet, but he never had time really to enjoy the experiences, for the parents accompanied each one with a barrage of words. Most of the words were polysyllabic. The overstimulation and the pattern of complex language were too much for him. The result was that he gave up trying to speak and became a child with "delayed speech."

Both the school and the community also provide stimulation for language development. If the child's school is a place where one of its prime aims is to further effective communication and to help the child engage in speech situations successfully, he will grow faster than the child in a school where the teacher is the dominant person and where the listening phase of the communication cycle is emphasized to the detriment of the speaking phase. When the experiences that the school offers are the kind that stimulate conversation, discussion, debate, reading aloud, and when the teacher is the kind of person who truly wants the give and take necessary in a democratic classroom, the child will learn to speak more clearly, more fully, and more accurately.

If the child lives in a community where people live cooperatively and where much communication takes place, he will grow faster in language. If his community consists of people who speak well, clearly, and easily, he will also have an advantage. The influence of the neighborhood, church, library, and playground is decisive in the child's language growth. Even the amount and kind of television available makes a difference. In fact, Templin (37) points out that the import of increased travel and television may be reflected in the greater similarity of children's experiences. As socioeconomic statuses become more nearly equal in a community, the level of certain language skills may become more nearly alike. The need for providing experiences to stimulate language development is elaborated more fully in Chapter 8.

Sex

Girls do seem to be more fluent than boys, and some authorities believe that they have more facility with language at an earlier age than boys. McCarthy (22) points out that the reason for the girls' superiority may be that girls are able to identify with their mothers, their first teachers of language, more easily than boys do. Studies have shown varied levels of differences in the development between the two sexes. Davis (4) notes that in nearly every phase of language study girls retained up to the nine-and-one-half-year level the superiority in language development including articulation, word usage, and length, complexity, and grammatical correctness of sentences. She indicates that girls use more personal pronouns and conjunctions than boys and less slang. She found sex differences more marked in children of lower socioeconomic status than those of higher socioeconomic status. Templin (35) states that her study does not entirely substantiate the more precocious development of girls over boys found in previous studies. She notes that while girls do tend to receive higher scores than boys, the differences are not consistent and are only infrequently statistically significant. She indicates that in articulation of sounds, the boys took about one test interval (.5 year) longer than the girls to reach a comparatively mature level of articulation. In general, she states that her results support findings of earlier studies showing that girls tend to arrive at articulatory proficiency somewhat earlier (one-half year) than boys. Boys tend to exceed in word knowledge. She explains her reduced differences on the basis that over the years differences in language ability of boys and girls may have become less pronounced because of a shift toward a single standard in child care and training in the last few decades (35, p. 147).

Two other studies minimize the sex differences. Winitz (41) reporting a study on sex differences in language development of kindergarten children notes that in a study of 75 boys and girls essentially the same in chronological age, intelligence, socioeconomic status, and family constellation, the statistically significant differences were found in favor of the girls on two measures, length of responses and one of three-word fluency measures. No significant differences were found in articulation or vocabulary. He indicates that the hypotheses of no difference between the sexes with regard to the major verbalization measures (length of response, number of different words, structural complexity, articulatory skills, vocabulary skills, and three- of four-word fluency measures) is tenable. Sampson (25) writing in the *British Journal of Educational Psy-*

chology says that sex differences in language development are very small. He does state that there is some evidence in his study to indicate that in the performance of five-year-olds, boys are superior in precision of language usage and girls in fluency of expression.

Development of Speech in Children

When a proud father hears his ten-month-old child say "da-da," he frequently jubilantly exclaims, "Johnny's talking!" In some instances, Johnny in saying "da-da" means "Daddy, I'm glad you're home." In others, he evokes by chance that particular bit of jabber at the moment his father enters the room. In any case, using words with meaning is one aspect of a child's language development. Other aspects include: (1) The particular sounds the child speaks or uses in words and the relationship of the number of vowels to the number of consonants; (2) the grammatical composition of his speech, which involves the length and complexity of his sentences and the parts of speech he uses; and (3) the purposes of his speech, which may be to hear the sound of his own voice or to gain a response from others. All these factors are concerned with the child's ability to speak. His capacity to comprehend is also important. This capacity depends not only on his understanding of the words spoken but also on the speaker's gestures, his tone of voice, and the immediate situation.

Children develop language at varying rates. Johnny may speak his first word at nine months, Alex at 15 months. Helen at six may say every sound except *s* perfectly but Katy at six may substitute *t* and *d* for the two *th* sounds, *l* for *r* and *w*, and *p* and *b* for *f* and *v*. The remarks of Helen at four years are almost entirely two-word sentences while Janey at the same age uses as many as ten words in a sentence. Jimmy at 4½ said with obvious understanding when a child was having difficulty learning to ride his bike, "No self-confidence." Helen of the same age more normally said, "Mark no go?" These examples demonstrate the variability of development of speech in children of the same age. As the averages are given on the following pages, the reader must remember that they are averages and that the development of individual children differs considerably.

Birth Cry

The first sound heard is the birth cry, the purpose of which is to establish normal respiration and provide oxygen for the blood. This first vocal activity is part of a purely reflexive total response to chemical-nervous stimuli within the baby's organism. Expiration of breath sets the vocal cords into vibration and gives rise to the birth cry. For language it means little except that it shows that the elementary laryngeal and respiratory mechanisms are normal. Irwin (13) notes that the sound may be the vowels in the words *met, calm, cat, cup,* or the first vowel in the word *about.*

First Two Months

During the first two months the child responds to pain, hunger, noises, and other strong stimuli by crying. During the first month the cries which follow the birth cry are reflexive, totally bodily responses which lack specificity and direction. The child is responding to pain, hunger, noise, cold, thirst and other strong stimuli by crying. The character of the cry is not significantly different in response to different stimuli. During the second month, however, the character of the cry does become characteristic of certain stimuli. For example, the hungry child utters a type of cry that mothers often recognize as a hunger cry. These cries thus establish a special kind of communication with the mother, for through crying the child indicates his wants. Lewis claims that the origin of the vowels and consonants is the result of the expression of the child's vital needs and their satisfaction (15, p. 114). Lewis points out that a child's progress in speech will to some extent depend on the way in which others respond to the child's cries and gurglings. If he is often allowed to cry for long periods without response from anyone, his cries will not easily be connected by him with the satisfaction of his needs. His crying then is uncommunicative. If when he gurgles, no one joins him with a smile and a gurgle, again communication is thwarted. But if, on the other hand, the adult pays too much attention and anticipates the child's every need, his progress in speech may be slowed down. If the parents come the minute he cries and if he is so carefully cared for that he never needs to cry, the incentive is weakened. Similarly, if someone is always there to play with him, he will have no need to gurgle to attract attention (14, p. 26).

In crying and gurgling, the child uses the vowels found in *met*, *hit*, and *cup*, and the consonant *h*. In the early stages the child uses a preponderance of front and middle vowels. As he grows older, he uses more back vowels (10). Front vowels are those which are produced in the front of the mouth with the blade of the tongue most active. They are found in such words as *hit, cat,* and *met*. Back vowels are those which are produced in the back of the mouth with the back of the tongue most active. Back vowels are found in such words as *calm, root, law,* and *rope*. Middle vowels are those in which the midsection of the tongue is most active and are found in such words as *cup* and *burn*. By the end of the second month the child is using many of the front and middle vowels and about one-fourth of the consonants (13, p. 114). He pays attention to sounds and attends to speaking voices.

Three to Six Months

At this time the child, while not giving up his reflexive crying, does enter the stage where he is vocalizing, playing with sounds, or *babbling*. He produces most of the sounds at random. As he grows older, however, he repeats. He babbles "ga-ga, goo-goo, bah-bah, uggle-uggle." Something happens through some combination of tactile, kinesthetic, or auditory sensory avenues which facilitates reproducing sound. In addition, he responds to others. He squeals with delight as his mother brings his red ball or with pain if she pricks him with a pin. When he sees his daddy coming with arms outstretched, he expresses his eagerness and happiness. But when daddy takes away the teddy bear, he quickly shows his displeasure.

He also distinguishes between the scolding note he sometimes hears and the friendly tone he normally hears. Gesell and Thompson say that 42 percent of babies coo at eight weeks and three-fourths of them at 12 to 16 weeks (7, p. 249). In all of this cooing, crying, and babbling Irwin (13) says that the child uses almost all consonant and vowel sounds although he does not use diphthongal sounds.

It is not completely clear how important the stage of babbling is. Children frequently produce an *l* and *r* at this stage, but, when they reach the age of four, the same children cannot produce the sound in a word. But at some stage, the babbling comes together with perceptual development. Lewis (14) believes that the babbling stage is very important. He notes that in babbling the incentives present in the child are reinforced by the behavior of others. As the child makes sounds for fun, his fun is increased when he finds that his babbling brings pleasure to others. Lewis claims that there are impulses in the child to make sounds and that these rudimentary sounds will grow into language only if they are nourished by the responses of others. Since the roots of a child's development in speech lie in his own nature, development will be encouraged and sustained only if his little world is favorable to his growth as a speaker (14, p. 46).

Seven to Twelve Months

During these next months the child is getting ready to say his first word. He expresses satisfaction when daddy gives him his favorite ball and exclaims when daddy tosses him in the air. He imitates his own sounds for fun. He says "da-da" or "abble-abble," listens intently, and then repeats the sounds. This repetition, wherein the child is responding to the sound he has produced, is called *lallation*. Even though he does not understand the sounds, he enjoys saying and hearing them. He likes to listen to familiar words; for instance, he enjoys mom's saying "Bye-bye" and frequently responds by waving. At 10 months or so he begins to imitate sounds that he hears others make. This step is called *echolalia*. As his mother says, "Come on, eat," he responds with "eat, eat." At the stages of lallation and echolalia, the child acquires a repertoire of many sounds and combinations of sounds which he will ultimately produce at will and use in meaningful speech.

At this age, other evidences of language development appear. The child understands "no." His mother says "no" as he tries to turn his plate of food upside down or grab her eyeglasses. She prevents his action or shows displeasure in some way. Now he stops his intended action when he hears "no."

Around 12 months the child says one or two words. Darley and Winitz (2) reviewed the literature on age of appearance of the first word. They state that it appears that the average child begins to say his first word by approximately one year. They further state that delay of appearance of the first word beyond 18 months may indicate a serious physical, mental, or hearing involvement. Almost always the first word is a monosyllable or repeated monosyllable. Winitz and Irwin (42) report that their findings are in agreement with reports in literature that the syllabic structure of first words are either disyllables such as "baba" or monosyllables such as "ba." They also give a possible explanation of the discrepancy between Iowa studies, which suggest that the first consonants uttered in the early months of life are back consonants with infrequent labials, and other earlier studies, which suggest that the most frequent sounds are labials. They point out that their study shows that labial consonants are the most frequent elements in word structure. The inference then seems feasible that the earlier studies were not made in the early months of the child's life but were made as the infants were saying their first words.

"Da-da" comes to mean daddy and "ma-ma" comes to mean mother and "ba-ba" comes to mean ball. A pleasurable reaction follows closely upon the utterance of such sounds which were probably spoken by chance in a seemingly meaningful way. As the mother or father repeats the sound with obvious satisfaction and the child echoes him, the word becomes associated with pleasure. At this point the child utters the word with meaning; he has established a conventionalized speech reaction as a response to a socially presented stimulus. The child may use the one word to express different meanings. "Ca-ca" may mean "I want to get in the car," "There's a car in the street," or "Give me that toy car." Gesell and Thompson (7) indicate that at 44 weeks, 69 percent of the babies said one or more words. Twelve percent used one or more words at 32 weeks. At 52 weeks some children still had not spoken. These figures are significant in that they show how children vary in this one phase of language development.

Twelve to Eighteen Months

This is a period of preparation for true speech although the child is not speaking many words. He is so concerned with walking and discovering objects in his environment that his language development may seem slow. According to Gesell (7) the norms are four words at 15 months and five or more at 18 months. The child vocalizes a great deal in a kind of conversational jargon, and he still imitates syllables and words. He can follow simple commands and stop at "No" or "Don't do that." When his mother says, "Give me that," he understands. The vocabulary he comprehends is much greater than his spoken vocabulary. The control of his voice is not stable. It is inconsistent.

Eighteen to Twenty-Four Months

At 18 to 24 months there is a real spurt. The child joins words to make a sentence such as "Me go." He names objects and pictures, comprehends simple questions, begins to use pronouns, and includes phrases in his conversation. McCarthy points out that at two years nouns make up 39 percent of the words whereas at 18 months they make up 50 percent (17, p. 114). M. E. Smith (31) indicates that a two-year-old child has a vocabulary of 272 words, which contrasts decidedly with five words at one year. She also notes that the average two-year-old will speak about 80 words during an hour period of free play. More than half of what the child of two says is comprehensible, compared with only about one-fourth of what the child of 18 months says (17, p. 51). The child of this age has better control over voice as a whole. Inflections, however, are unstable and poorly controlled (19). All these facts give evidence of decided development of language.

Three Years

At three years the child is chattering. He is using more than half the sounds in the English language, and adults can understand almost all that he says. He now uses only 19 percent of nouns as compared to 39 percent a year ago (17, p. 114). He uses many simple sentences with an increase in the proportion of articles, conjunctions, and prepositions. His sentences contain about four words and in them he uses "we," "us," and "you." Typical sentences are "That's all" (dasall), "What's this?" (wasis), "What are those?" (watadoz) (19, p. 44). The voice of the three-year-old is, in general, of an even loudness and often a low, soft tone (19, p. 44).

Four Years

The loquacious four-year-old enjoys talking, and his parents and friends easily understand what he has to say, for he is making most of his sounds accurately. As the relative frequency of simple sentences decreases, that of complex and compound sentences increases. His sentences contain from six to eight words. He uses more articles, conjunctions, and prepositions and not as many interjections (45). He is easily excitable, and his voice reflects the excitement. He can control the modulation of his voice. He uses inflection for dramatic emphasis (19, p. 48).

Five Years

The five-year-old continues to like to talk. He exchanges information with others and asks many questions. He tells what happened on his trip to his grandmother's. He relates the story of *The Three Bears* that his mother has read and told him. He enjoys being read to.

Six Years

The talkative six-year-old is interested in everything about him. Because he really wants a response to his ideas, he communicates more fully with his classmates and friends. He still likes to hear stories, and he tells them himself with many gestures. Children in the first grade recognize 24,000 basic derivative words; they know 16,900 basic words. The range is from 6,000 to 48,800 (33).

Later Development

From here on the child matures rapidly in his language usage. Studies indicate a fairly steady growth of vocabulary through the school years. In the twelfth grade, he recognizes 80,300 words with a range from 36,700 to 136,500 (33). The maturing child uses language for many purposes: He learns to carry on conversation with real give and take with adults and children. He argues with other children and supports his statements. He reads stories to give enjoyment to younger brothers and sisters. His speech becomes less egocentric. He begins to increase the ratio of abstract to concrete words. He speaks not only of the present and the future but also of the past. He talks about his problems, helps plan the work of his classroom, and discusses processes and solutions. Finally, he generalizes and makes deductions.

Fluency

The child's speech is not completely fluent at any level. It contains many dysfluencies. Children repeat words, syllables, and sounds. These repetitions are characteristic of the normal speech of all age levels. Davis (3) points out that the average child repeats a sound or phrase forty-five times per thousand spoken words in spontaneous free play speech. Winitz (40) investigated the repetition of speech sounds in the vocalizations and speech of children in the first two years of their lives. The results of his investigation indicate that from one-fourth to one-third of the vocalized breath exhalations during the first two years contain repetitions of sounds or sound patterns. Both the teacher and the parent must expect hesitancy in a child's speech and must not set standards for fluency too high.

Acquisition of Sounds

Templin (35) in a definitive study gives the ages at which 75 percent of the children first uttered various types of sounds correctly. She found that final consonant elements are less correctly produced than initial or medial consonant elements until about 90 percent correct articulation is achieved (35, p. 43). A table indicating norms for ages for acquisition of types of sounds follows (35, p. 47).

Age at Which 75 Percent of Children First Uttered Various Types of Sounds Correctly

Chronological Age	Sounds
3	Initial, medial, and final nasals,* initial, medial plosives;* initial, medial semivowels, vowels, diphthongs
4	final plosives
5	final semivowels, final combinations, initial double consonant blends
6	initial, medial, final fricatives, final double consonant blends, reversed triple consonant blends, reversed double consonant blends†
7	initial, final, triple consonant blends

The following table gives comparison of ages of acquiring specific consonant sounds in the Templin and Poole studies (35, p. 53).

*These terms are explained in Chapter 6.
† Examples of blend: "*pl*" forms an initial consonant blend sound in *play*.

Sound	Templin	Poole	Sound	Templin	Poole
m	3	3.5	r	4	7.5
n	3	4.5	s	4.5	7.5†
ng	3	4.5	sh	4.5	6.5
p	3	3.5	ch	4.5	‡
f	3	5.5	t	6	4.5
h	3	3.5	th	6	7.5†
w	3	3.5	v	6	6.5†
y	3.5	4.5	l	6	6.5
k	4	4.5	th	7	6.5
b	4	3.5	z	7	7.5†
d	4	4.5	zh	7	6.5
g	4	4.5	j	7	‡
			hw	*	7.5

* Sound tested but not produced correctly by 75 percent of subjects at the oldest age tested.

† In unpublished study Poole notes that *s* and *z* appear at 5.5 then disappear and return later at 7.5.

Th appears at 6.5 and *v* at 5.5.

‡ Sound not tested or not reported.

Since in many communities, as in Philadelphia for example, the *hw* sound (as in *where*) is rarely heard, and the use of *w* is widespread, its lack of acquisition from the standpoint of language development is not important.

References and Suggested Readings

1. BILTO, W. E., "Motor Abilities of Children with Defective Speech." *Journal of Speech Disorders,* **VI** (December 1941), 187-203. (Compares the muscular abilities of children with articulatory defects and stuttering with those of children with normal speech.)

2. DARLEY, F. L., and H. WINITZ, "Age of First Word: Review of Research." *Journal of Speech and Hearing Disorders,* **XXVI** (August 1961), 272-290. (Reports on 26 groups. Includes sample, collection of data, and definition of first word, and age of appearance of first word for boys and girls.)

3. DAVIS, D. M., "The Relation of Repetition in the Speech of Young Children to Certain Measures of Language Maturity and Situa-

tional Factors." *Journal of Speech Disorders,* **IV** (December 1939), 303-318, and **V** (September 1940), 235-246.

4. DAVIS, E. A., *The Development of Linguistic Skill in Twins, Singletons with Siblings and Only Children from Ages Five to Ten Years.* Minneapolis: University of Minnesota Press, 1937.

5. DAVIS, E. A., "Developmental Changes in the Distribution of Parts of Speech." *Child Development,* **IX** (September 1938), 309-317.

6. DAWE, H. C., "A Study of the Effect of an Educational Program upon Language Development and Related Mental Functions in Young Children." *Journal of Experimental Education,* **XI** (December 1942), 200-209.

7. GESELL, A. I., and H. THOMPSON, *Infant Behavior: Its Genesis and Growth.* New York: McGraw-Hill, 1934. (Includes material on the development of language and the ability of children to comprehend.)

8. GODA, S., and K. SMITH, "Speech Stimulation Practices among Mothers of Preschool Children." *Journal of Speech and Hearing Disorders,* **XXIV** (May 1959), 150-153. (Gives parental ratings showing time children spend in various speech stimulation activities and the parents' opinions of their order of importance.)

9. HARMS, I. E., and C. C. SPIKER, "Factors Associated with the Performance of Young Children on I.Q. Scales and Tests of Speech Development." *Journal of Genetic Psychology,* **XCIV** (March 1959), 3-22. (Substantiates Irwin and Chen on the fact that girls tend to be superior to boys in the production of different sounds.)

10. IRWIN, O. C., "Infant Speech: Development of Vowel Sounds." *Journal of Speech and Hearing Disorders,* **XIII** (March 1948), 31-34.

11. ———, "Infant Speech: Effect of Systematic Reading of Stories." *Journal of Speech and Hearing Research,* **III** (June 1960), 187-190. (Studies the effect of parents' reading to infants on the amount of their production of sounds.)

12. ———, "Speech Development in the Young Child." *Journal of Speech and Hearing Disorders,* **XVII** (Sept. 1952), 269-279.

13. ———, and H. P. CHEN, "Speech Sound Elements during the First Year of Life; a Review of the Literature." *Journal of Speech Disorders,* **VIII** (June 1943), 109-120.

14. LEWIS, M. M., *How Children Learn to Speak.* New York: Basic Books, 1959. (Gives the patterns and growth of development in children's language.)

15. Lewis, M. M., *Infant Speech*. London: Kegan Paul, Trench, Trubner and Co., 1936. (Carefully describes early stages of linguistic development.)

16. McCarthy, D., "Language Development in Children." In L. Carmichael (ed.). *Manual of Child Psychology*. (Rev. ed.) New York: John Wiley and Sons, 1954, 492-630. (Thoroughly reviews studies of language development.)

17. ———, *The Language Development of the Preschool Child*. Institute of Child Welfare Monograph Series, No. 14. Minneapolis: University of Minnesota Press, 1930. (Includes such aspects of language development of the preschool child as the use of the various parts of speech and comprehensibility of the child's speech.)

18. Marge, M., "Home Background Influences on the Development of Speech Skills in Older Children," *ASHA*, I (November 1959), 113. (Shows the home background influences on the development of oral communication skills in preadolescent children.)

19. Metraux, R. M., "Speech Profiles of the Pre-School Child 18 to 54 Months." *Journal of Speech and Hearing Disorders*, XV (March 1950), 37-53.

20. Milner, E., "A Study of the Relationships between Reading Readiness in Grade One School Children and Patterns of Parent-Child Interaction." *Child Development*, XXII (June 1951), 95-112.

21. Myklebust, H. R., "Babbling and Echolalia in Language Theory." *Journal of Speech and Hearing Disorders*, XXII (September 1957), 356-360. (Explains the early development of language. Indicates that babbling occurs as a concomitant to psychological process of identification and manifests the beginning of internalization.)

22. National Conference on Research in English. *Factors that Influence Language Growth*. Chicago: The National Council of Teachers of English, 1953. (Contains articles on the child's equipment for language growth and the influence of home, school, and community on the development of language.)

23. Poole, I., "Genetic Development of Articulation of Consonantal Sounds in English." *Elementary English Review*, XI (June 1934), 159-161. (Indicates the age at which boys and girls normally obtain the mastery of certain speech sounds.)

24. Reid, G., "The Etiology and Nature of Functional Articulatory Defects in Elementary School Children." *Journal of Speech Disorders*, XII (June 1947), 143-150.

25. SAMPSON, O. C., "Speech and Language Development of Five-Year-Old Children." *British Journal of Educational Psychology,* **XXIX** (November 1959), 217-222. (Studies the language development of five-year-olds in relation to I. Q., vocabulary, sex, and socioeconomic status.)

26. ——, "Study of Speech Development in Chidren of 18-30 Months." *British Journal of Educational Psychology,* **XXVI** (November 1956), 194-201. (Gives results of a study of 50 children between 18 to 30 months—longitudinally over a 12-month period.)

27. SAYLER, H. K., "The Effect of Maturation upon Defective Articulation in Grades 7-12." *Journal of Speech and Hearing Disorders,* **XIV** (September 1949), 202-207. (Indicates sounds most commonly missed.)

28. SCHNEIDERMAN, N., *An Investigation of the Relationship between Articulatory Ability and Language Ability.* Master's thesis (Brooklyn College, September 1953).

29. SHIRLEY, M. M., *The First Two Years: A Study of Twenty-Five Babies:* Vol. III *Personality Manifestations.* Institute Child Welfare Monograph Series, No. 8. Minneapolis: University of Minnesota Press, 1933.

30. SMITH, D. W., "Factors Affecting Speech Development." *Education,* **LXXX** (April 1960), 452-454. (Shows the factors of language development in relation to the child and his environment.)

31. SMITH, M. E., *An Investigation of the Development of the Sentence and Extent of Vocabulary in Young Children.* University of Iowa Studies: Studies in Child Welfare, **III**: 5 (1926).

32. ——, "Some Light on the Problem of Bilingual Children in Both of the Languages' Use." *Journal of Genetic Psychology,* **LXXIV** (June 1949), 305-310.

33. SMITH, M. K., "Measurement of the Size of General English Vocabulary through the Elementary Grades and High School." *Genetic Psychology Monographs,* **XXIV** (1941), 311-345.

34. SPRIESTERSBACH, D. C., and W. B. MCKENSIE, "Speech, an Index of Maturity." *Childhood Education,* **XXVII** (February 1951), 26-31. (Explains speaking behavior, development of speech sounds, obstacles to fluency in speech, language development, and persistence of baby talk.)

35. TEMPLIN, M. C., *Certain Language Skills in Children: Their Development and Interrelationships.* Minneapolis: University of Minne-

sota Press, 1957. (Presents norms on the development of articulation, sound discrimination, sentence structure, and vocabulary and the interrelations of these language skills in children of preschool and elementary school age.)

36. ———, "Norms on a Screening Test for Articulation for Ages 3-8." *Journal of Speech and Hearing Disorders,* **XVIII** (December 1953), 323-331. (Compares the time of acquisition of articulatory ability of boys and girls.)

37. ———, "Relation of Speech and Language Development to Intelligence and Socio-Economic Status." *Volta Review* **LX** (September 1958), 331-334.

38. VINEYARD, E. E., and H. W. MASSEY, "Interrelationship of Certain Linguistic Skills and their Relationship With Scholastic Achievement When Intelligence is Ruled Constant." *Journal of Educational Psychology,* **XLVIII** (May 1957), 279-286.

39. WILLIAMS, H. M., "An Analytical Study of Language Achievement in Preschool Children." University of Iowa Studies: Studies in Child Welfare, **XIII**: 2 (1937), 9-18.

40. WINITZ, H., "Repetitions in the Vocalizations and Speech of Children in the First Two Years of Life." *Journal of Speech and Hearing Disorders,* Monograph Supplement 7 (June 1961), 55-61.

41. ———, "Sex Differences in Language of Kindergarten Children." *ASHA,* **I** (November 1959), 86. (Compares the language skills of 75 boys and 75 girls of kindergarten age.)

42. ———, and O. C. IRWIN, "Syllabic and Phonetic Structures of Infants Early Words." *Journal of Speech and Hearing Research,* **I** (September 1958), 250-256.

43. WOOD, K. S., "Parental Maladjustment and Functional Articulatory Defects in Children." *Journal of Speech Disorders,* **XI** (December 1946), 255-275.

44. YEDINACK, J. G., "Study of the Linguistic Functioning of Children with Arithmetic and Reading Disabilities." *Pedagogical Seminary,* **LXXIV** (March 1949), 23-59. (Describes a study of second-grade children with articulatory or reading problems that shows that articulatory and reading problems are coexistent. Indicates that there is no significant relationship between articulatory ability and intelligence.)

45. YOUNG, F. M., "An Analysis of Certain Variables in a Developmental Study of Language." *Genetic Psychology Monographs,*

XXIII (1941), 88-89. (Studies the language of 74 nursery school children aged 30 to 65 months. Compares the language development of children of parents of usual economic status with a group whose parents were on relief.)

Problems

1. Listen to a boy and girl on each of the following age levels: two, four, and six years. Note differences in accuracy of articulation, in sentence length, and in vocabulary usage.

2. Listen to a child whom you consider very bright and one of the same age whom you consider of average intelligence. Are there any differences in sentence length, vocabulary, and proficiency of articulation between the two children?

3. Listen to children in the kindergarten and to children in the fifth grade. Notice the differences in articulation.

4. Read and report on one of the following references: 1, 8, 14, 22, 34, 37, 40, or 43.

5. Find a provocative picture in a magazine. Ask a five-year-old, an eight-year-old, and a twelve-year-old to tell a story based on the picture. Note the differences in: (*a*) vocabulary, (*b*) length of sentences, (*c*) ideas involved, and (*d*) length of the story.

8

Stimulating

Language

Development

BOTH THE classroom teacher and the correctionist are involved in the speech curricula of the elementary and high school. These curricula implicitly pursue three aims for each child: (1) to correct any speech difficulty which calls attention to itself, causes the child undue concern, or detracts seriously from his communicative ability; (2) to help him eliminate minor articulation and voice difficulties and substandard articulation and voice; and (3) to assist him to become an effective speaker and listener. The first aim is usually achieved by speech and hearing correctionists or therapists. The program for it is ordinarily entitled "speech and hearing correction" or "speech and hearing therapy." The last two aims are usually achieved by the classroom teacher under supervision. These two aims are incorporated in a program called "speech improvement," "language arts," or "speech arts."

Administration of Speech Improvement

The first aim is clear cut; the responsibility for achieving it lies clearly in the hands of those in charge of the remedial speech and hearing program. The second and third aims, which are aims of the speech improvement program, however, are not as specific, and the responsibility for achieving them may rest within several programs. In a study (3, pp. 81-82) conducted by a subcommittee of the Research Committee of the American Speech and Hearing Association (Geraldine Garrison, Chairman, Frederic Darley, Hilda Amidon, and Verna Breinholt), 70 percent of the 98 supervisors consulted replied to a questionnaire concerning the administrative organization of the speech improvement program. Of the supervisors questioned, 35 percent reported the program to be part of remedial speech and hearing services; 21 percent, part of language arts; 5 percent, separate programs; 6 percent, part of both remedial services and language arts; and 3 percent, part of other units. In the same study an analysis was made of nine outstanding speech improvement programs which had been in operation for some time. Of the nine, five are part of a remedial program in speech and hearing; one is a separate speech improvement program coordinated with remedial service; one is identified with the language arts program, but speech clinicians direct the speech work; and one is part of a two-year research study headed by remedial speech and hearing personnel.

Stimulation and Language Development

Since all three aims are directly concerned with the language development of children and since speech stimulating practices and an atmosphere designed to further speech are important factors in language development, we shall be occupied in this chapter with the activities and the atmosphere which stimulate speech. The preceding chapter on language development contains many bits of evidence which point to the need for such stimulation: The Milner study shows the result of parental conversation on development of language. The Irwin-Winitz study indicates the value of reading stories and talking about them as stimulus to developing sounds in children. The Dawe study tells of the effect of an educational program, involving children's literature and the taking of short trips, on the language development of children living in an orphanage. Studies concerning home background influences emphasize the importance of a warm, democratic, accepting atmosphere to nurture language development.

Speaking activities which stimulate take place in all kinds of environments—home, playground, speech correction session, and classroom, and they range in a continuum from the very informal to the formal. The kindergartner may be telling a fellow kindergartner on the way to school what a fuss his family makes over a little bit of hot weather. Here the ideas are informally expressed by one person to another person. Organization is almost completely lacking. The kindergartner's only purpose is to express his feelings about one of the idiosyncracies of adults. On the other hand, the president of an elementary school student council may make an address to all the students of the school. This situation, the purpose of which is to welcome the students at the beginning of the school year, is a formal one involving hundreds of students. The president has planned his address carefully and has organized it according to a definite pattern. But the basic ingredients of these two speaking situations are the same. They include participants who are small or large in number, who are friendly or hostile, democratic or undemocratic, warm or cold, relaxed or rigid. These participants have ideas, dull, mundane, or exciting, which they organize effectively or ineffectively and which they speak to achieve a particular purpose. The other participants listen carefully or carelessly, critically or uncritically, graciously or ungraciously, in an atmosphere secure or insecure in a particular room, comfortable or uncomfortable, small or large, attractive or unattractive. In school or home situations, the teachers, the speech correctionist, or the parents control these factors to some degree, regardless of the type of speaking situation, and regardless of where it occurs on the informal-formal continuum.

Factors in Speaking Situations

Kinds of Speech Situations

CONVERSING, TALKING, DISCUSSING.   One of the most frequent situations in speech is imparting ideas that inform or persuade. At the informal end of the continuum such talk is conversation. Conversation occurs both in the classroom and in the speech correction room. For instance, both the teacher and the correctionist use the ingredients of "show and tell." Both strive to make "show and tell" a truly sharing time where students give and receive ideas. Both try to motivate children to express ideas that interest themselves but at the same time are exciting and vital to their listeners. The choice of ideas in this conversational speaking activity, as in other speaking activities, matures as the child grows older. Both the teacher and the correctionist encourage this maturing process subtly and sensitively. For example, some first graders and many kindergartners are at the developmental level where they need the security of an actual object—like a small, furry make-believe kitten. The timid child manages only to show his treasure. Then he tells its story just to the teacher or to the clinician. With adult encouragement, he tells it to the whole class or to a group.

In this sharing period, the correctionist is not particularly concerned with organization, but the teacher is; he helps the children to organize their ideas. In the early part of the first grade, the teacher may, as the child talks, quietly and unobtrusively write on the blackboard the central idea of the sharing experience. As children mature, the teacher asks them to phrase their own central ideas as:

> We have a new blue and white rug.
> My daddy flew to California.
> My baby brother discovered his toes.

The teacher encourages the other youngsters to listen and then talk about the main idea and stay with it. With the flexible guidance of a good conversationalist, the teacher promotes an onward, somewhat organized flow of language. Consequently, as the child matures, he becomes more facile both with the expression and the organization of his ideas.

The informal end of the continuum of expressing ideas to inform or persuade is particularly important for the child with a speech defect. This child needs to feel that what he has to say is worthwhile and that others wish to listen to him. He needs to perceive himself as being adequate in a group speaking situation. Consequently, the teacher and the speech correctionist often work together to give him the kind of stimulation to speak which will enhance his self-concept.

Mary Ann was a child with average intelligence, but with general marked language retardation, including many sound substitutions, use of short very simple sentences, meager vocabulary, and little use of articles, prepositions, and conjunctions. Very few adults could understand her. The teacher and the correctionist conferred on ways to stimulate Mary Ann to speak. Some were very ordinary; for instance, one day in the classroom the teacher asked Mary Ann to talk to Tommie's dog so that the dog wouldn't be lonesome. When Mary Ann became more sure of herself, the teacher encouraged her to read a poem she had dictated to the speech correctionist to her classmates. At this time, Mary Ann was working on f and v:

Fee, fie, foe fum
I come, I come, I come.
Vee, vie, vo vum
The big, big, big bums
They go, they go, they go.
Fee, fie, fo, fum
Vee, vie, vo vum
The five big bums
They dive, dive, dive
Like jive, jive, jive.

The first-grade children responding to her bit of nonsense laughed with her. In fact, one child said, "You ought to bring 'the wives' in now." Whereupon another remarked, " '*Live*' goes with it, too." Later on, when Mary Ann was ready, she talked to a stranger. The day the class went on a trip to a canning factory, the teacher asked its owner to respond to Mary Ann as Mary Ann thanked her for allowing the children to visit. The owner (fortunately a former speech correctionist) graciously responded, understood Mary Ann's jargon, and provided another step forward in the child's language development.

At the high school level, informal conversation exists both in the classroom and in the speech correctionist's room. A speech class had attended a college play, *The Death of a Salesman*. The conversation that took place in the classroom as a result was spirited. One boy contributed considerable information about Arthur Miller's other plays. Another interposed, "He was married to Marilyn Monroe." Still another, "He just finished a new book." From here on, the teacher guided the conversation to include an analysis of the characters, the opposing forces in the play, and how the costuming and scenery helped to interpret it. The situation was informal; the ideas flowed onward with organization because of the teacher's skillful guidance. The classroom hour was an exciting one of good conversation made possible because all the students had shared the same stimulating experience. If the speech correctionist's student or students had attended the performance, the play might have provided a topic of conversation for the therapy session.

More nearly at the formal end of the continuum, four high school enthusiastic students of ballet participated in a panel on "What Makes a Good Classical Ballerina?" One girl, reporting on John Martin's *Introduction to the Dance* (New York: W. W. Norton, 1939), traced the history of the ballet and told of the contribution of Nijinsky, Fokine, and Novarre. Another, reporting on Agnes De Mille's *Dance to the Piper* (Boston: Little, Brown and Company, 1952), revealed the enchantment linked with a career in ballet and at the same time made clear that preparation for ballet is necessarily grueling. The third, reporting on Nicolaeva Legat's *Preparation for Ballet* (London: Hunt, Barnard and Company, 1953), gave an account of Legat's advice concerning such items as selection of instructor, conditioning of the body, and the music of the dance. The last girl, reporting on an article in *Dance Magazine* (vol. XXVII, December 1954, 51-57), told how this article explains and describes the reflections and experiences of a Russian ballerina. In this discussion, each girl stood, addressed her audience, and made her remarks follow a fairly formal style. This continuum of giving talks can contain many speaking situations ranging from telephone conversations, interviews, reports to a class, discussions, and debates to very formal addresses.

Books furnish the stimulation for much of this talk both in the classroom and in the therapy session. They often make a special day or event significant. The first grader on Valentine's Day may enjoy Pamela Bianco's *The Valentine Party* (Philadelphia: Lippincott, 1955). The excitement of Pamela's finding that the party is for her rubs off on first graders. On Hallowe'en, the primary child may well delight in Nora Unwin's *Proud Pumpkin* (New York: Aladdin, 1953). Everyone, glowing on Hallowe'en, admired the pumpkin. But then the pumpkin was lonely until a chipmunk made him his winter home. Or at Christmas the same child may well find pleasure in Will and Nicolas' *The Christmas Bunny* (New York: Harcourt, 1952) which tells of a young boy who, because of a rescue, is rewarded with a visit to the animal's Christmas in the woods. The beautiful illustrations of this book foster conversation in the classroom and in the therapy session.

Toys, visits, bulletin boards, and plants also promote talk. A farm run by high school boys near a speech and hearing center is a truly exciting place for the center's children to visit. A visit furnishes plenty to talk about. On all levels in all classrooms and in the home, the more experiences the child has, the more he has to talk about and concomitantly the more to listen for. The richer his environment is, the greater will be his language development.

READING ALOUD. A second effective activity is reading aloud.

Here again both the classroom teacher and the correctionist use oral reading to stimulate language development, and again the situation ranges from the informal to the formal with the formal situation occurring in the classroom. Sometimes the teacher or clinician reads a poem so that the children can talk about its ideas. Recently a teacher read to a group of nine-year-olds Rose Fyleman's poem about the rain coming down 'til the water was all over the town. It goes on to tell about cabs and buses floating, about everyone's living on the second floor. One nine-year-old responded with: "She'd have to row. I did once at Shawnee. I'd play in a boat—right in the middle—right out in the street—and pretend I was on the ocean. I'd like to take one of my friends with me. We'd talk, tell each other stories. Maybe I'd take my lunch in the boat, too. But if you'd open the door, the water would come in." Thus, the poem stimulated a flow of language. This same informal flow could take place in the clinician's room.

The same teacher read Rose Fyleman's poem which begins "Widdy-widdy wurkey is the name of my turkey." One of the children asked the teacher to read the poem a second time. After the second reading, the child remarked, "It's nonsense and silly but I like it. You know the names all rhyme. Remember? Wurkey, turkey, back again and hen, loose and goose." This child obviously had listened to the words and to their similarity in sound. Such stimulation to listen can occur in the classroom or in the therapy session.

One teacher motivated her youngsters first to think about the clouds in the sky and then to write about them. She asked a child to read to the class Rose Fyleman's poem about the bulls, wolves, and buffaloes in the sky—about their swimming, running, and flying. That afternoon and evening the children looked at the sky. When they returned to class next morning, they talked about what they had seen. Then they wrote about it. Finally they shared their selections with each other.

Another teacher uses sounds as a basis for original writing. Children listen to the sounds in the winter time. They hear tires screeching as they spin, doors banging, sleet hitting the windows, and wind whistling. Then they write about the noises and share their compositions with each other. Sometimes the teacher suggests that they use kitchen noises: The kettle whistling; the coffee pot going "ploppety, plop, plop, plop;" the toaster going "zing;" the dishes clattering; the pans banging; the stove bell saying "brrr;" the floor mop going "swish, swish." Such listening makes children in the classroom or therapy session more aware of sounds. The same group also uses the sounds of children's names as a basis for a poem like:

> Our little Jane likes sugar cane
> But chocolate ice cream to her is a pain.
> Now our big Jim likes to go to gym
> But drawing pictures is not for him.

A child comes to school prepared to like poetry, for he is intrigued with rhythm, the sounds of words, and the sensations of touch, taste, sound, and smell. His own rhythmic reactions are poetic in nature, as evidenced by his response to music. He is delighted with the way words sound. One six-year-old lovingly and caressingly used the word "delicious." The feeling of a fur piece was delicious. His stroking of fur, saying "delicious" at the same time, indicated his enjoyment and response to the sensation of touch. "Delicious" applied to ice cream showed his reaction to taste. Just as vivid to him are sensations of sight, sound, and smell. He likes the sensuous quality of many of his experiences. Most teachers, by making use of this preparation to like poetry, enrich the child's school day by reading poetry aloud.

The teacher and the children read poetry aloud to bring out its melody, tones, movements, and quality. The teacher encourages children to select verse that meets their needs in terms of interest, emotion, and development. On the first day of a beautiful heavy snow, the teacher may read Frances Frost's *The Snow Man*, a poem about making the snow man, sticking the pipe in his mouth, tying a red scarf around his neck, and putting in his eyes. The children may do just that on their own initiative after school. Or why not provide an opportunity for them to build the snow man during school hours? Either the classroom teacher or the clinician may provide this opportunity. The day may be dull and need livening. On such a day a ten-year-old read Beatrice Brown's *Johnathon Bing.* Johnathon, going to Court, to visit the King, discovered that he forgot his tie and his hat and finally that he was wearing pajamas. The children responded to this peculiar man Johnathon in this ludicrous situation. The dull day was brighter. Children also like lyric poetry that creates mood and calls forth pictures. One group of children again and again read and listened to Christina Rossetti's *Lullaby* with its pictures of the lambs sleeping, the stars up in the heavens, the moon peering, and with its mood of everyone quietly falling a-sleeping. Last, children like narrative poetry, such as Eugene Field's *Orphan Annie,* that tells of the adventures of an individual or a group of individuals. The good teacher and the perceptive clinician are alert to opportunities for sharing poetry suggested by the activities of the classroom and the school day.

At the more formal end of the reading aloud continuum one girl may be reading a particular poem or bit of prose to the entire class. Or the whole group may be speaking a poem together. The choral speakers may even perform in assembly. For example choral speaking choirs may furnish the thread of the narrative for the Christmas story. Or the choral speaking may be background for modern dance. Perhaps the poem tells the story of cities—like Sandburg's "Chicago"—while the modern dancers interpret it. At assemblies students frequently read a selection from the Bible. One vocational high school speech teacher said as a boy read, "He used to have trouble with his *l*'s and *r*'s. Now listen to him." The boy read well —with meaning and feeling.

Reading aloud in both the classroom and in the speech correction room can be dreary. When the child is trying to read material that he does not quite understand, that he finds dull, and for which he feels no need, no stimulation is present. In a correctionist's room when the only drill is reading loaded sentences over and over again, the result is equally dreary. Material to be read aloud should be material that in some way will stimulate the reader. It may have to do with the child's interests; it may be related to the occasion; it may be the kind of nonsense that appeals to him; it may express his particular feelings at a particular time. But it should prove stimulating. In each instance the children should have found out the meaning and feeling of the poem, understood them clearly before they read aloud. The teacher then helps them to impart this meaning and feeling to the audience.

DRAMATIZING. Theater activities may range, as the others, from completely informal to the quite formal. From time immemorial children and parents have played a story as evidenced in Robert Browning's poem "Development":

> My father was a scholar and knew Greek.
> When I was five years old, I asked him once
>   "What do you read about?"
>   "The siege of Troy."
>   "What is the siege and what is Troy?"
>   Whereat
> He piled up chairs and tables for a town
> Set me a-top for Priam, called our cat
> Helen, enticed away from home (he said)
> By wicked Paris who crouched somewhere close
> Under the footstool, being coward,
> But whom—since she was worth the pains, poor puss—
> By taking Troy to get possession of.
> Towzer and Tray, our dogs, the Atreidai,
> —sought
> —always when great Achilles ceased to sulk,
> (My pony in the stable)—forth would prance
> And put to flight Hector—our page boy's self.
> This taught me who was who and what was what:
> So far as I rightly understood the cast

At five years old; a huge delight it proved
And still proves—thanks to that instructor sage
My Father, who knew better than to turn straight
Learning's full glare on weak eyed ignorance,
Or, worse yet, leave weak eyes to grow sand-blind
Content with darkness and vacuity.

Such playing stimulates language learning. For example, Robert Browning learned the meaning of *siege, Troy,* "who was who" and "what was what."

Teachers use this same kind of activity. One sixth-grade teacher wanted to prepare her children to view the television production of Shakespeare's *The Taming of the Shrew.* After she told the story, the children decided on what was to happen in each scene and who was to play Bianca, Catherine, Petruchio, and Hortensio. They then played *The Taming of the Shrew* in three scenes. As a result of this preparation, they watched the television production with understanding and interest. The discussion following their viewing was a lively one where the children began to learn some of the important elements of theater.

Teachers use not only stories as a basis for creative dramatics but also narrative poems, pairs of words like ugly and beautiful, sets of properties like an old bag, a scepter, and a blue teapot, and pictures that motivate but do not portray a story. Stories built from these sources stimulate children's language development. The degree of maturity makes a difference in the reaction to the stimulus. For example, two children, one aged seven and the other thirteen, were asked to make up stories which they could later play about the same picture. The picture was of a small girl looking rather wistful and dressed in a loose-fitting, white robe. The seven-year-old was mostly concerned with outward appearance and with descriptions, but the thirteen-year-old was interested in the relationship among persons. The seven-year-old saw just the present, but the thirteen-year-old viewed the past and looked to the future. The seven-year-old gave simple explanations and descriptions; the thirteen-year-old gave more complex ones. For example, she went into the motives of the child and her reasons for her actions. In addition, she saw the situation as a psychological problem of the child.

Speech correctionists, as well as classroom teachers, frequently use creative dramatics as material for teaching children to speak more clearly. A study by McIntyre (21) evaluates the effect of a program of creative activities upon the consonant articulation skills of adolescent and preadolescent children with consonant articulation disorders. She selected 32 children from the speech therapy program of the Pittsburgh, Pennsylvania, public schools, who needed further therapy, and placed 16 in an experimental group and the remaining 16 in a control group. The experimental group participated in creative activities with 185 children for a six-week summer program of creative dramatics, creative music and dance, and arts and crafts. When the groups were retested, significant improvement in articulation was evidenced by a greater percentage of the children in the experimental group than was evidenced by children in the control group.

Many children's stories emphasize particular sounds so that if the correctionist is working on a sound, he can find a story which contains many words with the sound. For example, a first grader with a defective *k* and *g* might well play *Ask Mr. Bear* by Marjorie Flack (New York: Macmillan, 1954). Danny tries to decide on a birthday gift for his mother. He meets a hen who suggests an egg, a goose who suggests a feather pillow, a goat who suggests cheese, and a cow who suggests cream. But finally Danny meets Mr. Bear who suggests a bear hug. All are happy. A second grader working with *k*'s might like to play Esphyr Slobodkina's *Caps for Sale* (New York: William Scott, 1947) which is the tale of a peddler and some monkeys and their monkey business. After going to sleep, the peddler looks up to see all of the monkeys wearing caps. A third grader who is working on *l* and *r* might enjoy playing Phyllis McGinley's *The Plain Princess* (Philadelphia: J. B. Lippincott, 1945) which involves a plan to make Esmeralda, the princess, beautiful. She goes to live with Dame's five beautiful daughters and learns not to be the spoiled princess but rather a person who is happy doing things for others. Thus, the princess becomes beautiful.

Adolescents, too, enjoy creative drama. A story such as Dorothy Canfield Fisher's *A New Pioneer* contains many *r* sounds and at the same time is the kind of material that interests adolescents. Magda is in bed crying, dreaming of all the horrible things that happened to her in Austria. Her grandfather comes to comfort her, telling her that everything will be all right now that they are in America. In school, some of the girls find her odd and different. As the students prepare for a Thanksgiving program, Magda writes and reads a prayer of Thanksgiving that she is now living in America. Her classmates are moved by her sensitive prayer.

All of the activities just mentioned are variants of dramatic activities on the informal end of the continuum. As the stories acquire more structure, as the "play" includes exposition, rising action, climax, falling action, and final outcome, as the teacher gives more direction, as the lines become set, as costumes and scenery are added, and as the size of the audience increases, the creative drama becomes less informal and approaches the more formal end of the continuum.

At the formal end of the continuum is the play where lines are learned, where the director gets exactly the results he wants, where the scenery and costumes are designed with care, and where the production is put on before an audience who pays to get in. But sometimes children learn lines and give plays to just another class. The direction is not as detailed. The costumes and scenery are improvised, and the result may be even less formal than a carefully staged creative dramatic activity.

Relationship of Speech Activities to Curriculum

Speech education involving such stimulating speech activities is part and parcel of all school curricula. Teachers at both the elementary and high school level frequently plan their work with their students. As the work of the unit progresses, many speech activities take place. Children give talks, report, discuss, debate, interview, read aloud, and dramatize.

For example, children in an eighth grade were studying the early history of New York State. While studying this era, one twelve-year-old, reporting on his trip across New York State on the Thruway compared the Thruway with the Erie Canal. The report of this trip motivated members of the class to study the building of the canal more thoroughly. The writer of their social studies text explained the reasons for the building of the canal and its values to the country, but the children wanted more information than their text contained. They discussed what more they would like to know about the Erie Canal. Specifically they wanted answers to:

What were the factors that made a canal seem advisable?
Who decided a canal was necessary?
Why was Van Buren opposed to it?
Why did Clinton approve the building of the Canal?
What were the times like in the early 1800's?
What kind of clothes did people wear then?
What did they do for entertainment?
How did they live?
What did they do for a living?
How was the building of the Canal planned?
What was the route of the Canal?
What were some of the difficulties encountered in building the Canal?
Who built the Canal?
What was its opening like?
What were the effects of its opening?

After they had listed these questions on the blackboard, they broke into groups to decide how to do their research and how to report on their findings. The project demanded oral communication in its planning and in its execution.

Throughout this activity groups frequently gave progress reports. As the children read, they found other items that they thought should be included. Finally, individuals and groups of individuals reported on what they had read. One boy gave an account of the way people talked in the 1800's. This item was not included originally, but he and the members of his group felt it added to their understanding of the period. "Oh, go sandpaper your nose" became one of the favorite expressions of the group. Another panel of students gave a very interesting discussion of the songs sung during this era. Through such activities children learn to speak better and to participate in discussion more capably.

The teacher helped these children in a number of ways to prepare for and to give their talks. He reminded them of the necessity of gaining and holding the interest of their listeners. He suggested ways and means of collecting material and of organizing it. He stressed their having a thorough knowledge of their topic, a real interest in it themselves, and a desire to communicate this interest to their listeners.

The teacher also taught them to be more successful participants in a discussion group. He taught them how to state a problem, analyze it, and examine its solutions. The children learned that they must have a basis for the choice of a particular solution. Although these children had already learned to be fairly effective members of a discussion group, the teacher reinforced their learning. Frequently he stressed that they must have knowledge and background before speaking. Because the discussion sometimes went off on a tangent, he emphasized that they must keep it relevant. He helped the students to consider all points of view, participate well, and listen carefully. He encouraged each boy and girl to be a responsible member of the group.

In this work on the Erie Canal the students found it necessary to read aloud from various sources. One boy read the speech made by Dewitt Clinton at the opening of the Canal. The teacher helped him to prepare this speech for reading aloud by making sure he understood the material both intellectually and emotionally. As the boy mentioned bringing together the waters of the Hudson River and Lake Erie, his classmates felt pride in his voice. Because he knew the background so well, he needed almost no help in preparing his material to read aloud.

Finally, as a culminating activity, the class wrote and produced a play which depicted the struggle to build the canal. The play included a chorus of singers who sang about the Erie Canal and a choral speaking group who, dressed in overalls, carrying shovels, and pushing wheelbarrows spoke, "We are digging the ditch through the mire." The play, rather elaborately staged and executed, ran for three nights. It was the most formal of the speaking activities involved in this unit.

Such school activity also provides material for conversation for the speech correction session.

Social Climate

In all of the speaking activities the stimulation to speak is increased or decreased by the social and physical environment. In classrooms and in therapy sessions, where the social climate is warm, friendly, and wholly accepting and where the teacher or correctionist listens graciously, carefully, and understandingly and where he places value on the contribution of each child, students are encouraged to talk, listen, and react. Such a climate cannot be created for speech situations alone; it rather must pervade every activity. It comes from a class framework which includes many opportunities for working together cooperatively in large and small groups at tasks or ideas that promote initiative. From such enterprise grows respect of group members for each other and for each other's contributions. Moreover, from such enterprise develops concern for the well-being of every member of the group. This setting provides the social climate conducive to a meaningful, gracious, and thoughtful interchange of ideas. Such climate should prevail both in the classroom and in the speech correctionist's room.

Physical Environment

Last, the teacher and the correctionist do what they can to encourage a favorable physical environment. When the classroom has tables and chairs, the teacher's task is easier than when it has permanently installed seats. A group at one table may be talking about last night's baseball game; another at a different table, about feeding dogs; another, about a visit to Disney Land; and still another, about an astronaut's latest trip. Similarly, the clinician's room should be comfortable, give the students a chance to walk around, and invite members of a group to talk with one another. Both the correctionist and the teacher bring to the environment materials that stimulate children. Books, magazines, toys, pictures, valentines, masks and jack o'lanterns on Hallowe'en, and puppets that induce the children to handle them and to talk for them. A good-looking, comfortable room with materials that stimulate but do not distract invites talk. Both the classroom teacher and the correctionist should provide such material.

Relationship of Speech Improvement to Speech Correction

Recently several studies have been completed which have investigated the effect of speech improvement upon articulation. One such study (10) is reported in the October 1960 issue of *ASHA*. Teachers, after an in-service training period which emphasized ear training (identification of the sound, listening for it, and discrimination between sounds), provided kindergarten and first-grade children with speech improvement lessons daily for 21 weeks. The experimental kindergartners achieved scores on two of the three articulatory measures and the one auditory discrimination test that were significantly different from the control group. The experimental first graders had scores on one articulation test that differentiated them from the control group; on word recognition the experimental first graders did significantly better than the controls.

Van Hattum (40) reports similar results in a study published in *Exceptional Child*. He instituted a speech improvement program in Rochester which provided ear training for part of the first-grade population. After the training period, he checked the number of students who needed speech work in the third grade. Of the 1,503 pupils who did not receive speech improvement, 20.1 percent had speech defects. Of the 467 students who did receive speech improvement, 12.9 percent had speech defects. Concomitant with the speech improvement program, the dismissals from clinic climbed from 19 percent to 41 percent.

A study done by Sommers and others (36) explores the effects of speech improvement and speech therapy upon the articulation and reading of first-grade children. The results of this study include: Speech improvement was found to affect reading skills, as expressed in reading factor scores in a significant way. Speech correction procedures did not significantly change reading comprehension scores for children with misarticulation or for children with normal articulation, but it did for a matched group of 25 children with severe articulation problems. Speech therapy did not affect reading factor scores in any significant way but it did improve articulation significantly more than did speech improvement. In fact, three months of speech therapy appeared about as effective in reducing articulation errors as nine months of speech improvement. Children receiving speech improvement improved significantly more in articulation than those who did not receive it. Children with severe articulation problems improved significantly when they received both speech therapy and speech improvement compared with a matched group who received speech improvement only (36, p. 37). This study was followed by one designed to test the effectiveness of speech improvement on reading and articulation of school children beyond the first grade. The data support these conclusions about articulation:

a. Speech improvement conducted by clinicians who used analytical ear training procedures was significantly better in improving articulation of first grade children when it was provided for nine months rather than 16 weeks beginning at the middle of the school year.

b. Speech improvement for eight weeks in second grade was ineffective in providing further improvement in articulation for children who received nine months of it in first grade.

c. The consonant sounds which were most easily corrected under a program of nine months of speech improvement in first grade and eight weeks in second grade were studied. They were found in order of highest to lowest percentage of correction to be: [v], 50%; [f], 41%; [r], 38%; [g], 37%; [k], 36%; [θ], 33%; [s], 26%; [ʃ], 22%; [tʃ], 20% and [l], 18%. Additional investigation was given to the [s] sound. Misarticulations of [s] were analyzed in terms of interdental and lateral sigmatisms. Twelve percent of children with lateral sigmatisms were corrected; 32 percent of the children with interdental sigmatisms were corrected (37A, p. 58).

The data support these conclusions about reading:

a. Subjects who were provided with speech improvement both in first and second grades made significantly higher reading factor scores at the end of the second grade than did subjects who were not provided with speech improvement.

b. Higher reading factor scores for subjects who experienced speech improvement in first and second grades did not result in higher reading comprehension scores at the end of the second grade compared with those who never received this treatment.

c. No significant difference was found in the improvement of reading factor scores for first-grade subjects who received 16 weeks of speech improvement compared with those who received nine months of this treatment (37A, p. 59).

A very important study referred to earlier (3) by a committee of the American Speech and Hearing Association also points to the need for a speech improvement program. To be clear as to what this Committee means by speech improvement, we include its definition of speech improvement and its statement of purposes of the program:

For the purposes of this study speech improvement takes place in the classroom. It consists of systematic instruction in oral communication which has as its purpose the development of articulation, voice, and language abilities that enable all children to communicate their ideas effectively. Speech improvement is not concerned with the work of the speech clinician with speech- and hearing-handicapped children outside of the regular classroom (3, p. 78).

The committee describes the purposes of the program:

Similarities in curriculum development and instructional practices in speech improvement are more common than are differences and contrasts. There appears to be general agreement on the purposes of instruction in speech improvement. Teachers indicate that curriculum experiences should be provided in the classroom to permit all children to develop the best speech, voice, and language patterns of which they are capable, correct minor speech and voice difficulties, and express their ideas clearly and effectively. There also seems to be general agreement that ability to hear and to discriminate between speech sounds is of first importance in speech and language development and in the correction of minor speech difficulties (3, p. 84).

The activities which accomplish these purposes include exercises in discriminating between similar sounds, in articulating and pronouncing clearly, in use of stress, and in use of voice. Seven speaking activities used as procedures in teaching speech improvement are auditory training drills, voice and articulation practice, discussion and conversations, dramatic presentations, oral reading, parliamentary procedure, talks, and reports (3, pp. 84-85). These seven activities fall into the categories mentioned earlier in this chapter.

The Committee says about measuring the effectiveness of speech improvement:

The principal means of measuring the effectiveness of speech improvement is judgment—the judgment of supervisors, teachers, parents, and children. However, 29% of the speech improvement teachers use articulation tests and 16% use voice ratings. While 67% of the teachers depend upon their judgment together with that of their supervisors, 31% use the judgment of parents and 45% use the judgment of children in evaluating speech improvement.

Teachers of speech improvement are strongly convinced that speech improvement helps children not only to develop good speech, voice, and language patterns but also to correct minor speech and voice problems. They also believe that children are helped to organize their thoughts and to express them clearly and effectively (3, p. 87).

Supervisors are not convinced that speech improvement decreases the number of students requiring speech therapy. Only 23 percent believe it does.

Except for those on the West Coast, speech and hearing clinicians throughout the nation, however, are more certain than their supervisors that speech improvement has decreased the number of children requiring therapy. Of the clinicians, 61 percent believe that speech improvement reduces the number needing therapy. The same committee makes suggestions for a model program in speech improvement, noting that all classroom teachers are teachers of speech improvement and that speech improvement programs should provide the kinds of assistance classroom teachers need to help all children learn to organize their thoughts and express them effectively in the best speech, voice, and language of which they are capable. They base their plan in part upon the description of ongoing programs of speech improvement. The following are the Committee's recommendations:

All children are carefully screened by speech and hearing personnel and records are kept on each child. Those children who indicate that they can respond to speech improvement techniques are not referred for remedial speech, although they may be later if they do not make expected progress.

When a program is being started, all elementary teachers are given in-service training covering a period of two to three years; the length of training is dependent upon the previous preparation and experience of the classroom teachers and the amount of time clinicians can devote to programs in the classroom. After the program is begun, in-service training is limited to teachers new to the system. In-service training includes a planned series of workshops and demonstrations held during the year either by the supervisor of speech improvement or by persons recognized for their leadership in the work. When possible, college courses in speech improvement are offered locally. Provision is made for teachers' attendance at regional and state conferences.

Speech improvement is not taught as a separate subject in any classroom from kindergarten through grade 12. Instead it is part of the regular curriculum in that it is integrated with subject matter areas and with school activities.

In the classroom during the in-service training period the clinician does demonstrations of speech improvement at least once a week to set a pattern for the classroom teacher to follow between demonstrations. Major emphasis is placed upon developmental and preventive aspects of speech, voice, and language, but attention is given to correction of minor speech and voice problems. Through conferences the clinician helps the teacher to integrate speech improvement with class and school activities, and she assists the teacher to conduct speaking activities as part of instruction. The clinician makes specific suggestions for helping children receiving remedial services to participate in speech improvement and to use newly acquired skills. The clinician assists the teacher to use standardized evaluative criteria as well as judgment in measuring the effectiveness of the work. With the period of in-service training completed, the classroom teacher assumes responsibility for speech improvement and the clinician serves as consultant.

Since parents can do much to help their young children develop speech, voice, and language abilities, an able clinician is assigned to work with parents of children in kindergarten and in grades one and two. Conferences begin with the initial visit of parent and child at school in preparation for the child's entering school. In larger school systems this clinician devotes full time to work with parents individually and in groups.

At the senior high school level speech improvement is integrated with work in fundamentals of speech, public speaking and debating, and dramatics and is correlated with academic subjects and with activities such as student government, class organizations, assembly programs, and clubs. In-service training and assistance are provided by the supervisor of speech improvement (3, pp. 90-91).

From these studies it seems obvious that schools need both speech correction and speech improvement programs. Speech correction services facilitate the handicapped to overcome their difficulties. Speech improvement services help all children to speak and listen better and reinforce the teaching given in speech therapy sessions. Stimulation to speak through speaking activities and through a democratic friendly classroom atmosphere is important in both speech improvement and speech correction.

References and Suggested Readings

1. ABERNETHY, R. L., "The Role of Storytelling." *The Speech Teacher,* IX (November 1960), 283-286. (Gives a preliminary report on the role of storytelling in the United States.)

2. ARBUTHNOT, M. H., *Children and Books*. Chicago: Scott, Foresman, 1947. (Considers how to select books for children and how to guide their reading. Contains excellent sections on storytelling and choral speaking.)

3. ASHA Subcommittee of Research Committee, "Speech Improvement." (Chapter 7) In "Public School Speech and Hearing Services." *The Journal of Speech and Hearing Disorders,* Monograph Supplement 8 (July 1961).

4. BERRY, A., "Listening Activities in the Elementary School." *Elementary English Review,* **XXIII** (February 1946), 69-79.

5. BIRCH, J. W., and J. MATTHEWS, *Improving Children's Speech.* Cincinnati: Public School Publishing Co., 1958. (Presents goals in speech improvement for various grades and means of achieving these goals.)

6. Board of Education of the City of New York, *Puppetry in the Curriculum.* Curriculum Bulletin I, 1947-48 Series.

7. ———, *Toward Better Speech.* Curriculum Bulletin V, 1952-53 Series.

8. BOWDEN, F. B., "Conversation and Discussion in the Elementary School." *Elementary English Review,* **XXIV** (May 1947), 293-302.

9. BROWN, H., and H. HELTMAN, *Let's-Read-Together.* Evanston, Ill.: Row, Peterson, 1950. (One of the most comprehensive and usable collections of poetry for choral speaking.)

10. BYRNE, M. C., "Results of a Speech Improvement Program for Kindergarten and First Grade Children." *ASHA,* **II** (October 1960), 360-361. (Studies the effect of a daily speech improvement program on articulation ability of kindergarten and first-grade children.)

11. CHAPIN, A. B., and M. CORCORAN, "A Program for the Speech-Inhibited Child." *Journal of Speech Disorders,* **XII** (December 1947), 373-376.

12. Contest Committee of the Speech Association of America, "A Program of Speech Education." *Quarterly Journal of Speech,* **XXXVII** (October 1951), 347-358. (Shows the place of speech in today's society.)

13. DAWSON, M. A., *Teaching Language in the Elementary Grades.* Yonkers, N.Y.: World Book Company, 1951. (Includes material on oral language activities such as conversation and speaking before groups.)

14. EISENSTADT, A. A., "Who Teaches Speech?" *American Childhood,* **XLIII** (May 1958), 26-27. (Stresses the importance of the class-

room teacher in developing acceptable patterns of speech in the child.)

15. ERWIN, J. C., "Speech Improvement in the Elementary School." *The Speech Teacher,* **VII** (September 1958), 185-190. (Reviews activities of classroom teachers in speech improvement.)

16. HAHN, E., "An Analysis of the Content and Form of the Speech of First Grade Children." *Quarterly Journal of Speech* **XXXIV** (October 1948), 361-366. (Shows that where speaking is fun, speaking skills are high. Explains that the length of response, sentence structure, and completeness of structure depend on the immediate situation more than the topic.)

17. HUNTER, M. A., "Lessons in Articulation." *The Speech Teacher,* **IX** (November 1960), 290-292. (Tells how classroom teachers can teach discrimination and production of sounds.)

18. IRWIN, R. B., "The Role of the Speech Therapist in the Speech Improvement Program." *The Speech Teacher,* **IX** (November 1960), 278-282. (Shows relationship of speech improvement to speech therapy. Suggests a limited role of speech therapist in speech improvement services.)

19. *Language Arts in the Elementary School.* Bulletin of the Department of Elementary School Principals (special issue), **XX** (July 1941), 259-316. (Gives suggestions for topics to talk about and principles to follow in speaking.)

20. LEASE, R., and G. B. SIKS, *Creative Dramatics in Home, School, and Community.* New York: Harper and Brothers, 1952.

21. McINTYRE, B., The Effect of Creative Activities on the Articulation of Children with Speech Disorders." *ASHA,* **I** (November 1959), 80.

22. MURPHY, G., "Conversation—a Lost Art," *Childhood Education* **XXVII** (February 1951), 256-260.

23. NURK, M., "Motivating Speech Improvement in the Upper Grades," *The Speech Teacher,* **IX** (November 1960), 301-303. (Tells how to use records of *My Fair Lady* and the story of *Pygmalion* to motivate speech improvement with upper elementary and junior high school students.)

24. OBERLE, M., "A Contemporary View of Elementary Speech Education." *The Speech Teacher,* **IX** (November 1960), 267-270. (Explains the importance of speech training to the elementary school child.)

25. OGILVIE, M., "Creative Speech Experiences in the Elementary School." *The Speech Teacher,* **VII** (January 1958), 5-10.

26. ———, "Oral Communication in Elementary School Living. "*The Speech Teacher,* **VII** (January 1957), 43-47.

27. ———, *Speech in the Elementary School.* New York: McGraw-Hill, 1954.

28. ———, and M. N. SEARLES, "The Important Place of 'Sharing Ideas.'" *The Speech Teacher,* **IX** (November 1960) 287-289. (Suggests how the teacher may guide the show and tell period.)

29. PRONOVOST, W., with L. KINGMAN, *The Teaching of Speaking and Listening in the Elementary School.* New York: Longmans, Green, 1959. (Includes guides for teaching speech activities in the elementary school program. Shows very clearly the integration of speech education with various elementary school academic areas. Contains many examples.)

30. RASMUSSEN, C., *Speech Methods in the Elementary School.* New York: Ronald Press, 1947.

31. ROBINSON, HELEN (ed.), *Oral Aspects of Reading.* Chicago: University of Chicago Press, 1955.

32. SCOTT, L. B., "What Values, Puppetry?" *Elementary English,* **XXX** (April 1953), 210-213. (Explains the use of puppetry in helping the speech defective child.)

33. SIKS, G. B., *Creative Dramatics.* New York: Harper and Brothers, 1958. (Tells how to guide and find material for creative drama.)

34. SIMMERMAN, A. J., "Lessons in Creativity." *The Speech Teacher,* **IX** (November 1960), 293-295. (Describes a creative experience involving poetry.)

35. SLADE, P., *Child Drama.* New York: Philosophical Library, 1955. (Gives directions to the teacher doing creative drama.)

36. SOMMERS, R. K., C. E. COCKERILLE, C. D. PAUL D. C. BOWSER, G. R. FICHTER, A. K. FENTON, and F. G. COPETAS. "Effects of Speech Therapy and Speech Improvement upon Articulation and Reading." *Journal of Speech and Hearing Disorders,* **XXVI** (February 1961), 27-37. (Explores the effects of speech improvement and speech therapy upon the articulation and reading of first grade children.)

37. SOMMERS, R. K. *et al.,* "Effects of Various Durations of Speech Improvement upon Articulation and Reading." *Journal of Speech and Hearing Disorders,* **XXVII** (February 1962), 54-61. A continuation of the preceding study.

37A. Speech Association of America (Carrie Rasmussen, chairman). *The Role of Speech in the Elementary School.* Washington, D. C.: NEA, Department of Elementary School Principals, 1946-47.

38. STRICKLAND, R. G., *The Language Arts in the Elementary School.* Boston: D. C. Heath, 1951. (Explains the purpose of oral communication in school. Gives the kinds of listening. Discusses conversation.)

39. THEMAN, V., "Techniques in Cultivating Effective Oral Interpretation, Appreciation and Tastes in Reading." In Wm. S. Gray (compiler). *Basic Instruction in Reading in Elementary and High School.* Chicago: University of Chicago Press, 1948, 188-191. (Explains how to further good oral reading and an appreciation of it in children.)

40. VAN HATTUM, R. J., "Evaluating Elementary School Speech Therapy." *Exceptional Child,* **XXV** (May 1959), 411-414. (Gives the effect of training in speech improvement upon number of cases of speech defects.)

41. VAN RIPER, C., "They Too Need Speech." *Journal of Exceptional Children,* **XII** (February 1946), 134-136. (Stresss the importance of communication for the handicapped. Shows the relationship of mental hygiene and speech.)

42. ———, and K. G. BUTLER. *Speech in the Elementary Classroom.* New York: Harper and Brothers, 1955. (Contains many suggestions for improving speech in the classroom. Particularly good for teaching sounds and for work on discrimination of sounds.)

43. WELLS, C., "Speech in the Full School Program." *Elementary English,* **XXVIII** (April 1951), 201-204. (Stresses the idea that every class is a speech class and every teacher a speech teacher. Describes a good climate for speech.)

Problems

1. Visit a classroom and list the different speech activities that went on while you were there. Did anything happen which could not be considered a speech activity?

2. Visit an elementary or high school classroom and analyze the effect of the seating arrangement, the social climate of the room, and the interests of the children upon their motivation to speak in the classroom.

3. Indicate in some detail specific classroom activities that may pro-

mote conversation, group discussion, creative dramatics, reading aloud, and speaking before the class.

4. Show how three pieces of children's literature could be used as a basis for speaking situations.

5. Find a story and three poems that the children of the level you intend to teach might well enjoy.

6. Read one of the following references: 1, 2, 3, 5, 12, 14, 15, 16, 18, 24, or 25. Indicate the use you might make of one speech activity for a specific grade in your school system.

7. Indicate how a speech correctionist might make use of creative drama in a therapy session.

9

Delayed or

Retarded Speech

Delayed Speech Development

THE CHILD with seriously delayed speech is not likely to be found in the "normal" classroom because serious speech delay is likely to result in nonadmission to school. In some instances, a child with moderately serious speech retardation may be enrolled in a class for exceptional children, or may be in a class with normal children of a younger age group. For the most part, however, the classroom teacher is more likely to have "delayed-speech" children, who began to speak at a significantly later age (perhaps at age four or even five) than most of the other children of the same grade. Another possibility is that the children never spoke much, or spoke and perhaps continue to speak with articulation so poor that they are not readily intelligible.

Delayed speech among school age children may vary from a complete failure to use oral language to an almost complete failure for a child to be understood despite evident strong effort in attempts at using oral language. In between we have the children who may have a limited but readily intelligible vocabulary to those who have a moderately large but only sometimes intelligible oral vocabulary. Some children rely to a considerable degree on gestures as substitutes for oral efforts or else use gestures to reinforce attempts at oral speech. Others may withdraw and become quiet "seen but not heard" children.

Many children who enter school with delayed language development are likely to present articulatory problems by the time they reach the second or third grade. The children do not suddenly develop their articulatory difficulties. For the most part, their articulatory proficiency was delayed along with their language development. By the time the children begin to manage language, the articulatory aspect of their overall development becomes more apparent. Children with serious delay in the language (oral words) *per se* are not likely to be advanced beyond the early primary grades. There are, of course, occasional and important exceptions. We sometimes find children with severe oral linguistic impairment who nevertheless learn to read and to write and so evidence their educational achievement. More often, however, children with serious delays in language development also have difficulties in learning to read and to write and are generally retarded in educational achievement.

For the most part, the classroom teacher of the nonexceptional child may have one or two children who have the residuals of delayed speech. These children often need the help of the speech correctionist to improve their articulatory proficiency.

Delayed Speech: Causes and Therapeutic Implications

Mental Retardation

The chief cause of seriously prolonged delayed speech is mental retardation. The child who is seriously retarded mentally may never learn to speak. The less severely mentally retarded child may learn to speak with a limited vocabulary of single words or short phrases. If we accept Newland's (8) use of the term *mentally retarded* to denote ". . . those children whose competently ascertained learning aptitudes are approximately one-half to three-fourths those of their chronological peers and whose limitations in this regard are believed to be attributable to biologic rather than psychologic or environmental factors," we would find a positive relationship between the degree of mental retardation and the amount of language delay as well as the quality of the language when it is acquired. We sometimes find children with moderate mental retardation who seem to have as many words as their age peers. A discerning listener may be able to note, however, that these children use the words less meaningfully and that the words lack depth and richness of concept. It is our observation that some mentally retarded children who are well trained and well taught are able to acquire appropriate words on a low level of meaning for many situations and events. We agree with Newland that even if the mentally retarded child ". . . is able to acquire as many lower-level tidbits of learning as the average . . . he would presumably integrate them less well, less meaningfully, less fully . . . to such an extent that the results of his integrations are discernibly different from those of his nonretarded brothers" (8, p. 81). Some mentally retarded children who "know the words but not too many of the meanings" may manage to get through the primary grades without too much trouble. These children, by virtue of the "halo effect" of their apparent linguistic ability, may not seem to be mentally retarded until they reach a level in school where the teacher begins to note their difficulty in dealing with concepts or ideas that cannot be readily objectified.

It is also important to recognize that there are some children whose difficulty with oral language makes them seem mentally retarded when they are not. Some children who are suspected of being mentally retarded because of their delayed development may, upon examination with nonlanguage tests of intelligence, turn out to be normal, or even above average, in intelligence. Other causes, such as slow general physiologic development, emotional disturbances, or hearing loss, may account for the speech delay. The possibility of error in arriving at a causal diagnosis of mental retardation for speech delay points to the need for a competent clinical psychologist or school psychologist to examine the suspected child and make an evaluation. If this cannot be done, the classroom teacher may entertain hypotheses about the concerned child, but judgments should be withheld until justified. The teacher should be especially careful to reserve judgment about possible mental retardation for the child with uneven school achievement. If the child does average or better work when oral language is not required, but does poorly in areas that require speech competency, we should seek the cause for the disparity rather than conclude that we are dealing with a "nontypical" but nevertheless mentally retarded child.

Therapeutic Approaches: The Mentally Retarded

Treatment for the mentally retarded child—for the one who, by our definition, is so for biologic rather than pathologic reasons—should take the form of education and training geared to the capacities of the individual child. Stimulation and improvement of the home environment, if this is possible, should help to bring the retardate to a level where his potential for language usage and articulatory proficiency become highly and positively correlated. Specific training for the correction of specific articulatory and vocal defects is indicated for the higher grade retardates. Such children may be members of slow progress or "special" classes. For most children a reasonable achievement objective is to strive for the proficiency level of a normal child whose chronological age is equal to that of the mental age of the retardate. In the absence of sensory, motor, or personality involvements, this level of achievements may be reached for most higher level retardates.

Hearing Loss: The Deaf[1]

A deaf child is one whose hearing was insufficient, at the time when speech normally is learned, to enable him to acquire oral language ability through the sense of hearing. Children with hearing loss severe enough to be diagnosed as deaf do not learn to speak unless specially trained to do so through the use of devices and

[1] The problems of the deaf and hard-of-hearing children are considered in some detail in Chapter 14.

techniques not necessary for normally hearing children. Even so, most of these children are likely to have significant defects of articulation and voice, and frequently of language development. The problems of the deaf child for language learning are frequently complicated by some degree of associated mental retardation or by slower mental maturation. The extent of delay in language development for many, if not most, deaf children may be appreciated when we realize that the normal hearing child has a speaking vocabulary of about 2,000 words by the time he is of school age. In sharp contrast, the deaf child who enters a school for the deaf at age five may not have any working vocabulary. There are, of course, many exceptions. These may be found among the bright deaf children, especially among those whose parents recognized that their children had hearing disabilities and initiated early training in lip reading and oral speech. Other exceptions may be found among deaf children with sufficient residual hearing to have made use of their hearing, especially when it can be reinforced by a hearing aid. Still other exceptions are found among children who were not born deaf but became deafened after they had established speech. In general, however, the incidence of speech defects is almost universal among preschool deaf children.

When the deaf child begins to acquire language, he continues to have difficulty with understanding what he is learning. Compared with hearing children of equal intelligence, most deaf children are linguistically retarded. Myerson (5, p. 148) sums up this aspect of the development of deaf children with this observation. "For the present and past generations of the deaf upon whom the test results were obtained, language and communication skills have lagged far behind intelligence, chronological age, and interests."

Hearing Loss: The Hard-of-Hearing

Language retardation is prevalent among children who are not profoundly deaf and may be classified as *hard-of-hearing*. In some instances, the hard-of-hearing may have little or no speech when they have reached school age. Both the quality and quantity of the language of the hard-of-hearing child depend on many individual factors. These include the intelligence of the child, the early recognition of the hearing loss, and the motivation of both parents and child toward speech learning. A bright child, well motivated and with well-informed parents, may be helped to considerable speech through combining lip (speech) reading and the maximum use of hearing. Amplified sound and the use of a hearing aid, if possible and appropriate, may be of considerable help.

SPEECH DEFECTS ASSOCIATED WITH HEARING LOSS. Almost all children who are hard-of-hearing have some degree of difficulty in articulation and appropriate vocalization. Depending in part on the type and degree of hearing loss, distortions and omissions of consonants, and especially fricative sounds, is common. There is also likely to be some difficulty in the distinguishing between voiced and voiceless cognates such as *b* and *p, d* and *t, v* and *f,* and the *th* sounds. Vowels and diphthongs may be distorted. (See pages 348-349 for a more detailed discussion of this problem.)

The improvement of the speech of the child with a recognized and appreciable hearing loss is the task of the professional speech clinician rather than the classroom teacher.

INTERMITTENT OR OCCASIONAL HEARING DIFFICULTY. Many teachers have had children who on occasion seem to have some difficulty in hearing. It is possible that some of these children have relatively slight and chronic difficulty with hearing, but are usually able to make up for the loss by good attentive effort. However, if such a child has a head cold, or suffers from enlarged adenoids because of a temporary inflammation, his hearing problem may be temporarily increased. Fatigue or ill health may produce comparable results. There are, of course, other children who for reasons related to their emotional problems in or out of the classroom on occasion seem not to be able to hear. Perhaps these children block out human speech sounds because of difficulties that arise when they hear, understand, and respond to speech. If the teacher suspects the latter to be the case, an understanding of what may be the basis for the nonhearing rather than a scolding is in order.

Whenever hearing loss is suspected, an audiological evaluation is recommended. If hearing loss is found, its cause and possible treatment should be determined by a physician. Fortunately, in some instances medical treatment can minimize or entirely clear up temporary difficulty in hearing resulting from pathology.

The teacher can be of appreciable help in the classroom for a child believed to have a hearing loss. Among the things he can do to be of direct help to the particular child are:*

1. Make certain that he is looking in the direction of the child when giving the class instruction or direction.

2. Seat or reseat the child so that he will be both close to the teacher and readily able to see his face when he is speaking. This means that if the teacher is to stand in any part of the room for any length of time, the child suspected of hearing loss should be permitted to change his seat.

3. Speak louder and somewhat more slowly, when an activity involving a specific response from the child suspected of having a hearing loss is anticipated.

Emotional Problems

The history of many children with speech delay includes an item indicating that they began to speak at an age within normal limits but then seemed to give up speaking. On questioning, one or both parents may reveal that the cessation of speaking seemed to be associated with an unhappy familial situation. In some instances it becomes apparent that the parents were disturbed about their own relationship, and frequently spoke harshly to each other in the presence of the young child. Occasionally an admission is obtained that when the parents spoke to each other at all, it was in emotional outbursts. The young child, we would gather, became afraid of the consequences of speech and retired into the relative safety and security of not speaking. Such a child may, after he resumes speaking, continue to be fearful about its consequences when he enters school. If he meets with any penalty resulting from speech behavior

---

* See Chapter 14 for a more complete discussion of the teacher's role.

during his early school experiences, his original fears may be reconfirmed. This is the type of child who may prefer to be thought uninformed, or prefer to be given a talking-to for his apparent inattention rather than risk the assumed greater penalty of saying the wrong thing. He may well decide that it is better to be the "quiet one" than the one who gets involved in difficulties by verbalizing his thoughts.

Another situation associated with regression or cessation of speech and occurring frequently enough to be worthy of note is the birth of a new child. The two- or three-year-old may look upon the crying, nonspeaking infant as a usurper of attention and affection. With what seems fair logic, the older sibling may decide that he may be able to regain his original position in the family if he imitates some of the behavior of the newcomer, and so gives up speech.

Responses to Parental Attitudes

At the community speech and hearing center affiliated with Queens College, investigation has shown that the parents of delayed-speech children are frequently unrealistic in their expectations about their children. Both parents, but mothers more often than fathers, expected their children to develop and learn more rapidly than is normal according to the Gesell Development Schedules (2) for children of comparable age. Individual case histories revealed that the children who failed to develop speech before age three were often children who were toilet-trained before one year of age; some were expected to feed themselves at an age when their peers were still being helped by their parents. Many of the parents expected their children to talk by the end of the first year and began to be anxiously concerned when they were not using words by fifteen months.

Other findings indicate that the parents of delayed-speech children are often inclined to be rigid and restrictive in their demands on their children, as well as upon each other. Possibly as a result of the frustration experienced by the parents, there is an air of excessive tension in the conduct of the home. Many of the parents admit to being "perfectionists" but use the term with pride rather than insight. It is possible that children brought up in such homes unconsciously feel rejected. It is possible also that the parents, consciously or unconsciously, are rejecting their children. Certainly these parents are rejecting the efforts and accomplishments of their children, and the children respond to this attitude as if they were entirely rejected. If a child's early speech attempts are ignored as being unworthy of notice, or criticized for not being readily understandable, he may well hesitate to talk so as to avoid an unfavorable parental response.

Some of the feeling of apprehension continues to characterize the behavior of children who were once delayed in speech. The classroom teacher in the first or second grade would do well to be permissive in attitude and to avoid correcting the articulation or pronunciation of children who have a delayed-speech history. These children need the security of acceptance of themselves as they are so that speech efforts will not be conducive to disapproval or fear. Speech correction of specific speech faults may well wait until the third or fourth grade for these children. Of course, indirect efforts at correction take place whenever the child is exposed to a kind and permissive environment which stimulates good but not perfectionistic speech. An attitude of permissiveness, incidentally, should be consistent and should not vary from day to day according to the whims of the adult.

Faulty Motivation

A child is not likely to acquire any new skill, speaking included, unless it provides him with a sense of satisfaction not otherwise obtainable. The child whose wants are anticipated may be denied the need and opportunity to develop the skill of speaking through which wants are announced and so satisfied. Parents who are overprotective, who because of a possible fall hover over their child when he attempts to walk, who cannot wait until the child completes even a gesture before he is overwhelmed with a number of things he might possibly mean by the gesture, is denied the need for learning to do things for himself, speaking included. Such a child, unless he is able to identify himself with others in his environment who are less anxiety-ridden and less anxiously protective, may be delayed in speech. Fortunately, the child is likely to acquire a normal understanding of speech and may, despite his parents, develop a pantomime language. By developing these aspects of symbol behavior, he is at least not completely without tools for acquiring conventional speech if his environmental situation improves. Among the immediate improvements sought are:

1. An understanding on the part of parents, and any other overanxious, overzealous members of the child's environment, that he is deserving of the right to entertain a want or a need, even if he has to cry about it.

2. When an attempt at speech is made, the attempt is to be heard out before the adults jump to do something about it.

3. A repeated vocalization, especially if it accompanies a repeated gesture in association with a given situation, may be the beginning of word usage. The adult should imitate the vocalization in the recurring situation, before responding to the act of gesture and vocalization. In this way attention is directed to the oral activity rather than to the pantomime.

4. Once repeated vocalization is established, the parent should take the initiative and give a simple monosyllabic name to a toy or object frequently used and desired by the child. This name should include sounds the child has successfully made and repeated in his sound-play activity. For example, if "da" is frequently uttered by the child, the name "da" can be given to a doll or some other plaything enjoyed by the child. The sound should be spoken by the parent each time the object is given to the child, and each time the adult, when present, observes the child reaching for the object. After one or two days of this practice, the object should be with-

held until the child makes some attempt to utter the sound name for it. If the child is reasonably successful in making a sound which closely resembles, if not directly reproduces the sound-name, he should be given quick approval for his effort. This, however, *does not mean* that he is to be rewarded by another toy or overwhelmed with a flow of words too numerous and too rapid for assimilation or understanding.

Bilingual Environment

As indicated in our discussion on language development, children who come from a multilingual environment may be seriously delayed in the onset and growth of their own language abilities. Many children are without question able to acquire two or more languages that they are exposed to from infancy. Research data strongly suggest, however, that for an appreciable number of children the effect of multilingual (usually bilingual) exposure beginning at an age before a single language is established is to cause some degree of impairment in overall language proficiency. As we indicated earlier, Smith (9) who studied the effects of bilingualism (Chinese and English) among children in the Hawaiian Islands, found that as a group the children had vocabularies of below-average size in both Chinese and English. Beyond this, Smith found that even when the vocabularies of the two languages were combined, only two-fifths of the children exceeded the expected norms for monolingual children. On the strength of her data Smith concluded that ". . . only the superior bilingual child is capable of attaining the vocabulary norms of monoglots . . ."

Occasionally we find that the single significant factor in a delayed-speech child is multiple language exposure. On the whole, it would seem much safer for a child to have one language well established before he is exposed to a second. If multiple language exposure cannot be avoided, as is the case in many homes and many cultures, it would seem that the use of a given language be identified consistently with a person or a situation. Some children seem to find it necessary to fit themselves and the speaking situation into a linguistic "groove" and to maintain that "groove" in a consistent manner. For example, if the parents spoke only English, and the grandparents, nurse, or housekeeper spoke a second language, the child would learn to associate a language pattern—a way of speaking—with a person and so have less conflict than if his own parents spoke English on some occasions and a second language on others. When the other times are unpredictable, or when the other times are reserved for admonishments, difficulty with the second language may increase. So also, unfortunately, may the child's attitude toward language behavior in general.

If a child who has been exposed to more than one language appears to have difficulty in learning to speak, we strongly recommend that the parents decide which language is to be essential for the child and that he be exposed to only that one until speech behavior has become established. This frequently calls for control and modification of the home environment as well as aspects of the environment outside of the home. Though this is not always easy to achieve, it is important that it be done.

Twins

As indicated in our discussion in Chapter 7, the incidence of delayed speech and slow language development is greater among twins than among single children. Day (2) for example, found that preschool age twins had age interval increments approximately half of that of single-born children. Language retardation among twins may be attributed to both organic and atypical environmental causes. Both will be briefly considered.

According to Nelson (6) most twins are prematurely born. Prematurity of birth is associated in many instances with vascular defects and with brain damage. Even when there is no clear evidence of damage to the brain, there is considerable evidence of lag in overall physical maturation which continues at least until the time the child is of age to enter school. Lags in psychological and social development parallel those for physical development. These disadvantages, we should emphasize, are associated with the combination of training *and* premature birth. Though there is evidence that some prematurely born children "never catch up," we are more inclined to accept the point of view of the geneticist Newman (7), who maintains that, if twins survive the hazards of being born and the consequences of prematurity, by the time they are well along in school they are as capable as their single-born peers.

Twins provide an atypical environment for one another. As they grow up they seem to be satisfied with their mutual social situation and so are less demanding of the attentions of older persons. Even if attention is demanded, it must be divided. Unfortunately, twins are not well qualified as language stimulators. The result is that they are exposed less to adults than are single children and more to poor language stimulation. An interesting linguistic phenomenon among twins is their development of a special code for expression and communication—an idioglossia—which seems to serve twins adequately but baffles all other members of the family. Because of the evident satisfaction twins derive from their idioglossia, they may not be motivated to learn the language of their homes or their more extended environment.

If twins arrive at school age still using their special language, we recommend that if at all possible they be put in separate classes. If this is not possible, they should be put in separate groups so that they may associate with children using more conventional language.

The Role of the Classroom Teacher with Delayed-Speech Children

As indicated in the opening of this chapter, the classroom teacher is not likely to have many children with seriously delayed speech among his pupils. By the time children of normal intellect who began as being delayed in speech reach school age, they are likely to be speaking well enough to be accepted in the regular class. However, some of the residuals of the problems may remain. Some of the children formerly delayed in speech may still be apprehensive about speaking and show anxiety when responsibility for communication is fixed upon them. These children are likely to be freer when responding as members of a group than when they are required to recite alone or to speak with rather than before their classmates. Others may have limited vocabularies or more than a normal number of speech faults. If the teacher can determine which of the causes of delayed speech were present for any of the children, he can be of great help in controlling or preventing the pressures associated with the original cause for speech retardation. These children need to learn that speech is enjoyable before they become aware that with the acquisition of speech there is an assumption of communicative responsibility. When pleasure replaces apprehension, goals for increased speech proficiency can be set. The child should be gently directed toward these goals about which, incidentally, it is best that he have no conscious awareness at the outset of his school career. The teacher should, if possible, share information and objectives with the child's parents so that the proper attitudes may prevail in the home as well as in the school.

References and Suggested Readings

1. BERRY, M., and J. EISENSON, *Speech Disorders: Principles and Practices of Therapy.* New York: Appleton-Century-Crofts, 1956, Chapter 5.

2. DAY, E. J., "The Development of Language in Twins." *Child Development,* III (1932), 179-199.

3. GESELL, A. I., *The Psychology of Early Growth.* New York: Macmillan, 1938.

4. HEJNA, R. F., *Your Child's Speech.* Madison, Wis.: College Typing Company, 1955, Chapters 1, 2, 5. (Explains in simple terms the development of language and the problems of children who are slow to talk. Recommended as reading for parents.)

5. MYERSON, L., "A Psychology of Impaired Hearing." In Cruickshank, W. M. (ed.). *Psychology of Exceptional Children and Youth."* Englewood Cliffs, N.J.: Prentice-Hall, 1955, 148.

6. NELSON, W. E., *Textbook of Pediatrics*. (7th ed.), Philadelphia, Saunders, 1959, 305.

7. NEWMAN, H. H., *Multiple Human Births*. New York: Doubleday Doran, 1940. (An interesting discussion by a geneticist of multiple births and their implications for the individual and the race.)

8. NEWLAND, T. E., "Language Development of the Mentally Retarded." *Monographs of the Society for Research in Child Development*, **XXV**: 3 (1960), 71-87.

9. SMITH, M. E., "Measurement of Vocabularies of Young Bilingual Children in Both of the Languages Used." *Journal of Genetic Psychology*, **LXXIV** (1949), 305-310.

10. STINCHFIELD, S. M., and E. H. YOUNG. *Children with Delayed or Defective Speech*. Stanford: Stanford University Press, 1938.

11. VAN RIPER, C., *Speech Correction: Principles and Methods*. (3rd ed.) Englewood Cliffs, N.J.: Prentice-Hall, 1954, Chapter 6.

12. *The Nervous Child*, **IX** (1951). (This number is devoted to problems of delayed speech in children.)

Problems

1. What are the chief causes of delayed speech?

2. What is the relationship between emotional upheavals in the family and possible speech delay?

3. Check with the parents of some children as to the ages when their children began to speak. Average the ages for the boys and for the girls. Which group had an older average age?

4. Twins have been found to begin to speak at a later age than single children. How do you account for this?

5. Read the article by Ruth W. Metraux, "Speech Profiles for the Child 18 to 24 Months," *Journal of Speech and Hearing Disorders*, **XV** (1950), pages 37-53. Check the language development of a child you know between the ages of 18 and 54 months with the Metraux profiles. If there are any differences, can you account for them?

6. There is considerable evidence that children who have difficulty in learning to read include more than a "normal" number of children with delayed-speech onset. Can you account for this?

10

Defects of
Articulation—I

Definition and Diagnosis

OF ALL speech disorders, teachers encounter articulatory defects most frequently. Three percent of youth between five and 21 have articulatory defects (1). The number is more than all the other speech difficulties combined; in fact, in the school-age population about three-fourths of all speech defects are of an articulatory nature.

Definition of Articulatory Defects

Articulatory defects fall in general into three categories: (1) the substitution of one sound for another; (2) the omission of sounds; and (3) the distortion of sounds.

Substitution of One Sound for Another

The substitution of one sound for another is the type of articulatory error that children in the primary grades make most frequently (39). One child may substitute a sound easier for him to make for one more difficult for him. Another may substitute a sound more readily visible for one less visible. In instances of other children, the correctionist cannot arrive as easily at a rational explanation for the substitution. The sound of w[w] is frequently substituted for l[l] and r[r], f[f] and v[v] or t[t] and d[d] for th[θ] and *th* [ð]. Sometimes t[t] and d[d] are used instead of f[f] and v[v]. Many other substitutions occur. An unvoiced sound such as p[p] may be substituted for such a voiced sound as b[b].

The following are typical of substitutions made by Jimmy, a seven-year-old boy:

stûr'ĕl [stɝ əl]	for squirrel
prŭsh [prʌʃ]	for brush
trŭm [trʌm]	for drum
lĕ lō [lɛ lo]	for yellow
fĕd' ĕr [fɛd ɚ]	for feather

Jimmy substitutes t[t] for k[k], p[p] for b[b], t[t] for d[d], l[l] for y[j], and t[t] and d[d] for th[θ] and *th*[ð].

The following represent the usual substitutions made by Mary, a six-year-old girl in a large school system:

sûm [sʌm]	for thumb
tōōs' brŭsh' [tusbrʌʃ]	for toothbrush
tăt [t æt]	for cat
stōs [stos]	for stove
nīs [naIs]	for knife
tĭ ki [tI kI]	for chicken

Mary substituted s for several sounds: th[θ], sh[ʃ], f[f], and v[v]. She also substituted t[t] for k[k] and k[k] for ch[tʃ]. Her g[g], the voiced counterpart of k[k], was made accurately.

Most children are not seemingly consistent in their substitutions. They may substitute f[f] for th[θ] in one word and not in another. They may substitute f[f] for th[θ] but substitute th[θ] for s[s]. Consistent patterns of substitution occur infrequently. In general, children are more likely to make errors when the sound occurs in the middle or at the end of a word, rather than when it occurs at the beginning of a word.

Omission of Sounds

A sound may be omitted. The following are examples of omissions of sounds by David, a ten-year-old boy:

bĕd [bɛd]	for bread
dĕs [dɛs]	for dress
tī [taɪ]	for try
tān [ten]	for train

Most youngsters will not be as consistent as this child in omitting sounds. Their omissions may be more like Susie's, a five-year-old, whose examples follow:

âr yŭ dō ĭn [er ju do ɪn]	for Where are you going?
mē ŏntȧ ō tōō [mi ɑntə o tu]	for I want to go too
Ī ōr? [aɪ or]	for Why for?

Omissions occur much more frequently in the young child's speech than they do in the older child's speech. Children omit final consonants more often than the initial or medial consonant. They commonly omit one of the sounds in blends of two consonants, such as *tr*[tr], *pr*[pr], *st*[st], or *sl*[sl].

Distortion of Sounds

A sound may be distorted. The listener recognizes the sound for what it is, but is distracted by it. The way the sound is made calls attention to it. Laymen, in describing a distorted *s,* make such remarks as: "Her *s* whistles" or "Her *s* has a slushy *sh* sound." In the whistling *s,* too much air is escaping and, in the slushy *s,* air is escaping over the sides of the tongue.

Degree of Severity of Articulatory Difficulty

The severity of an articulatory difficulty depends on how greatly it reduces the intelligibility of the speech of its owner and the concern it gives him. The degree of intelligibility is related to the number of sounds omitted and the number of substitutions; the distortion of sounds is of least importance in intelligibility. When the child omits many sounds and when he substitutes many sounds for others, his speech becomes almost unintelligible. Children judge the severity of the articulatory defects in accordance with the number of errors. Kleffner (27) notes that fourth-grade children react unfavorably to a consistent error on a frequently occurring sound and even more unfavorably when many errors are present. When a sound which occurs frequently in our language, like t[t] or s[s], is defective, it has more effect on intelligibility than a sound, like sh[ʃ] or zh[ʒ], which occurs infrequently. The simplest way for a classroom teacher to evaluate the severity of a defect is to count the number of sounds that are omitted, substituted, and distorted. Many quite complex systems of evaluation of degree of severity have been devised. Most of these still need refinement and are used only by speech correctionists.

The child may either accept and acknowledge his difficulty, reject it and insist that it does not exist, or be overly concerned with it. A teacher is of inestimable worth in fostering the attitude of acceptance and of motivating the student to do what he can to correct the difficulty. Both the teacher and the correctionist may have to help the child who believes his inadequate speech is adequate. They must assist him in isolating the error and in perceiving it. In some cases parents help insulate the child against therapy because they believe that a particular error is attractive. On the other hand, overperfectionist, nagging parents may cause the child to be unduly anxious about his difficulty. In one instance the deviation or difference is approved; in the other it is penalized. The teacher must be aware of how the child perceives his own difficulty.

Related Difficulties

Other difficulties are closely related to articulatory difficulties. For example, the child with a denasal voice has three defective sounds: m[m], n[n], and ng[ŋ]. The child with the muffled voice keeps his mouth almost clenched shut; the quality is due in part to the lack of clear-cut articulation of sounds. These two difficulties are labeled voice disorders. The term *delayed speech* includes many articulatory defects—omissions, substitutions, and distortions; in fact, some writers include their discussion of the articulatory defects of the primary grade children under delayed speech. Delayed speech, however, does connote, in addition to articulatory difficulties, small vocabulary, overly simple sentence structure, and, in general, retarded language development. Cleft palate speech and defective speech due to impaired hearing are also characterized by articulatory difficulties. Even in cluttering, because of its rapid rate, the child noticeably slurs over and distorts the consonantal sounds. Thus, defective articulation may be a single problem to a child or it may be a symptom of a more complex syndrome.

Articulatory Disorders and Maturation

Because some parents show undue concern about their young children's ability to articulate, teachers must be particularly aware of the need for recognition of the maturing factor in diagnosing articulatory defects. One mother of a five-year-old boy in kindergarten came to a school to demand speech help for him. The only error he made with any consistency was to substitute *t*[t] and *d*[d] for the two *th's*[θ], [ð]. But at times even these sounds were correct. Occasionally he said a *w*[w] for *l*[l]. The mother insisted his speech was not "normal," explaining that his sister had spoken better at the same age, that his cousins of the same age spoke very well, and that the neighborhood youngsters who were even younger spoke more clearly. The little boy was a verbal child who expressed himself unusually well with very few articulatory errors. The teacher explained the part maturity plays in the development of articulation. Because the mother remained unconvinced, the teacher called in the correctionist to reassure the mother. The teacher also suggested that the mother remain in the kindergarten room to listen to how other kindergartners spoke.

Studies made where no speech correction was available show

that maturation alone takes care of many articulatory errors in the first four grades, but that it does not have any appreciable effect in the higher grades. Roe and Milisen (44) indicate that the percentage of children making articulatory errors decreases from grades 1 through 6, and that the average number of errors decreases as the grade level increases from grades 1 through 5. A statistically significant difference between grades 1 and 2, 2 and 3, and 3 and 4 reveal that growth and maturation eliminate many articulatory errors in these grades. But the lack of a significant difference in grades 4 and 5 and 5 and 6 tends to prove that maturation does not affect any noticeable improvement in the speech sounds of higher grades. Sayler (45) notes that there was a slight decrease in the average number of articulatory errors from grades 7 through 10. Landers (28) did a study with 22 matched pairs of kindergarten children including children with incorrect productions of between five and nine sounds in one or more positions. To one group he gave speech therapy; to the control group he did not. It appeared that the children improved their speech as much by maturation and the regular kindergarten curriculum as by both of these factors and speech therapy.

Some studies, however, show that speech therapy brings an increased rate of decline in articulatory errors in kindergarten and in very young children. Reid (41) found that speech correction produced a greater decline of articulatory errors than could be attributed to maturation alone. Ventura, Ingebo, and Wolmut (60) showed that speech correction in the kindergarten classroom with the whole class participating achieved the greatest change in articulatory ability and that speech correction outside the classroom achieved the greatest change in the articulation of certain consonants. Both methods, however, achieved significantly greater change than maturation alone. A study by Carter and Buck (11) determined the feasibility of including first-grade children in a speech therapy program. Their control group received two 30-minute speech therapy periods weekly for nine months; of these 72.2 percent made 100 percent final correction while only 9.1 percent made no correction. Of the 26 children in the experimental group who received no therapy, eight made 100 percent correction, while about one-half made no correction of their defective sounds.

Norms for Acquisition of Sounds

A table on page 124 shows the age at which most children are able to articulate certain sounds. Poole (40) points out that girls attain mastery of all sounds approximately a year before boys. Templin notes that by eight years essentially mature articulation of speech sounds is attained. At this age about 95 percent of correct articulation, as measured on a 176-item test, has been reached. Only fourteen sound elements are not articulated correctly by 90 percent of the children, and, with the exception of wh[ʍ], most of the sound elements approach this level of accuracy (52, p. 144). Using terminal status scores in the articulation of consonant sounds, the boys took one test interval (.5 year) longer than the girls to reach a comparatively mature level of articulation (52, p. 147).

Prognosis for Improvement Through Maturation

Since maturation may take care of some of the articulatory difficulties in the primary grades and not of others, guidance is needed in the selection of children for therapy. Such guidance has been provided by two studies. The results of a study by Carter and Buck (11) suggest that therapy be given to those children who cannot correct their articulation when given a nonsense syllable test. From their study it appears that the higher the percentage of correction on the nonsense syllable test, the more accurate is the prediction of achieving accurate articulation without therapy. A study by Steer and Drexler (51) indicates that certain measures at the kindergarten level can predict later articulatory ability. The most effective and reliable predictive variables appear to be: (1) the total number of errors in all positions within words; (2) errors in the final position; (3) errors of omission in the final position; and (4) errors on the *f, l* consonant group. The amount of improvement in articulatory ability, independent of the number of errors, in the kindergarten level also appears to be significant.

Testing for Errors

When a child's articulation does call attention to itself or when the child himself is disturbed about his difficulty, the teacher should determine what errors the child is making. The teacher can get a general impression of the child's speech through conversation. For younger children pictures cut from magazines motivate conversation. Pictures that tell a story, such as children having a good time at a birthday party, a small child crying as he looks at a broken doll, a farmer feeding his cows, or children playing in the sand and building castles, are particularly effective in motivating conversation. Certain picture books promote talk. For example, Mrs. Newberry's *Percy, Polly and Pete* (37) contains pictures that induce children to comment about the activities of the three cats. With older children, the teacher may talk about common interests, hobbies, vacation plans, or some other interesting topic. From such conversation, the teacher gains a picture of the child's speech.

Often times, however, a teacher wants a more accurate analysis and wishes to test each sound. Jordan (24) shows that such an analysis does give valid information on how the child says the sounds even in connected speech. He studied the relationship between measures of articulation from phonetic analysis and measures of articulation obtained from listener ratings of connected speech. He found that the articulation test responses provided valid information on articulatory behavior in connected speech. In addition, he discovered that listeners' reactions to defective articulation are dependent on (1) the frequency with which articulatory defects occur and (2) the degree of the defect. To the listener, omissions are more deviant than substitutions and substitutions are more deviant than distortions. The number of defective sounds is highly related to the measure of articulation derived from listener response to connected speech.

Frequently the teacher is asked to refer students to the speech correctionist. A Subcommittee on Diagnosis and Measurement of the Research Committee of the American Speech and Hearing Association (2, p. 52) indicates that for speech screening, surveys and referrals by teachers are used most frequently. Since the teacher does often make the referral, she should make the referral for articulatory defects on some organized basis—preferably an articulatory test which tests all the consonantal sounds. His purpose is not to evaluate the precise articulatory abilities of the children but rather to decide whether their abilities lie within the normal ranges of the group. The speech correctionist to whom the child is referred will take care of the more detailed therapeutic examination.

A study by Siegel (47A) suggests that classroom teachers can be trained to test articulation. The experiment consisted of three articulation testing occasions. On the first occasion two experienced and two inexperienced examiners each tested 26 mentally retarded children with the Templin-Darley Screening Articulation Test and with the criterion measure being the number of correct responses. The inexperienced examiners were then given about four hours of training and experience in articulation testing. After this training, all the examiners retested 22 percent of the children. The next week, all the examiners tested a new group of 21 children. The results indicated that inexperienced examiners could be trained to be quite reliable with a minimum of training. Reliability, however, did not guarantee examiner equivalence since, in spite of high reliability, examiners tended to differ significantly in absolute scores assigned to children.

Sounds are usually tested in three positions: initial, where the sound begins the word, medial, where it is in the middle of the word, and final, where it ends the word.[1] For the young child the teacher may test with pictures.

---

[1] Authorities now debate whether the medial position should be legitimately included since a sound in a medial position usually begins or ends a syllable. If one considers position in relation to syllables, only initial or final sounds would be included. Curtis and Hardy note that Stetsons' analysis of articulatory dynamics, supported by considerable experimental data, appears to indi-

Irwin and Musselman (22a) have devised a picture articulation test which checks more than one sound in a word and which includes all of the consonants in the initial and final positions, all of the vowels, and all of the diphthongs. The 61 phonetic elements are incorporated in the following 27 words which in the study were represented by original India ink drawings.

WORD	SOUND		
	Initial	*Medial*	*Final*
pig	p	ɪ	g
boy	b		ɔɪ
teeth	t		θ
door	d		r
cage	k		dʒ
book		ʊ	k
garage	g	ɑ	ʒ
fish	f		ʃ
valentine	v	æ	n
glove		ʌ	v
thumb	θ		m
this or that	ð		
smooth		u	ð
saucer	s	ɔ	ɚ
mouse		aʊ	s

cate that a consonant's function as either an initiating or terminating element of a syllable may be more significant than its position in a word (12, p. 245). They note that classifying a sound as medial denotes the possible difference in functions, since a consonant in the medial position may be either initiating or terminating with respect to the syllable. Hence they use the classification as to whether the sound occurs before a vowel (prevocalic) or after a vowel (postvocalic) within a syllable. Keenan (26) also suggests that the medial concept be discarded and that the classification be based, as Curtis recommends, on whether the consonant begins a syllable and precedes a vowel, whether it ends a syllable and follows the vowel, or whether it is part of a blend (as the *l* in *pl*). Certain writers also express concern about the effect of neighboring sounds on the sound to be tested. Most current tests do not take these factors into consideration.

WORD		SOUND	
	Initial	*Medial*	*Final*
zebra	z		ə
ship	ʃ		p
hand	h		d
church	tʃ	ɝ	tʃ
jail	dȝ	eɪ	l
music	m	ju	
nose	n	oʊ	z
leaf	l	i	f
web	w	ɛ	b
white	ʍ	aɪ	t
yellow	j		o
ring	r		ŋ

The study showed that this test may be used to evaluate more than one error in a word with reliability by both experienced and inexperienced judges. This test takes half as much time to administer as the conventional test. The study also showed that there was no significant difference between the experienced and inexperienced judges.

We have constructed a test wherein pictures of the following objects may be used. We have indicated the sound in the left column and have suggested pictures which will test the sound in the three positions:

$p[p]$	paint	puppy	step
$b[b]$	banana	cabbage	tub
$t[t]$	tiger	kitten	bat
$d[d]$	doll	ladder	bread
$k[k]$	cat	doctor	chalk
$g[g]$	girl	tiger	pig
$f[f]$	farm	coffee	leaf

$v[v]$	very (check in conversation)	movie	stove
$th[\theta]$	thumb	birthday	month
$th[\eth]$	they (check in conversation)	father	
$s[s]$	circle	bicycle	face
$z[z]$	zoo	scissors	cheese
$sh[\int]$	sheep	machine	fish
$ch[t\int]$	child	kitchen	match
$j[d3]$	jelly	soldier	page
$m[m]$	moon	mommy	home
$n[n]$	nut	dinner	hen
$l[l]$	lettuce	dollar	doll
$r[r]$	rabbit	Europe	car
$ng[\eta]$		monkey	tongue

Sounds only in initial position:

$y[j]$	yellow	$h[h]$	horse	$wh[\text{м}]$	white
$br[br]$	breakfast	$dr[dr]$	dress	$tr[tr]$	train
$pl[pl]$	plate	$st[st]$	star	$sl[sl]$	slipper

We have chosen these objects carefully so that the young child is likely to know their names. The only one not taken from lists of recommended words is *zoo*. In some cases, however, the teacher may have to tell the child the word and ask him to repeat it. In such instances, the teacher does not wait; he supplies the word. Whether the child repeats what the teacher says or whether he names the object spontaneously makes no appreciable difference in the testing (54). At times, the picture may bring forth a different response from what was expected. When it does, the teacher may say something like this: "It has a different name, too. You can also call it a_____. Say it for me."

The teacher may also administer the test by asking the child to guess the object from his description of it. For instance, the teacher may say for paint: "This is something you use that changes the color of your house." For puppy, he may say: "This is a small animal that children like to play with; it barks." The teacher makes the guessing game easier or more difficult to meet the needs of the child he is testing.

For younger children, the following story includes the sounds in their various positions. The teacher gives the child a copy and asks him to read it with her. As the child makes an error, the teacher checks it inconspicuously on his own copy. Later he transfers his results to the list of words also included here. The number over a letter or letters of a word in the story indicates the sound in a particular position being tested. This word is repeated in the list. The number makes it easy to find. The words in this story are from the first 2,000 of the Thorndike-Lorge List (57) with three exceptions: the name *Rags* given to the dog, *terrier*, and *zoo*. The teacher may well explain these three words to the child before he begins to read. When he has difficulty, the teacher helps him read the selection aloud.

RAGS

Rags was a funny little brown dog. He was very, very small, no bigger than a cat. He didn't live with a mommy, a daddy, and children; he lived all alone with Mr. Man in a big, big house. Each morning Mr. Man took him outside for a walk. All the other dogs were much bigger. When they saw Rags, they looked and looked again. They thought maybe he came from the zoo. They could not believe that he was so small. And they never saw him walking with a mother or with brothers or sisters. He was always with Mr. Man.

One day, Jack,[41] the big, big dog moved close to Rags to talk to him. He looked and looked some more. Then he asked, "What kind of a dog are[57] you?[58] Where do you live?"

Rags told him, "I am a small terrier[53] and I live way up in the big house with Mr. Man. I bark "hello" to everyone who comes to the door. When anybody[5] rings[51] the bell, I start to bark and don't stop[3] until the person[1] leaves. Mr. Man says I should[35] be ashamed[36] and I should stop barking[14] at everything[26][50] and everybody. All day long I wait in the kitchen[39] for Mr. Man to come up the steps[62] because he works[56] all[47] day. At night he and I go for walks and play[59] hard. Ever since I was a little dog, almost all my life,[21] I have lived with Mr. Man."

Mr. Man and I eat breakfast together. Mr. Man[49] likes coffee,[20] toast, and an orange,[43] but I like fish[37] and milk best of all. Sometimes[34] I open my mouth[27] wide and Mr. Man drops in his last piece of toast. Mr. Man and I eat all our meals together. At night he sometimes puts me in a tub[6] and washes me hard.

Jack said, "I've liked visiting[33A] with you. I think[49A] you and Mr. Man have good times together."

When Jack told[7] all the other[29] dogs about Rags, they[28] all became good friends.[60] When Mr. Man walked with Rags, Jack, the other dogs, and Rags played together happily[2] on the grass.[16] Mr. Man talked to the brothers, sisters, mothers, and fathers. They enjoyed[42] each other and all of them had fun.[19]

Sound	Initial Position	Medial Position	Final Position
p[p]	person (1)	happily (2)	stop (3)
b[b]	believe (4)	anybody (5)	tub (6)
t[t]	told (7)	little (8)	cat (9)
d[d]	dog (10)	Daddy (11)	played (12)
k[k]	cat (13)	barking (14)	walk (15)
g[g]	grass (16)	bigger (17)	dog (18)
f[f]	fun (19)	coffee (20)	life (21)
v[v]	very (22)	never (23)	live (24)
th[θ]	thought (25)	everything (26)	mouth (27)
th[ð]	they (28)	other (29)	
s[s]	small (30)	sisters (31)	house (32)
z[z]	zoo (33)	visiting (33A)	sometimes (34)
sh[ʃ]	should (35)	ashamed (36)	fish (37)
ch[tʃ]	children (38)	kitchen (39)	each (40)
j[dʒ]	Jack (41)	enjoyed (42)	orange (43)
m[m]	morning (44)	mommy (45)	came (46)
n[n]	night (47)	funny (48)	man (49)
ng[ŋ]		think (49A)	everything (50)
r[r]	rings (51)	very (52)	terrier (53)
l[l]	lived (54)	children (55)	all (56)
y[j]	you (57)		
wh[ʍ]	where (58)		
pl[pl]	play (59)		
fr[fr]	friends (60)		
br[br]	brown (61)		
st[st]	steps (62)		

For older children the following sentences are suggested for testing. The vocabulary is taken from the first 5,000 words of the Thorndike-Lorge list (57).

p[p]   Peter composed a poem about his cap.

b[b]   The bulletin told of the job of those who were able to attend the game.

t[t]	His main talent was an ability to act.
d[d]	He went to Detroit to buy a Ford in the middle of the summer.
k[k]	He took a quart of milk on the picnic.
g[g]	Margaret likes to dig in the ground.
f[f]	The officer laughed at the fancy dress of the boys.
v[v]	Are you going to move to a new village in November?
th[θ]	Edith had a birthday party on Thanksgiving Day.
th[ð]	Neither of them would bathe the dog.
s[s]	Alice suspected that Johnny put the snake in her bed.
z[z]	Much to the amazement of his aunt, Dick tried to arouse Mary's interest in the zoo.
sh[ʃ]	Shall I dash to the fashion show now?
zh[ʒ]	Casually, he walked to the garage.
ch[tʃ]	Charles went to Richmond to do research work.
j[dʒ]	Jim went to college to learn to be an engineer.
m[m]	Mary, the temporary chairman, called the meeting to order in Room 112.
n[n]	Nan entertained all the candidates.
l[l]	During the strike the landlord found running an elevator dull.
r[r]	On rare occasions he rode the ferry.
ng[ŋ]	He did not sing a single song for us.
y, wh[j, ʍ]	Do you live in the yellow or the white house?

Avant and Hutton (1a) have devised a measuring tool to: (1) permit examination of articulation in connected speech with reliability and validity; (2) permit evaluation of such other facts as rate, voice quality, pitch, loudness, and breathing; (3) use a stimulus which produces a consistent response; and (4) administer quickly and easily. The tool is a short reading passage for upper elementary school children. In constructing the test, they emphasized: (a) inclusion of a wide variety of speech sounds with emphasis on those occurring most frequently and those most often defective; (b) readability (simple structure; vocabulary from first 1,000 words of Rinsland list); (c) rapidity in administration.

The tester may use phonetic transcriptions. Instructions on a scoring procedure for articulatory errors include: (a) an omission by marking a diagonal line through the symbol for the omitted sound; (b) a substitution by writing the phonetic symbol; (c) a distortion by a question mark above the symbol; and (d) an added sound by an insertion of the phonetic symbol representing the sound.

The selection follows:

One day Jim was looking out the kitchen window. "Mary," he called, "Father is coming in the front door with a big white box."
"I have something to show you," said Mr. Jones.
"Is the box for us?" they both cried.
When he took the paper off, they saw it was a red doll house.
Jim said, "There are some people in it. The man is reading and the woman is washing a baby."
"She looks like Mrs. Green," Mary said.
"Do you see the girl in the play room?"
Mary saw the girl was sitting on a large ball.
Just then Mother came in. Mary and Jim said, "Look at the pretty toys Father gave us. Thank you very much for them" (1a, p. 41).

For the speech correctionist, testing may well become more precise. Barker and England provide a way of giving a numerical measure of articulation by assigning numerical values to sounds according to their frequency of occurrence in American speech. Furthermore, these sounds are arranged in developmental order based on Templin's study to provide an indication of articulation age. This measure has high validity when compared with professional judgment and is simpler than the detailed form used primarily by research workers. It is useful in comparing different kinds of therapy, in evaluating progress of the speech defective, in selecting case loads, and in discussing speech development with parents (6a).

Factors Associated with Articulatory Difficulties

Low Intelligence

Any number of studies show a high incidence of articulatory defects among children who are definitely feebleminded. Many organic conditions, such as brain injury, contribute both to the deficient articulatory and mental ability. Speech defects are more frequent among children of low than of high intelligence. Gladys Reid (42), however, points out that articulatory ability is not related to and cannot be predicted from intelligence when the intelligence is above that indicated by an I.Q. of 70. Yedinack (66) also indicates that there is no significant relationship between articulatory defects and intelligence. Similarly, a study by Steer and Drexler (51) predicting later articulatory ability of kindergartners, notes that intelligence as measured at the kindergarten level appears to be unrelated to articulatory ability five years later.

Hearing Loss

We have already stressed the relationship between adequate hearing and the ability to learn to speak. Although the child's hearing may be sufficient for understanding conversation and what goes on around him, it may be insufficient for learning to make all the sounds. Some sounds the child may not hear at all. His own speech, therefore, reflects his inability to hear. When D. J. Mase (30) was selecting his subjects for a study of the etiology of articulatory defects, he discovered five boys with pronounced hearing loss. No teacher or principal was aware of a hearing loss in any one of these five boys even though the symptoms of total monotony and inarticulate speech were clearly evident. Peripherally deaf children almost always have defective articulation, for they are unable to imitate sounds. They cannot compare the sounds they utter with those produced by others. In fact, they cannot hear the sounds of any model. Their abilities to see and to feel cannot make up for their inability to hear. We will discuss the problem of the child with a hearing loss in Chapter 14.

Emotional or Personality Difficulty

A child learns to speak to help him adjust to his environment. A large part of man's social adjustment to his surroundings is verbal. His environment and surroundings influence his ability to adjust through verbal means. Some children's environment is so difficult that they cannot learn to adjust to it. An articulatory defect may be a symptom of this inability to adjust. Solomon (48) in a study reported in *ASHA* notes that the child with the functional articulatory difficulty tends to be passive and to internalize his responses. He indicates that this child is characterized by submissiveness, timidity, and a need for approval. He interprets the findings to indicate that speech and behavior problems are found together and may both represent refusals to acquire socially acceptable functions because of unfavorable stress or environmental pressures.

Wood (65) did a study on the adjustment of parents who had children with articulatory defects. He found, by administering personality tests, that the mothers of children with articulatory defects as a group were more neurotic in tendency, more submissive, and more self-conscious than average mothers as measured by test norms. Furthermore, the scores of the mothers of children with articulatory defects were lower than the test norms in self-adjustment, social adjustment, and total adjustment. The scores of the fathers on one test did not differ significantly from test norms; on another they showed that the fathers rated lower on self-adjustment than the norms. He concludes that articulatory defects are definitely and significantly associated with maladjustment and undesirable traits of the parents and that such factors are usually centered in the mother. As mentioned in Chapter 7, his study also indicated that when the mothers of children with articulatory defects were treated clinically to help them secure better adjustment, their children improved more quickly with speech correction help than did children whose parents were not treated. Moll and Darley (33) studied the attitudes of mothers of articulatory impaired children. They found that mothers of articulatory impaired children have higher standards and are more critical of their children's functioning than are mothers of nonspeech impaired children.

Structural Abnormalities

Anomalies of the tongue, lips, teeth, and palate have long been associated with articulatory difficulties. Recently, however, attitudes have changed on the responsibility of organic deviations of the articulatory mechanism for articulatory defects. For instance, the literature in the field of speech correction presents opposing viewpoints on the responsibility of dental abnormalities for defective articulation. Undoubtedly, for some children, malocclusion of the teeth or an abnormally large tongue contribute to the child's lack of articulatory development. But some children with similar organic difficulties do not misarticulate the same sounds whereas other children with a normal mechanism do misarticulate them. Poor structures may, however, be a contributing factor in explaining poor articulation.

TEETH AND GUM RIDGE. The teeth and/or the gum ridge are involved in the sounds $f[f]$, $v[v]$, $th[\theta]$, $th[\eth]$, $s[s]$, $z[z]$, $sh[\int]$, $zh[3]$, $ch[t\int]$, and $j[d3]$. In $f[f]$ and $v[v]$ the upper teeth touch the lower lip. In $th[\theta]$ and $th[\eth]$ the tongue tip is placed against the biting edge of the upper teeth or between the two rows of teeth. In the sibilant sounds, the air is directed against the teeth in a variety of ways. In some cases the teeth have difficulty reaching the lower lip, the biting edge is badly located, or the teeth are so formed that it is difficult to find a surface of teeth against which to direct the air.

The condition where the upper front teeth protrude abnormally beyond the lower teeth is called an overbite. When the upper lip meets the lower one with difficulty, $p[p]$, $b[b]$, and $m[m]$ may be defective. The tongue lies forward in the mouth, sometimes over the lower teeth. The lower teeth are so far back that they cannot provide the necessary friction to make a good $s[s]$ or $z[z]$. With this condition the lower jaw usually recedes.

In other cases the lower jaw protrudes and the lower front teeth project over the upper front teeth. This condition is called an underbite and is usually associated with an undershot jaw.

In still other cases a space occurs between the upper and lower teeth when they are brought together. This condition is called an open bite. Normally the upper incisor overlaps its counterpart on the lower jaw so that about one-third of the surface of the visible lower incisor is covered by the upper incisor. In an open bite *s*[s] and *z*[z] are most frequently defective since the narrow stream of air cannot be directed against the cutting edge of the teeth. Sometimes *sh*[ʃ], *zh*[ʒ], *th*[θ], and *th*[ð] are distorted. If the lips cannot be brought together, *p*[p], *b*[b], and *m*[m] may be defective. When the lower lip cannot touch the teeth easily, *f*[f] and *v*[v] may be inaccurate.

Finally, a space may occur between the central incisors or the canine teeth may be irregularly placed. In both these instances *s*[s] may be defective. When the space occurs, too much air is allowed to escape. Where the teeth are irregularly placed, they may interfere with the tongue so that the air is allowed to escape over one or both of its sides. Frequently, however, individuals themselves, finding compensatory movements, speak well in spite of teeth that are very irregular.

Snow did a study on articulation proficiency in relation to certain dental abnormalities; the purpose of the study was to study the articulation of six consonant sounds [f], [v], [θ], [ð], [s], and [z], for which the upper central incisor teeth are ordinarily considered important. She found that a statistically significant larger proportion of "normal" first-grade children with missing or abnormal upper central incisor teeth misarticulated [f], [v], [θ], [ð], [s], and [z] compared with children with normal teeth. However, she notes that most of the children with missing or abnormal teeth made the sounds correctly and some children with normal teeth did not make the sounds correctly.

TONGUE. The term "tongue-tied" is applied when the frenum of the tongue (the little web of tissue underneath the front part of the tongue) is abnormally short so that the tip of the tongue cannot move to points such as the ridge behind the upper teeth. This condition, where it severely disturbs articulation, is comparatively rare in children.

Other conditions may involve the tongue. The sounds which

may be disturbed because of the tongue are k[k], g[g], ng[ŋ], th[θ], th[ð], l[l], r[r], s[s], z[z], sh[ʃ], and zh[ʒ]. In some few cases the tongue is so large or sluggish that it cannot make the small, precise, and quick movements necessary for certain sounds. Sometimes the tongue may be paralyzed or weak. At other times, there may be poor muscular coordination. Occasionally a thyroid deficiency causes sluggishness and poor control of the tongue, the result of generally poor motor coordination.

In l[l] and r[r] the tongue tip points to the teeth ridge. In s[s] and z[z], the tongue is grooved to direct a small stream of air against the teeth. In n[n], t[t], and d[d], the tongue touches the teeth ridge. In sh[ʃ] and zh[ʒ], the tongue directs a broader channel of air against the teeth. In the sibilant sounds the tip of the tongue may reach toward the upper gum. In teaching the sibilants, however, correctionists sometimes find it better not to have the child try to reach toward the upper gum but to have him reach toward the gum behind the lower teeth. The tongue is obviously an important articulatory agent.

TONGUE-THRUST. Increasing interest is being focused on a neuromuscular syndrome commonly called "tongue-thrust." The features of the syndrome include: a deviant swallowing pattern because (1) unusual tension exists in the mouth-enclosing musculature, (2) perceptible contraction of swallowing muscles decreases or is absent, and (3) the tongue is thrust forward, causing it to protrude between the teeth. As a result, the oral cavity may be changed and dental irregularities produced. Associated with these modifications are sound production defects, especially of the sibilants. Fletcher and others (18) found that a child with a tongue-thrust swallow is more likely to have a deviant s than the child with a normal swallow. They indicate that further information is needed to establish more clearly the role of the speech therapist in tongue-thrusts.

PALATE. In sounds such as sh[ʃ] and zh[ʒ], the palate plays a part. When it is abnormally high and narrow, the child's tongue may have difficulty in making the necessary contacts. When an opening occurs along the middle line of the palate, the condition is serious. This condition is discussed in a later chapter.

Motor Ability

Some children are poorly coordinated. Quite obviously some youngsters run, go up- and downstairs, and jump much more easily than others. One youngster will put a jigsaw puzzle together and fit the pieces with little or no effort. Another will struggle with it. This motor ability develops with maturation. But children of the same age vary widely in this ability. Sometimes poor coordination is evident around the mouth; the tongue, jaw, and palate are awkward. Some studies have shown that children with articulatory defects tend to score significantly lower on tests of motor ability than do children with normal speech. Not all children with articulatory defects are deficient in motor skill but poor motor ability may be a contributing cause of the defect. Bilto (8) compared the muscular abilities of a group of 90 children who had articulatory defects or stuttered with a group of children with normal speech. The children with defective speech had no organic difficulties. Approximately two-thirds of the speech defective children were inferior to the children with normal speech on the test that included appropriate rhythm, coordination, and application of strength. Patton (39) found a tendency for children with articulatory defects to show less kinesthetic sensibility than children with normal speech. He defines kinesthesia as the sense by which muscular motion, weight, and position are perceived and as the sense whose organs lie in the muscles, tendons, and joints and are stimulated by bodily movements and tensions. A study by Karlin, Youtz, and Kennedy (25) indicates that children with defective speech are inferior to those with normal speech in ability to perform tasks requiring motor speed.

On the other hand, Mase (30) found no significant difference in his matched groups of intermediate elementary school children with and without articulatory defects on rate of movement of articulators and general muscular coordination. Reid (42) concludes from her study of functional articulatory defects that the degree of neuromuscular control and the degree of kinesthetic sensitivity are not related to articulation ability. She does point out, however, that, without doubt, there are minimum levels of maturity for these two factors. Maxwell (31) found no difference between normal speaking and articulatory cases in his tests of motor performance.

Auditory Memory and Discrimination

Some children may hear very well but have difficulty in retaining auditory impressions. Others with excellent hearing may have trouble in discriminating one sound from another. Mase (30) found no significant difference in either auditory memory or discrimination between the speech defective group and the normal speaking group. Reid (42) also found that the length of auditory memory span is not related to articulatory ability. She found, however, a significant relationship between articulatory ability and the ability to discriminate between speech sounds. Hall (20) found that articulatory defective children and adults are not inferior to normally speaking children and adults in auditory discrimination of either simple or complex speech patterns or in regard to auditory memory for speech sounds. Metraux (32) in a study of the auditory span of children ranging in age from four years to twelve years determined that there are significant differences in auditory memory span among the various age groups for both the vowel and consonant sounds. The scores for recalling both the vowel and consonant sounds gradually increase with age, although the peak for the vowel test is reached at age ten while the peak for the consonant test is reached at age twelve.

Other more recent studies emphasize that the ability of the child with an articulatory defect in auditory discrimination is inferior to that of the normal speaking child. Bruns (10) using the Templin modification of the Travis-Rasmus Test of Auditory Discrimination and the standardized Phonetically Balanced Kindergarten Word List found that the group of children possessing articulatory defects scored significantly lower on both the Templin test and the Phonetically Balanced Kindergarten Test than did the group of children with normal speech. Farquhar (17), in studying the value of a battery of imitative articulation and auditory discrimination tests in predicting speech development of two groups of kindergarten children, found that children with severe speech problems had significantly inferior auditory discrimination than children with mild speech problems. Mange (29) found that his group of normal speaking children achieved significantly higher scores in discrimination of pitch than did his group of children with functional misarticulation of *r*[r]. In this study, there was also a significant but low partial correlation between phonetic word-synthesis ability and the number of articulatory errors. Schiefelbusch (46) in a study to develop a new test for sound discrimination found that significant differences exist between the speech defective and normal speaking groups in relation to sound discrimination abilities in each form: rhyming, initial, and final sounds. He also found that the second-grade normal speaking groups had significantly better sound discrimination than the first-grade normals, but a similar gain was not found for the second-grade speech defective group in comparison with the first-grade speech defective group.

Faulty Learning

The child may have had no good models to imitate. One of the writers interviewed three children aged twelve, ten, and six from the same family. All of them were above average in intelligence. The two older children made so many substitutions for sounds that their speech was almost unintelligible. The youngest child had normal speech. The two older children grew up in a rural environment with no playmates. Their father's speech was normal but their mother's was the original edition of the two older children. The younger child, had, however, because of the illness of the mother, lived with her grandmother in town from the age of six months to five years. The model that the two older girls imitated was in all likelihood the cause of their articulatory disorder. Another example shows the influence of the child's playmates. A small child had parents with excellent speech. She, however, from three until six years of age played with children with a decided foreign accent. She had the same kind and amount of foreign accent as the children she played with.

Relationship of Articulatory Difficulties with Reading and Spelling Disabilities

Reading Disabilities

Research shows that speech and reading are related, particularly where oral reading is involved. Research, however, has not shown the extent of the relationship, for the amount of research is too small to prove or to disprove assumptions. We do know that speech defects and reading difficulties occur concurrently in a certain proportion of children.

Moss (36) showed that normally speaking children surpassed deficient speakers in speed of reading and freedom from reading errors. Monroe (34) in a study of 415 reading defectives (based on both oral and silent reading tests) found that 9 percent stuttered and 18 percent had articulatory defects. In a group of 101 nondefective readers, only 1 percent stuttered and 7 percent had articulatory defects. Robinson (43) found in a study of 30 retarded readers that 20 percent had articulatory defects. Bond (9) in a study of the auditory and speech characteristics of poor readers compared 64 poor readers with 64 good readers in second and third grades. In silent reading, he found no relationship between speech difficulties and reading difficulties. But he noted that 35 percent of those children who were poor oral readers, but good silent readers, had speech defects. No child who was a good oral reader, but poor silent reader, had a speech difficulty. Moore's (35) results differed from those just cited. In a study of 123 ninth-grade children with articulatory defects, he found that as a group they ranked above the grade median on the Iowa Silent Reading Test.

The interplay of several factors may cause both articulatory and reading difficulties. Writers in both fields mention similar causes: auditory difficulties, lack of motivation to read or to speak, poor instruction, improper materials for instruction, emotional disturbances, or delayed muscular maturation.

Wepman's results of a study of the relationship of auditory discrimination to speech and reading difficulties (63) seem to indicate that delay in the development of auditory discrimination relates positively and probably causally to poor speech articulation, poor reading ability, or both.

Eames (14) thinks that both reading and speaking disabilities are likely to have a common cause. For example, he believes that a neurological lesion of the language centers or a failure or inadequacy of auditory association and discrimination may be a common cause for speech difficulty and general linguistic deficiency. Emotional reactions may increase the degree of difficulty in both reading and speaking.

Hildreth (22) says that a large proportion of children with speech problems tend to be retarded in reading and that speech defects can be an important secondary cause of reading disability. She also makes the point that weakness in auditory discrimination is a common defect that interferes with progress in reading.

Eustis (15) says the relationship of the speech and reading difficulties may well lie in a delayed muscular maturation. He points out that 48 percent of children who have specific speech and reading disabilities also showed one or more of the following: lefthandedness, ambidexterity, or body clumsiness. He believes that these conditions suggest a combination of symptoms which involve, among other things, poor muscular coordination due to the slow maturations of coverings of the nerve fibers.

Weaver, Furbee, and Everhart (62), on the basis of data obtained from administering a speech articulation test and a Gates

Reading Readiness Test, conclude that reading readiness and acquisition of adequate speech are to some extent related, although the proportion of variance common to reading readiness measures and articulation measures is quite small. They say that it is possible that the Gates Reading Readiness Test measures part of an underlying variable causal to the acquisition of both reading and speech.

Articulatory defects may influence a child's ability to read aloud orally and silently. The child's concern about these errors may well reduce his ability to concentrate on his reading so that he does not comprehend as well as he otherwise might. The child's articulatory defect may disturb the rate of reading, interfere with his phrasing, and thus cause difficulty. A negative attitude resulting from his inability to read aloud well may be carried over to silent reading and discourage the child in an area where he might otherwise progress if he had more practice.

Spelling Difficulties

Two studies also show that some kind of relationship seems to exist between spelling and articulatory difficulties. A study by Ham (21) reports that words that are misarticulated tend to be misspelled more frequently than words that are pronounced correctly even though the spelling error is not related to the type of mispronunciation as a $w[w]$ for $r[r]$ substitution. He notes, therefore, that the presence of articulatory problems may tend to be accompanied by problems in the areas of language skills. He makes no decision as to whether articulation problems contribute to spelling and reading problems or whether all are facets of a general language skills deficit. A study by Young Zedler (67) shows the effect of phonic training on speech sound discrimination and spelling performance. After a series of training periods with stories that emphasize sounds and listening to them, she found that the written spelling performances changed significantly and favorably and that speech sound discrimination ability increased significantly. She notes that written spelling ability and speech sound discrimination are significantly related variables.

Relationship to Language Ability

Schneiderman (47) studied the relationship of defective articulation to language ability. She included in language ability spoken vocabulary, sentence length, and a rating by the classroom teachers on the children's ability to express themselves verbally. She found that children with the lowest level of language ability were also the children with the largest mean number of defective speech sounds, whereas the children with the highest language ability had the lowest mean number of defective speech sounds. She states that this relationship is due in large part to other factors such as mental age.

Since, however, the child with disabilities in articulation, reading, and language may be a slow-developing child, the teacher may well relate his language activities. They may be based on familiar concepts of the individual child. For example, they may center on home, school, his street, pets, store, the beach, and the like. Since these children need practice with the common everyday words, they must have experience with interesting, familiar, and frequently repeated vocabulary. The teacher provides such experiences with language through storytelling, choral speaking, and dramatic activities. He should do what he can to encourage conversation. When the children plan their work together, they are engaging in an interesting activity that encourages communication.

References and Suggested Readings

1. American Speech and Hearing Association Committee on Legislation. "Need for Speech Pathologists." *ASHA,* I (December 1959), 138-39.

1a. AVANT, V., and C. HUTTON, "Passage for Speech Screening in Upper Elementary Grades." *Journal of Speech and Hearing Disorders,* XXVII (February 1962), 40-46. (Contains a passage to test articulation and certain aspects of voice.)

2. American Speech and Hearing Association Research Committee, "Public School Speech and Hearing Services." *The Journal of Speech and Hearing Disorders,* Monograph Supplement 8 (July 1961).

3. AMATORA, SISTER M., "Psychological Implications of Speech Problems in the Primary Grades." *American Childhood,* **XLIII** (January 1958), 28-29.

4. ANDERSON, V., *Improving the Child's Speech* (Rev. ed.) New York: Oxford University Press, 1961, Chapter 6. (Tells how to test for articulatory difficulties. Explains their causes.)

5. ARTLEY, A. S., "A Study of Certain Factors Presumed to be Associated with Reading and Speech Difficulties." *Journal of Speech and Hearing Disorders,* **XIII** (December 1948), 351-360.

6. BANGS, J. L., A Clinical Analysis of the Articulatory Defects of the Feeble-Minded." *Journal of Speech Disorders,* **VII** (December 1942), 343-356. (Analyzes the articulatory deficiencies of the feeble-minded. Shows correlations between speech proficiency, chronological age, mental age, and intelligence quotients. Analyzes phonetic errors, the sounds most frequently preferred as substitutions for each sound, all errors for each sound, and the sounds most frequently omitted and added.)

6a. BARKER, J., and G. ENGLAND, "A Numerical Measure of Articulation: Further Development." *Journal of Speech and Hearing Disorders,* **XXVII** (February 1962), 23-27. (Explains the giving of a numerical measure of articulation.)

7. BERRY, M., and J. EISENSON, *Speech Disorders: Principles and Practices of Therapy.* New York: Appleton-Century-Crofts, 1956, Chapter 5. (Discusses possible causes of articulatory defects.)

8. BILTO, E. W., "Motor Abilities of Children with Defective Speech." *Journal of Speech Disorders,* **VI** (December 1941), 187-203.

9. BOND, G. L., *The Auditory and Speech Characteristics of Poor Readers.* New York: Bureau of Publications, Teachers College, Columbia University, 1935.

10. BRUNS, J. M., "Experimental Study of Auditory Discrimination Ability of Children with Articulatory Disorders." *Exceptional Child,* **XXIII** (March 1957), 264-266.

11. CARTER, E. T., and M. BUCK, "Prognostic Testing for Functional Articulation Disorders among Children in the First Grade." *Journal of Speech and Hearing Disorders,* **XXIII** (May 1958), 124-133.

12. CURTIS, J. F., and J. C. HARDY, "A Phonetic Study of Misarticulation of /r/." *Journal of Speech and Hearing Research,* **II** (Sep-

tember 1959), 244-257. (Suggests that phonetic context is an important factor in the articulation process.)

13. CYPREANSEN, L., "The Standardization of a Speech Articulation Test with the Use of a Colored Filmstrip." *ASHA*, **I** (November 1959), 103. (Presents an objective method of studying, recording, and comparing the speech articulatory differences of children.)

14. EAMES, T., "The Relationship of Reading and Speech Difficulties." *Journal of Educational Psychology*, **XLI** (January 1950), 51-55.

15. EUSTIS, R. S., "The Primary Origin of the Specific Language Disabilities." *Journal of Pediatrics*, **XXXI** (October 1947), 448-455. (Indicates that the relationship between speech difficulties and reading difficulties may well lie in a delayed neuromuscular maturation.)

16. EVERHART, R. W., "Literature Survey of Growth and Developmental Factors in Articulatory Maturation." *Journal of Speech and Hearing Disorders*, **XXV** (February 1960), 59-69.

17. FARQUHAR, M. S., "The Prognostic Value of Imitative and Auditory Discrimination Tests." *ASHA*, **I** (November 1959), 96. (Determines the value of a battery of imitative articulation and auditory discrimination tests in predicting the speech development of two groups of kindergarten children.)

18. FLETCHER, S. G., R. L. CASTEEL, and D. P. BRADLEY, "Tongue-Thrust Swallow, Speech Articulation, and Age." *Journal of Speech and Hearing Disorders*, **XXVI** (August 1961), 201-208.

19. GAINES, F. P., "Interrelations of Speech and Reading Disabilities." *Quarterly Journal of Speech*, **XXVII** (February 1941), 104-110.

20. HALL, M., "Auditory Factors in Functional Articulatory Speech Defects." *Journal of Experimental Education*, **VII** (December 1938), 110-132.

21. HAM, R. E., "Relationship between Misspelling and Misarticulation." *Journal of Speech and Hearing Disorders*, **XXIII** (August 1958), 294-297.

22. HILDRETH, G., "Speech Defects and Reading Disability." *Elementary School Journal*, **XLVI** (February 1946), 326-332.

22a. IRWIN, R. B., and B. W. MUSSELMAN, "A Compact Picture Articulation Test." *Journal of Speech and Hearing Disorders*, **XXVII** (February 1962), 36-39. (Contains a picture test which checks more than one sound in a word.)

23. JOHNSON, W., *et al.*, *Speech Handicapped School Children*. (Rev. ed.) New York: Harper and Brothers, 1956, Chapter 3.

24. JORDAN, E. P., "Articulation Test Measures and Listener Ratings of Articulation Defectiveness." *Journal of Speech and Hearing Research,* **III** (December 1960), 303-318.

25. KARLIN, I. W., A. C. YOUTZ, and L. KENNEDY, "Distorted Speech in Young Children." *American Journal of Diseases of Children,* **LIX** (June 1940), 1203-1218. (Compares ability to perform tasks requiring motor speed of children with defective speech with normally speaking children.)

26. KEENAN, J. S., "What is Medial Position?" *Journal of Speech and Hearing Disorders,* **XXVI** (May 1961), 171-177.

27. KLEFFNER, F. R., *A Comparison of the Reactions of a Group of Fourth Grade Children to Recorded Examples of Defective and Non-Defective Articulation.* Ph.D. thesis (University of Wisconsin, 1952).

28. LANDERS, M. T., "Maturation Versus Speech Correction at the Kindergarten Level." *ASHA,* **I** (November 1959), 80.

29. MANGE, C. V., "Relationships between Selected Auditory Perceptual Factors and Articulation Ability." *Journal of Speech and Hearing Research,* **III** (March 1960), 67-73.

30. MASE, D. J., *Etiology of Articulatory Defects.* New York: Bureau of Publications, Teachers College, Columbia University, 1946.

31. MAXWELL, K. L., *A Comparison of Certain Motor Performances of Children with Normal Speech and Children With Defective Consonant Articulation.* Ph.D. thesis (University of Michigan, 1953).

32. METRAUX, R. W., "Auditory Memory Span for Speech Sounds: Norms for Children." *Journal of Speech Disorders,* **IX** (March 1944), 31-38.

33. MOLL, K. L., and F. L. DARLEY. "Attitudes of Mothers of Articulatory-Impaired and Speech-Retarded Children." *Journal of Speech and Hearing Disorders,* **XXV** (November 1960), 377-384.

34. MONROE, M., *Children Who Cannot Read.* Chicago: University of Chicago Press, 1932. (Includes a study on relationship between reading and speaking difficulties and one on the influence of poor auditory discrimination upon reading.)

35. MOORE, C. E. H., "Reading and Arithmetic Abilities Associated with Speech Defects." *Journal of Speech Disorders,* **XII** (March 1942), 85-86.

36. Moss, M., "The Effect of Speech Defects on Second Grade Read-

ing Achievement." *Quarterly Journal of Speech,* **XXIV** (December 1938), 642-654.

37. NEWBERRY, C. T., *Percy, Polly* and *Pete.* New York: Harper and Brothers, 1952. (A delightful story of three cats, well illustrated.)

38. OYER, H. J., "Speech Error Recognition Ability." *Journal of Speech and Hearing Disorders,* **XXIV** (November 1959), 391-394. (Assesses speech error recognition ability of two groups of college seniors: 20 majoring in speech and hearing therapy and 20 majoring in elementary education. Finds there is no significant difference in speech error recognition ability between seniors in elementary education and seniors in speech and hearing therapy.)

39. PATTON, F. E., "A Comparison of the Kinaesthetic Sensibility of Speech of Defective and Normal Speaking Children." *Journal of Speech Disorders,* **VII** (December 1942), 305-310.

40. POOLE, I., "Genetic Development of Consonant Sounds in English." *Elementary English Review,* **XI** (June 1934), 159-161. (Includes the ages at which boys and girls normally attain the mastery of certain speech sounds.)

41. REID, G., "The Efficacy of Speech Re-Education of Functional Articulatory Defectives in the Elementary School." *Journal of Speech Disorders,* **XII** (December 1947), 303-312. (Tells how children with functional articulatory defects are inefficient in intellectual self-expression until they learn to speak correctly.)

42. ———, "The Etiology and Nature of Functional Articulatory Defects in Elementary School Children." *Journal of Speech Disorders,* **XII** (June 1947), 143-150.

43. ROBINSON, H., *Why Pupils Fail in Reading.* Chicago: University of Chicago Press, 1946.

44. ROE, V., and R. MILISEN, "The Effect of Maturation upon Defective Articulation in Elementary Grades." *Journal of Speech Disorders,* **VII** (March 1942), 37-50.

45. SAYLER, H. K., "The Effect of Maturation upon Defective Articulation in Grades 7-12." *Journal of Speech and Hearing Disorders,* **XIV** (September 1949), 202-207. (Indicates sounds most commonly missed. Shows a slight decrease in the mean number of articulatory errors from Grades 7-10.)

46. SCHIEFELBUSCH, R. L., and M. J. LINDSEY. "A New Test of Sound Discrimination." *Journal of Speech and Hearing Disorders,* **XXIII** May 1958), 153-159.

47. SCHNEIDERMAN, N., "A Study of the Relationship between Articulatory Ability and Language Ability." *Journal of Speech and Hearing Disorders,* **XX** (December 1955), 359-364.

47a. SIEGEL, G. M., "Experienced and Inexperienced Articulation Examiners." *Journal of Speech and Hearing Disorders,* **XXVII** (February 1962), 28-34. (Studies the ability of the inexperienced to test after they have been given minimal training.)

47b. SNOW, K., "Articulation Proficiency in Relation to Certain Dental Abnormalities." *Journal of Speech and Hearing Disorders,* **XXVI** (August 1961), 209-212. (Studies the articulation of six consonant sounds for which the upper central incisor teeth are ordinarily considered important.)

48. SOLOMON, A. L., "Emotional and Behavior Problems of First Grade Children with Functional Defects of Articulation." *ASHA,* **II** (October 1960), 378.

49. SOMMERS, R. K., W. J. MEYER, and A. K. FENTON. "Pitch Discrimination and Articulation." *Journal of Speech and Hearing Research,* **IV** (March 1961), 56-60. (Investigates pitch discrimination in school children with functional articulation errors in grades 3-12.)

50. SPRIESTERBACH, D. C., "Research in Articulation Disorders and Personality." *Journal of Speech and Hearing Disorders,* **XXI** (September 1956), 329-335. (Reviews literature which shows the relationship or lack of it between articulation disorders and personality.)

51. STEER, M. C., and H. G. DREXLER. "Predicting Later Articulation Ability from Kindergarten Tests." *Journal of Speech and Hearing Disorders,* **XXV** (November 1960), 391-397.

52. TEMPLIN, M. C. *Certain Language Skills in Children: Their Development and Interrelationships.* Minneapolis, University of Minnesota Press, 1957.

53. ———, "Norms on a Screening Test of Articulation for Ages 3-8." *Journal of Speech and Hearing Disorders,* **XVIII** (December 1953), 323-331. (Compares articulatory ability of boys and girls. Indicates when boys and girls reach approximately mature articulation.)

54. ———, "Spontaneous Versus Imitated Vocalization in Testing Articulation in Preschool Children." *Journal of Speech Disorders,* **XII** (December 1947), 293-300.

55. ——, "A Study of the Sound Discrimination Ability of Elementary School Pupils." *Journal of Speech Disorders,* **VIII** (June 1943), 127-132. (Contains a short test of sound discrimination. Indicates the relationship of position of discriminative element to error.)

56. THOMAS, B. M., "Informational Processing Ability of Children with Articulation Problems as Compared with Normal Children." *ASHA,* **I** (November 1959), 106. (Compares the informational processing ability of children with articulation problems with children with normal speech.)

57. THORNDIKE, E. L., and I. LORGE. *The Teacher's Word Book of 30,000 Words.* New York: Bureau of Publications, Teachers College, Columbia University, 1944.

58. VAN RIPER, C., *Speech Correction: Principles and Methods.* (3rd ed.) Englewood Cliffs, N.J.: Prentice-Hall, 1954, Chapter 7.

59. ——, and J. V. IRWIN, *Voice and Articulation.* Englewood Cliffs, N.J.: Prentice-Hall, 1958.

60. VENTURA, B. P., G. INGEBO, and P. WOLMUT, "A Comparative Evaluation of Speech Correction Techniques in the Primary Grades and the Role of Maturation on Misarticulation." *ASHA,* **II** (October 1960), 378.

61. VOEGELIN, C. F., and S. ADAMS, "A Phonetic Study of Young Children's Speech." *Journal of Experimental Education,* **XIII** (December 1934), 107-116. (Studies the substitution of sounds made by children. Shows the inconsistency existing in children's articulatory errors.)

62. WEAVER, C. H., C. FURBEE, and R. W. EVERHART, "Articulatory Competency and Reading Readiness." *Journal of Speech and Hearing Research,* **III** (June 1960), 174-180.

63. WEPMAN, J., "Relationships of Auditory Discrimination to Speech and Reading Difficulties." *ASHA,* **I** (November 1959), 96.

64. WOLFE, W. D., "The Nature and Frequency of Misarticulation Relationship to Method of Eliciting Speech." *ASHA,* **II** (October 1960), 374. (Measures and compares articulation responses of children during oral reading and conversation.)

65. WOOD, K. S., "Parental Maladjustment and Functional Articulatory Defects in Children." *Journal of Speech Disorders,* **XI** (December 1946), 255-275.

66. YEDINACK, J. G., "A Study of the Linguistic Functions of Children

with Articulation and Reading Disabilities." *Journal of Genetic Psychology,* **LXXIV** (March 1949), 23-50.

67. ZEDLER, E. Y., "Effect of Phonic Training on Speech Sound Discrimination and Spelling Performance." *Journal of Speech and Hearing Disorders,* **XXI** (June 1956), 245-250.

Articulation Tests

Blanton-Stinchfield Articulation Test. C. H. Stoelting Co., Chicago. (Contains 100 sounds with 100 test words and standardized pictures.)

Bryngelson-Glaspey Picture Test. Scott, Foresman and Co., Chicago. (Contains set of pictures and names of objects which test sounds in the three positions.)

Clark Picture Phonetic Inventory. Communication Foundation, Box 8865, University Park Station, Denver. (Provides for recording of sound substitutions, distortions, and omissions. Also provides for testing of vowels and diphthongs.)

Developmental Articulation Test. (Revised) Robert J. Hejna. Speech Materials Co., Box 366, Storrs, Conn. (Contains 26 picture cards designed to determine articulatory development of children. Sounds tested in three positions on a developmental scale ranging from 3 to 8 years.)

Laradon Articulation Scale. Laradon Hall, East 51st Street and Lincoln, Denver, Colorado. (Contains 90 items based on M. C. Templin's normative data.)

Templin-Darley Screening and Diagnostic Tests of Articulation. Mildred C. Templin and Frederick L. Darley. Bureau of Educational Research and Service, Extension Division, State University of Iowa, Iowa City, Iowa. (Contains 57 cards with 176 black and white drawings. The first 16 cards contain 50 screening items. Has lists of test words and sentences for use with older subjects.)

Auditory Discrimination Tests

Auditory Discrimination Test. Joseph M. Wepman. 950 East 59th Street, Chicago 37, Ill. (Tests to determine child's ability to recognize fine differences that exist between sounds in American English. Measures ability to hear accurately.)

A Picture Type Speech-Sound Discrimination Test. W. Pronovost and C. Dumbleton. *Journal of Speech and Hearing Disorders,* XVIII

(1953), 266. (This test is based on pictures with word pairs phonetically balanced so that only one sound varies in each word of a pair.)

Templin Auditory Discrimination Tests. Mildred C. Templin. In *Certain Language Skills in Children*. Minneapolis: University of Minnesota Press, 1957, 159.

Problems

1. Give the tests on Pages 182-185 to four children. How many of the children appear to have articulatory difficulties?

2. Give the test on sound discrimination from one of the sources suggested on Page 208 to five children of the same age. Indicate differences in their levels of ability.

3. Visit a high school or elementary school class. Indicate how many articulatory defects you heard and the kind of defects they were.

4. Visit a class conducted by a speech therapist. List the substitutions, omissions, or distortions of sounds of one of the observed children.

5. If a case history of a child with an articulatory defect is available to you in a school or clinic, check from it the information relative to the child's intelligence, hearing ability, emotional health, and structural abnormalities of the speaking mechanism.

6. Read and report on one of the following references: 3, 10, 11, 14, 16, 23, 29, 35, 47a, 51, 55, 62, or 67.

7. Plan and have a group discussion on the relationship of reading, spelling, and articulatory difficulties.

11

Defects of

Articulation—11

Treatment of Articulatory Difficulties

WE HAVE already discussed the possible causes for articulatory difficulties. Some of these causes point to the need for the assistance of other specialists in solving the problems of the youngster with an articulatory difficulty. The teacher, his supervisor, principal, and the speech correctionist must be aware of this need, for the child's defective articulation may be but the symptom of another difficulty.

Finding the Cause

Both the teacher and the correctionist take into account the stage of development of the child. The child of six who substitutes a *w*[w] for an *l*[l] is probably in no need of immediate speech help, for in all likelihood maturity alone will take care of the difficulty. But when a child of the same age confuses *p*[p] and *b*[b], he is in need of help, because by six years of age he should be distinguishing accurately between these two sounds. As the child is learning to speak, he frequently omits sounds, distorts them, or substitutes one sound for another. These conditions in the young child are often part of a particular step in his development. The teacher and the correctionist must decide whether a child needs speech therapy. In the preceding chapter we discussed the part that maturation plays in articulation and cited the studies which take it into account in making a prognosis on an articulatory defect.

Because in some instances the child's speaking mechanism may be inadequate, the correctionist should observe it. He finds out whether the child has an underbite, overbite, or malocclusion that is an obstacle to his making certain sounds easily. As a result of his examination, he may recommend the child's seeing his dentist or orthodontist. The importance of organic factors should not be over-emphasized. As noted in the previous chapter, many children with oral anomalies such as marked overbites nevertheless do articulate proficiently. In many instances oral structural deviations constitute a contributing rather than a sole cause for speech difficulties. The correctionist also examines the child's health record to see whether another medical problem exists or has existed. The incidence of such problems as polio, cleft palate, cerebral palsy, or a thyroid deficiency may appear on his record. Furthermore, when obvious difficulty with muscular coordination or when symptoms such as constant colds or listlessness suggest a poor physical condition, the correctionist refers the child to his doctor through the health officials of the school.

When an emotional difficulty causes or partly causes the defective speech of a child, he may or may not respond to treatment for the articulatory disorder alone. If he does respond, the symptom, but not the cause, may be removed. In such instances, the school psychologist helps the child; his help may come before the child's speech correction or be given concurrently with it. The psychologist administers intelligence and personality tests to the child that assist the other persons who are teaching him to understand him and his problems. He advises those teaching the child how to handle him. Frequently the psychologist works with the child himself and with his parents to help them better understand themselves and those around them. With the aid of the psychologist, their adjustment to one another and to society improves.

No obvious reason for the many articulatory errors of an eight-year-old girl of average intelligence was evident. But as the school psychologist talked with the family, he found the mother to be oversolicitous and a sister, four years older, overprotective. The mother, confined to a wheel chair, wanted both girls to do well and set very high standards for them. She was a kind, likeable person, anxious to do all she could for her children. The psychologist conferred with the mother and helped the teacher and the correctionist to understand the child and the parents. He suggested to all three ways of assisting the child to develop self-confidence. The child began to take and accept responsibility. The older sister learned to let the younger child work out her own problems and to allow her to play and live with other youngsters more normally. Concurrently with the psychological help, the speech correctionist worked with the child's speech and the teacher reinforced the work. The psychologist's help made the work of both the correctionist and the teacher more effective. Not all children and perhaps not even most children with articulatory defects are so badly adjusted that they need help from a psychologist. Many of them use incorrect sounds simply because of faulty learning. When needed, however, psychological help is important and uniquely effective.

Interpreting the Articulatory Test

The examiner gains considerable information about the child's articulatory difficulty through testing. He finds out which sounds are omitted or distorted and what sounds are substituted for what other sounds. He discovers whether the deviant sounds occur at the beginning or end of syllables, whether they are incorrect in a blend, and whether they are ever correct. For instance, the sound may be correct in all but a blend. He learns whether the child can say the sound accurately in nonsense syllables. For example, he says to the child who does not make *k* correctly, "Repeat after me."

kay may	[ke me]
meekeem	[mi kim]
fawk	[fɔk]

When the child makes the sound correctly when substituting it for another sound, when he makes it correctly in certain positions, or when he makes it accurately in nonsense syllables, retraining is obviously easier.

The correctionist considers various other factors. For example, he finds out whether the sounds the child is missing are those that he should have acquired early or late. This information helps him to determine in part the influence of maturity. He checks to see whether or not the sounds the child says incorrectly are those readily visible. He learns whether they are high- or low-frequency sounds, for a hearing loss may cause the lack of perception of these sounds for a particular individual. He ascertains whether other members of the same family make the same substitutions, distortions, or omissions.

Finally, the examiner finds out which incorrect or omitted sounds influence the child's pattern of speech the most. Bud, a ten-year-old boy who made a *th*[θ] sound for *s*[s], said, "The kith thay I talk like a thithy. My th'th you know." He realized that his speech sounded out of place. This boy, who liked to box, ride a bike fast, and play baseball, was "all boy." Although he said *t*[t] and *d*[d] for *th*[θ] and *th*[ð], *t*[t] and *d*[d] for *ch*[tʃ] and *j*[dʒ], *w*[w] for *l*[l] and *r*[r], he himself was most concerned about his *s*[s]. To his listeners the *w*[w] for *l*[l] and *r*[r] was also a part of the "sissy speech." Bud went on to tell the correctionist that almost every word has an *s* in it; he pointed out that he lived on Sycamore Street. In this instance, the correctionist attacked the *s*[s] first. Bud was so strongly motivated that his improvement was rapid.

Some sounds occur more frequently than others. Mader (54) indicates the relative frequency of consonant sounds in the speech of children in the primary grades. Five sounds, *n*[n], *t*[t], *d*[d],

$r[r]$, and $s[s]$, make up 40 percent of the total occurrence of all sounds.

The factors just mentioned help the therapist to determine the order in which the child and he will attack the sounds. In general, the correctionist works first with the sounds the child can correct most easily, for success brings approval and a feeling of well-being to the child. As the child hears his correct speech recorded, he is happy. Sometimes, however, the sound most easily corrected is not the sound that distorts the child's speech the most—or it is not the sound about which the child is most concerned. In such cases the therapist and the teacher use their best judgment.

Motivation for Correction of Sounds

Not all children are as strongly motivated as Bud, the ten-year-old lisper. Some children do not even know that they are making sounds incorrectly. Others seemingly do not care. As in all learning, children must want to speak acceptably. The classroom teacher, particularly in the lower grades, can build an attitude that acceptable speech, like good manners, is a personal asset. After a speech correctionist had worked several years with both children and teachers in a small school system, the principal of the school said, "I am *most* pleased with the improvement of speech at the basketball games. The boys and girls sound grown up." The comment not only reflected the attitude of the principal and his teachers but also showed that their attitudes had influenced the children.

Because children do not hear themselves accurately, a recording device proves helpful. At first, they may not believe their own ears, but as they listen to the recordings of the speech of others, they become convinced that the recording of their own speech is accurate. When for the first time a seventh-grade girl heard herself making $f[f]$ and $v[v]$ for $th[\theta]$ and $[\eth]$, she did not believe that it was herself speaking. As she became convinced that the recording was accurate, she was astonished and hurt. She wailed, "Nobody ever told me." As she was strongly motivated and intelligent, she improved rapidly. When she left the school, her teacher offered her the record on which her speech was recorded. Her response, "I don't ever want to remember I talked like that," was revealing.

Correcting the Sound

Cases the Classroom Teacher Handles

When the distorted or incorrect sound is the result of structural or organic difficulty, the classroom teacher needs the help of the speech correctionist. For example, if the malocclusion of the teeth is such that a wide space is apparent between the two sets of teeth, the classroom teacher will rely on the correctionist to teach the *s*. The correctionist will teach the child a compensatory way of making the sound. He will find out how the child attempts to produce the sound and discover what structures the child does have that he could use for the essential mechanics of the sound. By explaining to him how to make the sound, using a mirror, and showing him how to manipulate his mechanism, the therapist helps the child to make the sound. For such correction, specialized knowledge and training are necessary.

Where, however, the child does not need to be taught compensatory movements and where he can make the sound correctly by imitating the teacher's nonsense syllable, the teacher can retrain him. But the teacher must be careful to remember that his own way of making a sound may be unorthodox and that variations occur in the making of a sound. *S* for example, may be made with the tongue pointing to the teeth ridge or to a point behind the lower teeth. In fact, the teacher must have training and practice before working with children with speech difficulties. Furthermore, it is advisable that the classroom teacher's speech correction work be done under the supervision of a correctionist.

Steps in Correcting the Defective Sound

The steps in correcting the defective sound frequently are:

1. Teaching the child to recognize both his error and the correct sound.

2. Teaching the correct sound in syllables.

3. Teaching the correct sound in a limited number of commonly used words.

4. Teaching the child to carry over the correction into his everyday speech.

Teaching the Child to Recognize His Error and to Perceive the Correct Sound

As preparation for this step, teaching the child to recognize his error and the correct sound, the correctionist may have to teach the child to listen carefully to discriminate between sounds and the teacher may reinforce the learning. Not all children with defective articulation need this training, but many seemingly do. Tests for ability to discriminate are found in Van Riper's *Speech Correction: Principles and Practice* (65), in an article by Templin, "A Study of the Sound Discrimination Ability of Elementary School Pupils," found in the *Journal of Speech Disorders* (61), in Templin's *Certain Language Skills in Children* (60), and in Berry and Eisenson's *Speech Disorders* (43).

LISTENING GAMES. Any number of games help teach the child to listen more carefully. These games are adaptable to classroom use. All children can profit from training in auditory discrimination. A game that can be played in primary grades is one in which the children guess who is speaking. One child is the caller. All the others put their heads down on their tables. As the caller tiptoes around the room, he taps one child. The child who is tapped raises his head and says aloud, "He tapped me." The caller then calls on someone to guess who was tapped. If the child guesses correctly, he is the caller. If not, the caller calls on different children until someone does guess who was tapped.

A similar game is one in which a child is seated in the middle of the room with his head down. Another child comes up, rings a bell, and says, "I am ringing your bell." The child who is seated guesses who rang the bell. This game can also be played with sides, each side trying to guess the larger number of bell ringers accurately.

Another type of listening game is one in which children indicate whether sounds are alike or different. When some of the children do not know the meaning of "alike" and "different," the teacher demonstrates and explains the concepts of the two terms. He may then strike each of two glasses containing different amounts of water and ask, "Are the sounds alike or different?" He follows with pairs of other sounds: hitting a block of wood and a piece of iron; ringing two different kinds of bells; ringing the same bell twice. Finally, he may use pairs of nonsense syllables such as: *ray, way; ray, ray; fay, kay; thee, zee; zee, zee; mow, now; mow, mow.*

Games can also emphasize particular sounds, for the child with a defective sound needs to be bombarded with the sound, to hear it in as many different words and situations as possible. Pictures, whose subjects' names contain the sound, may be hidden around the room. For example, if a child makes *k* and *g* incorrectly, pictures of candy, gum, a wagon, a pig, a gate, and a garden may be hidden. Or the children may play the game where they are going on a trip, taking articles beginning with a particular sound. Various members of one group were going to take silver, a spoon, a sled, a sweater, socks, a slip, and stockings; finally one lad decided to take a circus along. Emphasis is on the sound and not the spelling of the word. Sometimes a teacher places a large picture on a bulletin board and the children find all names of objects on it that begin with a particular sound, or they find all the objects that have names with a particular sound in them.

Teachers take children on "listening walks." The children take a walk, listen, come back, and tell each other all the sounds they heard. Members of one group heard the following sounds: the squeak of the tires as a car went around a corner quickly, the click when gas is poured into a tank of a car at a gas station, the burr of the airplanes, the chug, chug of the slow train, the rustle of leaves being blown in a street, the clink of a coin being dropped on the sidewalk, and the buzz of a bee going to get honey from a flower.

STORIES THAT EMPHASIZE LISTENING. Stories that stress

sounds can be used in a number of ways to further the child's auditory perception: After the teacher has read the story, the students can discuss it and its sounds or different children may make the sounds as the teacher rereads the story. Or the stories may motivate the children to listen for similar sounds in their own environment. Many such stories are available: Lois Lenski's *The Little Fire Engine* (Oxford Press, 1946) includes the noises of the alarm bell, the engine starting, the bell on the fire engine, the siren, water, and the squirting of water. Helen Sewell's *Blue Barns* (Macmillan, 1933) is the story of two white geese that contains the calls of many animals. Alvin Tresselt's *Rain Drop Splash* (Lothrop, Lee and Shepard, 1946) gives all the sounds of the splashing of the rain. Margaret Brown's *Shhh Bang, A Whispering Book* (Harper, 1949) wakes up a whispering town with a bang. Margaret Wise Brown has also written a series of books about a little dog Muffin who hears sounds in all sorts of places. These books include *The Country Noisy Book, The Seashore Noisy Book, The City Noisy Book, The Quiet Noisy Book, The Noisy Book,* and *The Summer Noisy Book* (Harper), all of which are geared for the age group of four through eight. Sounds also play an important role in Berta and Elmer Hader's *Cock-a-Doodle Do* (Macmillan), Phyllis McGinley's *All Around the Town* (Lippincott), and Petersham's *The Rooster Crows* (Macmillan). Through the use of these books a teacher can help develop auditory perception in his students.

Some books have been especially prepared for listening in speech correction. Zedler's *Listening for Speech Sounds* (Harper, 1950) and Scott and Thompson's *Talking Time* (Webster, 1951) represent this category. For instance, *Talking Time* contains rhymes which indicate that a particular sound occurs in one word but not in another. Through such procedures, children are motivated to listen for sounds.

AUDIO-VISUAL AIDS TO LISTENING. As is the case of books, some records are on the market which, while not especially prepared for speech correction, do prove very helpful in emphasizing listening to sounds. Teachers frequently use these records. Two inexpensive Little Golden Records, *Choo Choo Train* and *Tootle,* containing many sounds the trains make, suggest ways to listen to trains, cars, and planes. The Children's Record Guild puts out *Let's Help Mommy* which includes a variety of household noises. *Aural Imagery* (American Book Company) also emphasizes listening to sounds in general. A series of three records *The Sounds Around Us* (Scott, Foresman), especially prepared to teach sound discrimination, gives sounds of the house, farm, and town.

Several other records are designed specifically for motivating listening and are used mainly by speech correctionists. Van Riper's *Fun With Speech* (Encyclopedia Britannica Films), Mikalson's *Speech Development Records for Children* (Pacific Records Co., Pasadena), and Larsen's *Consonant Sound Discrimination* (Indiana University Audio-Visual Center) teach better auditory discrimination. *The Down Town Story* by Helen Gene Purdy (Folkway Records, 117 W. 46th Street, New York City 26) trains auditory perception of young children. Bresnaham and Pronovost's *Let's Listen* (Ginn and Co.) develops speech sound awareness and promotes a desire to improve articulation. For the immature child *The Speech Initiation Babble Record* (Children's Music Center, 2858 W. Pico Blvd., Los Angeles), using familiar situations, presents beginning speech sounds and provides stimulation of early speech development.

Two film strips give practice in the discrimination among sounds. *Film Strip for Practice in Phonetic Skills* (Scott, Foresman) gives practice in rhyme and consonant sounds. L. B. Scott's *Talking Time* (Webster) creates an awareness of consonant sounds through visual, auditory, and kinesthetic approaches. Both the teacher and correctionist may make use of these film strips.

The speech correctionist works hard to get children to listen to the way other people make particular sounds. Normally the child with the articulatory defect listens to comprehend; that is, he is listening for ideas and not for sounds. In fact, most of us do just this. But the child with defective articulation must be taught to listen for sounds as well as for ideas, for he needs this stimulation to correct his own inaccurate sounds. In encouraging the child to listen, the teacher and the correctionist stress listening to all sounds —and then to particular sounds. Sounds must be made important, for children must perceive them. Since the teacher is with the child over much longer periods, since stimulation to listen can be achieved in a classroom situation, and since it is beneficial to all children, the teacher often plans her work to include it.

In addition to hearing and recognizing the acceptable sound, the child must be able to identify it. The correctionist may make the unacceptable sound and then incorporate both it and the acceptable sound in words or phrases, whereupon the child is asked to identify the unacceptable sound. The teacher may reinforce this training. For example, he may indicate the names of pictures of articles, sometimes with the sound correct and sometimes with the sound incorrect, as he shows them to the child. When the teacher speaks the words with the sound made incorrectly, the child indicates that the sound is incorrect. Many teachers and correctionists have found it helpful to name the correct and incorrect sounds. For example, the $r[r]$ may be the airplane sound, the $s[s]$ the snake sound, the $z[z]$ the bee sound, the $th[\theta]$ the air sound, and the $l[l]$ the lullaby sound. Or the $r[r]$ may be a roar, the $s[s]$ a hiss, the $z[z]$ a buzz, the $k[k]$ a cough, the $g[g]$ a gurgle, and $ch[t\int]$ a chug. Such names help to make more vivid the auditory impression of the sounds. By such means the child learns to recognize both the correct and the incorrect sound. With older children the procedure is less a game. The speech correctionist, after making both the unacceptable and acceptable sounds, explains the characteristics of both. The child listens carefully and then indicates which of a pair of sounds, made by the correctionist, is acceptable. If he can, he makes both the acceptable and the unacceptable sound.

At this stage, recording the child's speech is a good teaching device. The child hears the words as he says them. He is frequently able by listening to his own recording to recognize the errors he is making.

Teaching the Acceptable Sound

In some instances, the child may not need to be taught how to make a sound. As he has learned to listen, to discriminate between the acceptable and unacceptable sound, he may have also learned to make the sound acceptably in all phonetic contexts. When he has, the only remaining problem is for him to incorporate the sound in his speech. In such cases, the classroom teacher who has had speech correction training may act as correctionist to help the child to be consistent in using the newly acquired sound.

In other instances, however, the child, even though he hears the unacceptable sound and can identify it, cannot make it accurately in all or in some phonetic contexts. In these cases the correctionist must teach the child to make the sound. Since his parents, teachers, and classmates have already stimulated him with words, phrases, and the sound itself and he has failed to respond, the correctionist must try other modes of attack. To this child wope [wop] for rope [rop] sounds right. He has always made a *w*[w] for *r*[r] and the habit is firmly established. He must learn the new sound thoroughly first in simple syllabic combinations, then in words and phrases. The sound throughout must be a vivid stimulus and, as a result, it is repeated and prolonged.

The correctionist first attempts to teach the child to make the sound through stimulation and imitation. In teaching the child to make the *th*[θ], he may tell him that this is the air sound and that air is being let out. Then he makes the *th*[θ] sound for the child. Together they may make a game of the sound with a small car. The pump (a piece of string) lets air into the tires and as long as the string is attached to the tire, the air goes in to the accompaniment of the *th*[θ] sound. In many instances, the child will learn the sound from such stimulation as this.

Where he does not, the correctionist may tell the child how to make the sound. While he looks in a mirror, the correctionist tells him that in the *th*[θ] sound, the point of his tongue is at the place where his upper teeth bite, and that a stream of air is coming out.

The child feels the stream of air coming from the correctionist's mouth. Looking in the mirror, the child follows the directions. He, therefore, feels where his mechanism is to go and imitates where the teacher has placed his mechanism. At times, the correctionist uses diagrams to show children where to place parts of their articulatory mechanism.

Sometimes the correctionist begins with a sound the child makes correctly and, using its placement as a basis, teaches a new sound. The child may make a t[t] correctly but use a th[θ] for the s[s] sound. The correctionist asks him to say tar [tɑr]; usually the t is made with the tip of the tongue on the teeth ridge. He then asks the child to keep his tongue in the same position for s[s] as for t[t] except that he must slightly drop the point of his tongue and say star [star]. The correctionist must also explain that in saying s[s] he must move the tongue tip just a bit away from the teeth ridge to let the air escape. With this instruction, the s[s] sound will frequently be correct. In teaching r[r], the teacher may ask the child to say d[d], draw the tongue back, but maintain the contact the tongue is making, and say the d[d]. The result is often a dr[dr] sound. For those children who have difficulty making an s[s] or r[r] by moving from a sound with an analogous position, the correctionist may well experiment with combinations of sounds made in quite different articulatory positions. For example, he might ask the child to try making the s[s] in combination with a k[k] or p[p].

The correctionist then gives the child opportunities to practice producing his new sound in nonsense syllables. Nonsense syllables are beneficial because, first, the material is completely new with no former associations. Second, the correctionist can keep the syllables simple. The correctionist will need to motivate this practice through games and stories. As a child learns the r sound, the correctionist may well incorporate it into such nonsense syllables as:

ray [re] tay [te]	een [in] eer [ir]	ayr [er]	ahr [ar]
bay [be] ray [re]	eeree [iri] ayray [ere]	owr [or]	awr [ɔr]
row [ro] tow [to]	eemee [imi] eeree [iri]	eer [ir]	
fow [fo] row [ro]			

As the child becomes more proficient, the correctionist makes the syllables more complex.

In the play situation the correctionist usually adds a vowel as ĭ[I], ă[æ], or *ah*[ɑ], since research has shown that syllables and not single sounds are the basic units of articulation, and since research suggests strongly that articulation therapy should be based on the syllable rather than on the isolated sound. The correctionist also usually utilizes the sound in the phonetic context that is made most nearly like the desired sound. A careful detailed analysis of the child's articulatory errors enables him to so utilize the sound.

Different correctionists use different approaches to articulation therapy. Some never use sounds in syllables or in nonsense words, preferring to use meaningful speech. Others, however, do use nonsense syllables. Still others use an eclectic approach—trying various techniques and using what seems to prove successful with the particular child or children. Our experience has been that nonsense syllables are effective in tenacious cases where the child does not respond readily to stimulation of sound and where he holds on to his error. Where the correctionist does use nonsense syllables, the teacher cooperates and reinforces the teaching in a variety of ways.

Practicing nonsense syllables can be fun for an entire class. One way to make the work enjoyable is through telling a story of nonsense animals who make nonsense sounds. The teacher can read the story or make it up as he goes along. Children, who play the parts of the various animals, say the nonsense syllables when the story demands the sound. For example, a teacher made up the following story:

THE ESCAPE OF THE MISHIKIN

Characters: Mishikin who says mish, mish, mish.
Karsikite who says kar, kar, kar.
Liger who says low, low, low.

Once upon a time long ago lived a tiny little mishikin, an animal no bigger than a spider who said_____,_____,_____. He was crawling under a desk in a classroom saying ———, ———, ——————— happily when into the room came a big liger, just like a tiger except he had a big red tail. He growled ———, ———, ——— and frightened the poor little mishikin who whimpered ———, ———, ———————. But the desk was so low that the liger couldn't get his head under to get a good look at the mishikin. The liger roared ———, ———, ——————— and the mishikin cried ———, ———, ——— in fright. The liger poked his head part way under the desk and upset it. When he pushed the desk over, he ———, ———, ——— and the poor little mishikin ———, ———, ———————. The mishikin crawled as fast as he could to a wall and up to the ceiling where the liger couldn't reach him.

The liger was roaring ———, ———, ——— up at the ceiling at the poor little mishikin ———, ———, ———————. In came a karsikite, a pretty little green, yellow, and purple long worm with a long needle sticking from his mouth just like a knitting needle. He said ———, ———, ——————— all the time that he hopped and jumped, for he could go just like lightning. He hopped in, poked his long needle into the liger, saying ———, ———, ——— and hopped away so fast the clumsy liger couldn't catch him. The liger was angry and bellowed ———, ———, ———————. The karsikite thought the liger funny and laughed ———, ———, ———————. All over the room went the big heavy liger after that perky, green, yellow, and purple karsikite.

The worm went up to the ceiling with the mishikin. The karsikite ———, ———, ——— and the mishikin ———, ———, ——————————. That's how they laughed. The liger got madder and madder and roared more and more ———, ———, ———————. Then the mishikin took the leg of the karsikite and they crawled down one story, two stories, and off to a field to play leaving the liger, oh so angry ———, ———, ———————. Poor liger!

With older children, the correctionist approaches the problem of teaching an acceptable sound more directly. The high school boy or girl usually accepts his difficulty and realizes that he must improve his speech for social reasons; to achieve his goal, he must concentrate on changing a particular sound. Consequently the high school boy or girl generally responds intelligently to the explanation of the correctionist on how the sound is made, makes more effective use of the audio-visual materials the correctionist supplies, understands the need for such techniques as nonsense syllables, and sees the value of drill. In the instance of older boys and girls, the successful achievement of a particular step is important. As they are successful in one step of the correction, they are anxious to go on to the next step.

Teaching the Correct Sound In Words

The correctionist may use word lists. When he does, the teacher has an opportunity to reinforce the training. As indicated earlier when the child can correct a sound through auditory stimulation alone, the teacher may feel justified in helping him incorporate the sound in words. In such cases the teacher says the word; the child watches, listens, and imitates. Then together they make up a phrase which includes the word. The teacher motivates the child to make up a phrase which he might well use. For example, using the word *game,* the child might say, "I like to play games" or "Screaming, yelling games are best." Or using the word *glad,* the teacher might ask, "What are you glad about?" The child might respond with, "I'm glad for the Good Humor Man," or "I'm glad my Daddy's home." Together the teacher and child might go on to think of all the things they are glad about. Short poems or stories that emphasize particular sounds may also provide topics of conversation for the child and his teacher.

It is important that the correction progress from making sounds in syllables to connected speech. Hahn (48) points out that adults accept their difficulty, discover its nature, desire to improve, and are able to extract the part from the whole while realizing its relationship. Adults know that drill and critical listening are needed. She notes that the same approach used with children often gets lost in "game land." She suggests that the phrase is our usual unit of expression and that the child should talk in phrases purposefully and maintain the rhythm and meaningful inflection of oral expression. She recommends speech therapy designed to: (1) stimulate desire to communicate; (2) help the child discover specific improvement needed; (3) show him a new way to make the sound; and (4) place the corrected sound in the communication of his ideas. An article by Black and Ludwig (44) also points to the dangers of using games and suggests sound criteria for them. We should remember that games must be used purposefully and that this drill is merely a step toward the correction of the sound in useful communication.

WORD LISTS AND SENTENCES FOR DRILL IN CORRECTING ARTICULATORY ERRORS. We have arranged the following exercises in two sections according to difficulty. In the first section the material is for children in the first four grades who have difficulty with particular sounds. We emphasize again that often children must first learn the sound in nonsense syllables and then learn to incorporate it into words. This material is to be used when the child has reached the stage of incorporating the sound into words. In preparing this material we used the list of words compiled according to frequency of the word in general by Thorndike and Lorge (62). In the material for the lower grades all the words are from the first thousand in terms of frequency in general use except where the words are marked by a dagger. Where they are so marked they are from the second thousand. These words have been selected so that the child in the lower grades with defective speech sounds will be trained with words which he will need to know how to pronounce. Thorndike and Lorge point out that the most important use of the list is to guide the teacher in his decision of what words he needs to teach the child so that they will be a permanent part of his stock of word knowledge (62, p. xi).

The words in the second section are taken from the first 6,000 words in terms of frequency of occurrence in general reading matter. According to Thorndike and Lorge, a child in the fifth and sixth grades may well be taught the words occurring with this frequency, provided the words are not adult words. The reading matter in the second section is for children in the upper grades. In the second section, we have purposely limited the words used to those within the first 6,000.

These lists, sentences, and stories are for the use of the classroom teacher. They are not to be turned over to children. Teachers will work with the material in different ways. One teacher may enjoy making up sentences with many *t* words with one youngster. Another may read one of the sentences and from it he and the child will build a story. The teacher will handle the stories included here in a variety of ways. He may read the story and then he and the child may discuss it; or they may add to it; or they may play it. The teacher will use the materials to make the drill on sounds beneficial and interesting. As much as possible, he will encourage the child to say the sounds in words in full sentences and in conversational situations.

Section 1. Exercises for Children in Grades 1-4

t [t]

Initial	Medial	Final
ten	eating	feet
time	history	gate
tire	matter	heart
told	notice	heat
took	until	knight
top	water	want
touch	winter	west
turn	writing	write

1. The captain went to a party for the benefit† of his sailors.†
2. The forty† men arrived at the gate about half past eight.
3. He could not decide whether to buy an automobile† or a boat.
4. The cat did not want to eat the twenty fish.
5. No matter how little you give, give.

A Trip in the Winter

Two little boys, Tom† and John, wanted to take a trip in the winter. One day a snow storm came and their big sister, Mary, told them she would take them out down the street. After they put on their snow suits, they went out into the storm. The trees, houses, and even the streets were covered with snow. The wet snow came down so fast and it was so cold that they decided not to go any farther but to turn and go back home. When they got home, they wrote a note to their aunt to tell her about their cold, cold trip in the wet, wet snow.

d [d]

Initial	Medial	Final
dare	hundred	food
dark	Indian	found
day	industry	glad
decide	under	hand
deep	wider	wind
did	window	wide
doctor	windy	wood
down	wonder	world

1. He did not dare to demand his dinner.
2. He took his dog† to the doctor.
3. She dreamed† of a dozen† new dresses, all red.
4. She decided to go to bed.
5. The kind lady let us play in her garden.

NINE DREAMS

One day nine little children were deciding what they would like to have if some kind lady or man would make their dreams come true. Jim† would like real live Indians to play with. Dan† wanted peace in the world. Dick† wished for good food for everybody.† Mary wanted a sand† pile† in her own back yard. Tom† would like to have a window full of colored glass. Elizabeth† wanted to be able to dance like her mother. Arthur wished for a dog. They knew they would not find the kind lady or man who would give them what they wanted but they liked telling each other about their dreams.

ng* [ŋ]

Medial	Final
thinking	being
England	belong
English	sing
longing	song
ringing	wing
singing	wrong
single	thing

1. He is going to England soon to stay for a long time.

* This sound does not occur in the English language at the beginning of words.

2. He is singing his favorite† song.
3. Do you belong to the club that meets in the morning?
4. You are selling the wrong thing.
5. Do you think you will go to the bank in the morning?

k [k]

Initial	*Medial*	*Final*
call	article	lake
carry	because	like
keep	include	look
kept	market	make
kill	record	mark
kind	require	milk
question	second	music
quick	taken	neck

1. The camp was kept quiet† during rest period.
2. The captain carried the case of food.
3. Do not mark the book.
4. Your uncle took a ride in the sky in a plane.†
5. Our cat can talk, answer questions, and count.

THE SICK PRINCE

The King, Queen, and the Prince lived high on a hill in a castle.† The King was a funny† man who loved to laugh and laugh. The Queen was a kind, sweet lady who loved to smile and smile. The Prince was a happy little fellow who loved to play and play. But one day the little fellow became very, very sick. The funny King didn't laugh any more. The kind, sweet Queen had a hard time smiling. The little Prince didn't play and play.

The King called all kinds of Doctors to Court. But they could not find out what was wrong with the Prince. The King began to sigh† The Queen began to cry. The little Prince just stayed in bed.

One day a new doctor, called Doctor John, came to Court. He said to take the sick little prince to the lake, put him in the water twice while music played, and then give him a big glass of milk. The King and Queen took the little Prince to the lake, put him in twice while music played, and gave him some milk. Quickly the Prince became well.

The funny King again laughed and laughed. The kind, sweet Queen smiled and smiled. The Prince played and played, and they all had a happy, happy time.

g [g]

Initial	Medial	Final
gain	again	big
game	agree	bag
garden	begin	dog
girl	finger	egg
give	forget	flag†
glad	longer	leg
gold	regard	
gone	stronger	

1. Take your dog to the gate.
2. Cut the grass in the garden again, please.
3. The girls grew gold flowers in the garden.
4. Don't forget to buy me a dozen† eggs.
5. Give her a glass of milk with an egg in it.

RAIN

No rain, no rain, no rain!
I'm sad,† sad,† sad,†
For the brown, brown grass
Will die, die, die.

Rain, rain, rain!
I'm glad, glad, glad
For the green, green grass
Will grow, grow, grow.

f [f]

Initial	Medial	Final
face	affair	enough
field	afraid	half
fire	afternoon	herself
fish	before	laugh
fly	different	life
food	fifty	roof
foot	offer	wife
fruit	often	

1. On this farm the farmer raises fruit.
2. I have five fingers on my hand.

3. Finally in the afternoon they found a place to fish.
4. Before we go, my friend must clean the floor.
5. The officer laughed when we refused the soft fruit.
6. Fish! Fish! Fish!
   One for thirty cents.
   Two for fifty cents.
   Fish! Fish! Fish!

THE FIVE WISHES

One day I met a man who looked like a fish. He told me that I could have any five wishes I wanted if I found a real red fruit. One afternoon I found a real red apple.† When I showed it to the man who looked like a fish, he asked me to decide what five wishes I wanted. Finally, I decided on these five:

I want to fly and follow the birds.
I want to live a long, long life.
I want never to be afraid.
I want to become famous.
I want to grow millions and millions of flowers.

Now life is fun! I'm never afraid when I fly like a bird. I grow flowers by the million. And just imagine!† I'll live a long, long famous life. Just imagine!

v [v]

Initial	*Medial*	*Final*
valley	cover	arrive
value	discover	believe
very	evening	five
view	ever	gave
village	everything	have
visit	heavy	leave
voice	never	love
vote	river	move

1. In the evening we went down to the river to look at the view.
2. We are going to visit the village.
3. They traveled in the valley.
4. He divides his cake† with his brother.
5. We are going to leave and move to a new village.

Traveling to the Wonderful Villages

One day I discovered that travel can be a wonderful adventure.† I was wandering† down the valley by the river, and decided I'd take my boat and visit a village along the river. The first village was all silver. The houses were silver. The stores were silver. The churches were silver. The streets were silver. It was good to see everything shining.

Because the visit was such a wonderful adventure, I decided to visit one more village. In the next village, I heard voices of children. I found seven of them around a corner playing King, Queen, and the Royal† Court. They voted for me for King. I loved being King. We all had a good time. My visit over, I wandered† back up the valley, up the river home.

s [s]

Initial	Medial	Final	Blends
safe	also	face	sky
seat	answer	France	sleep
sell	consider	house	small
silver	decide	kiss	smile
sing	escape	loss	snow
sink	herself	miss	spend
sister	person	peace	stand
sit	success	place	star

1. His sister listened to his story about the sea.
2. I sit in the second seat.
3. He used sand† for salt and was very sorry.†
4. In the spring the snow all goes away.
5. He sang a song about the sky.

Mary Likes Summer Time

Mary likes the summer time because she plays out almost every day. John, Mary's friend, and Mary play hospital;† and they take care of all the sick children. John is the doctor and Mary is the nurse.† On very sunny days Mary's sister takes her to the sea to swim† and to play in the sand.† Some days she builds a very special house in the sand† with shells† for windows. Once in a while her sister takes her sailing over the sea. Mary likes summer better than fall, winter, or spring. She likes summer best of all.

z* [z]

Medial	Final
business	does
busy	news
easy	nose
husband	size
music	surprise
newspaper	use
thousand	was
visit	wise

1. His cousin† was not given a reason for visiting Elizabeth.†
2. Her husband surprised her with roses.
3. He read the magazine† and the newspapers even though he was busy.
4. She does all the easy exercises.†
5. He was wise to make his business visit now.

sh [ʃ]

Initial	Medial	Final
shade	condition	accomplish†
shape	especially	brush†
share	issue	dish†
she	machine	finish
ship	mention	fish
shoe	nation	rush
short	ocean	wish
show	washing	wash

1. Finish your work at the shop.
2. The ship sails over the ocean.
3. Be especially sure to share your good news.
4. I wish I could fish all day.
5. Wash your dishes well.

The Sad Ship

The ship went sailing over the ocean.
The ship was in a very sad condition.
She dashed† and dashed† and dashed† some more
Then rushed and rushed and rushed ashore.

* No words beginning with z appear in the first 2,000 words.

zh* [ʒ]
division†
measure
pleasure
treasure†
usual†
usually

1. Usually he takes pleasure in measuring his goods.
2. They found the treasure† and agreed on its division.†

l [1]

Initial	Medial	Final	Blends
last	almost	fall	black
late	believe	fell	blue
laugh	belong	ill	clear
lead	family	hall	clean
length	follow	hole	flag†
let	million	hill	floor
letter	reply	mail	play

1. These flowers are yellow and blue.
2. The girl fell sound asleep.†
3. Tell me about your travels.
4. She likes to drink milk.
5. He plays police.

NIGHT

The silvery night rolls along.
The trees and flowers sing a song.
The stars and moon play a tune.**
The dawn† comes gently and too soon.

AUTOMOBILES

Millions of automobiles travel along,
Dashing† and rushing and racing around,

* The words listed below are the only words found in the first 2,000 of the Thorndike-Lorge list. No word in the English language begins with the *zh* sound. Words containing *zh* are used infrequently in the English language.
** The word "tune" is listed in the group of the third thousand words.

Covering millions and millions of miles of ground.
Powerful,† wonderful, and oh! so very strong!

th [θ]

Initial	*Medial*	*Final*
thank	Arthur	both
thin	authority†	beneath†
thing	method	earth
think	nothing	health
thirty	something	north
third		path
thousand		south
three		worth

1. Both Arthur and you are to find something worth doing.
2. Three thousand and thirty persons from this town think nothing of going South.
3. Thank Arthur for finding the North path.
4. Your health will be better in the South.
5. This month I'll try a new method.

th [ð]

Initial	*Medial*	*Final*
than	another	clothe
that	brother	
their	either	
them	mother	
these	father	
this	further	
those	gather	
therefore	neither	

1. Their mother and father gathered their clothes together.
2. Neither of the brothers wanted another ball.
3. These clothes are either too small or too big.
4. The brother, mother, and father went further than they planned.
5. I do not like the hot weather either.

r [r]

Initial	*Medial*	*Final*	*Blends*
write	America	dear*	break
rain	arrive	door*	cross
ran	article*	ear*	dress

r[r]
Initial

Initial	Medial	Final	Blends
rate	Europe	fear*	friend
rather	iron	fire*	ground
rise	morning*	four*	prince
river	marry	hear*	spring
road	Mary	wear*	true

* In some areas such as New England, the *r* sound in these words is not articulated.

1. They rode rapidly to the bridge.
2. They required water to put out the fire.
3. Mary is going to marry John tomorrow morning.
4. Your friend grew green grass even when there was no rain.
5. Did you really dream that you had to drink three glasses of water?

MARY'S REPORT

Mary gave a report on the American people and the British people. She explained to the class how the British have a queen and how the Americans have a president. She brought pictures to show the class. She told the children how the British live near Europe, across the sea from the Americans, and that the Americans and British are good friends. The children enjoyed hearing her report.

ch[tʃ]
Initial

Initial	Medial	Final
chain	catching	each
chair	kitchen	inch
chance	picture	much
change	reaching	rich
charge	marching	speech
check	teacher	such
children	teaching	teach
church	touching	touch

1. The children went to church each Sunday.†
2. When the child tried to catch the ball, he fell off the chair.

j[dʒ]
Initial

Initial	Medial	Final
general	danger	average†
gentle	enjoy	bridge

j[dʒ]

Initial	Medial	Final
job	imagine†	edge
John	judging	engage†
join	object	knowledge
joy	soldier	large
judge	stranger	manage†
just	suggest	village

JOHN AND HIS CLUB

John joined a club of little soldiers. Jim,† his big brother, suggested the idea to him when John reached the age of eight. John was soon chosen† to be the general. Because he did a good job as general, he enjoyed being general. He led his soldiers on long marches where they met many dangers. When he left the village to go to a new town, he left his club of little soldiers behind him.

Section 2. Exercises for Children in Grades 5-7

t [t]

Initial	Medial	Final
tablet	attic	advocate
tan	attire	ant
taper	automatic	absent
temper	attribute	acute
tenant	artistic	adapt
tenderness	bitterly	bait
tailor	bulletin	bet
telegram	courtesy	bite
tight	entertain	boast
tire	fatal	crept
tomato	fountain	frost
tune	kettle	part
turnip	literary	quiet
tutor	retire	scant

1. Albert ate turtle soup, steak, turnip, tomato, and potatoes for dinner.
2. He took attendance at the first meeting of the class.
3. The debate centered around the advisability of buying a fountain.
4. For the most part he wrote editorials about such topics as rent control, the British foreign policy, and the treatment of minority groups.
5. The tutor translated the text for his students.

d [d]

Initial	*Medial*	*Final*
dairy	abandon	bead
daisy	academy	beard
dale	additional	bird
dart	amendment	comprehend
daze	candidate	confide
deaf	candy	coward
deadly	endeavor	blade
deliberate	ending	blind
diameter	gardener	creed
dispute	hidden	fed
distinct	identical	fade
doll	ponder	Ford
dot	medal	lend
dramatic	riddle	pad

1. Teddy stood his ground.
2. The play was a comedy about a gardener and his hound.
3. The admiral abandoned the ship when it was doomed for destruction.
4. He pulled at his beard and laughed hard.
5. The builder finished the barn by midnight.

k [k]

Initial	*Medial*	*Final*
cabinet	academy	awake
cable	Africa	ask
camera	background	brake
candle	bacon	brick
cart	baker	buck
chemist	broadcast	clock
chorus	conquer	crack
combat	decade	creek
courtesy	dictate	dramatic
creek	echo	fork
cripple	exact	frock
Kate	maker	lark
kick	lecture	look
keeper	locality	relic

1. The speaker of the House kept his group under control successfully and skillfully.

2. The Academy gave the scholar an award for his study of Africa.
3. Because of her artistic background, Kay did a remarkable piece of decoration in the kitchen.
4. Skim the cream off the milk, please.
5. He ate so much turkey that he felt uncomfortable.

g [g]

Initial	Medial	Final
gallant	dragon	beg
gang	dignity	bug
gasoline	ignorance	catalogue
gasp	legal	dig
ghastly	magazine	dog
gift	Margaret	dug
glisten	neglect	egg
globe	Negro	fatigue
glove	signature	fig
glue	signify	frog
goal	stagger	hog
gold	tiger	pig
grain	ugly	rogue
guide	undergo	tug

1. The beggar begged at the gateway to the house.
2. He ordered a bugle from a catalogue.
3. The gold glistened in the sun.
4. Margaret neglected to buy the magazine.
5. His goal was to own a hundred hogs.

*ng**[ŋ]

Medial	Final
alongside	bang
amongst	cling
anguish	concerning
ankle	cunning
anxiety	finding
banker	flattering
banquet	fling
donkey	flung

* This sound does not occur in the English language at the beginning of words.

ng*[ŋ]

Medial	Final
Englishman	knowing
hanging	lasting
hunger	lining
inking	longing
mingle	pang
sinking	rang

1. The singer was singing the spinning song.
2. He got the string in such a tangle that he had to throw it away.
3. Duncan is the Englishman who works at the bank.
4. He sprained his ankle on the way to the banquet.
5. He was cleaning out the trunk.

sh[ʃ]

Initial	Medial	Final
chivalry	accomplishment	cherish
shabby	condition	diminish
sheriff	cushion	foolish
shield	essential	harsh
shift	hardship	marsh
ship	insure	parish
shirt	intention	publish
shone	mansion	punish
shove	membership	polish
shovel	nation	rash
shrill	patience	relish
shrine	ration	sash
shrink	session	smash
shrug	suspicion	wash

1. His ambition was a foolish one.
2. His wish to shovel snow was to insure his having money to pay for his books.
3. He accepted the invitation to membership in the club.
4. He polished his shoes every day.
5. He wore a clean shirt when he visited the sheriff.

* This sound does not occur in the English language at the beginning of words.

ch[tʃ]

Initial	Medial	Final
chalk	achieve	arch
chant	archer	attach
charity	bachelor	bench
chart	Massachusetts	beseech
cheat	merchandise	birch
cheerful	mischief	bunch
cheese	orchard	coach
childish	preaching	couch
chill	pitching	dispatch
chime	Richmond	ditch
chin	scratching	enrich
chosen	snatching	fetch
chuckle	stretching	hatch
church	treacherous	lunch

1. He spent his childhood in Richmond.
2. He swam the treacherous waters of the channel.
3. The rancher also had a peach orchard.
4. His favorite foods are chocolate cake and cheese.
5. While Charles sat on the bench, John pitched the whole game.

j[dʒ]

Initial	Medial	Final
gem	adjust	allege
generation	angel	avenge
genius	Benjamin	baggage
gently	cordial	besiege
George	digest	bridge
germ	engineer	cabbage
jaw	enjoyment	carriage
jewel	fugitive	engage
John	legion	enlarge
joint	legislature	foliage
joke	lodging	fringe
jolly	logic	luggage

j[dʒ]

Initial	*Medial*	*Final*
joyful	margin	pledge
juice	pigeon	postage
July	prejudice	rage

1. Roger wanted to be a surgeon; George, a clergyman; John, an engineer.
2. Joan is a jolly girl who enjoys a joke.
3. When the magician waved, the jewel jumped out of the package.
4. The voyage ended in tragedy.
5. The legislature adjourned in July.

s [s]

Initial	*Medial*	*Final*		*Blends*
cedar	ascent	base	flax	foster
cigarette	bicycle	bless	inspect	inspire
circus	conserve	brass	install	screen
sack	consume	coarse	screw	skill
Sally	deceive	coax	slap	slate
sample	essay	fierce	sleeve	smite
sandy	facility	fireplace	smoke	snare
sandwich	hillside	fox	snarl	Spaniard
sap	lessen	geese	sparrow	spin
sauce	mason	harness	skin	
sermon	municipal	hopeless	stall	
severe	pencil	immense	starve	
sew	persuade	mouse	stem	
sift	receive	rice	Sweden	
soup	sincere	voice	swung	

1. Sarah fixed soup and sandwiches for lunch.
2. Sally made herself a silk dress with short sleeves for the dance.
3. Sometimes Sam takes his bicycle to school.
4. The house has an immense fireplace in the living room.
5. Lucy announced the results of the baseball game.

z [z]

*Initial**	*Medial*	*Final*
zeal	amazement	abuse

*Only four words beginning with the sound of *z* are listed in the first thousand words in terms of frequency in the Thorndike-Lorge list.

z[z]

Initial	Medial	Final
zero	amusement	accuse
zinc	Brazil	advertise
zone	closet	advise
	crazy	amaze
	deserve	arise
	desirable	arouse
	dissolve	blaze
	frozen	bronze
	grizzly	cheese
	hazard	compose
	invisible	daze
	misery	ours
	noisy	poise
	refusal	sneeze

1. He visited the Roosevelt Museum at Hyde Park.
2. The allies analyzed the situation that arose.
3. He amazed them with his zeal.
4. He composed a poem about a grizzly bear.
5. This salesman sells cheese.

l [1]

Initial	Medial	Final	Blends
laborer	ability	arrival	blessing
lamb	balloon	camel	clever
lately	celebrate	chill	blew
laurel	delightful	detail	blank
leaf	delivery	earl	client
liberal	electrical	fertile	cloak
lily	elephant	hail	flake
liver	failure	hurl	flap
loaf	gallant	kneel	flare
loan	gallon	mule	gladly
lonely	Holland	oatmeal	glare
loom	millionaire	peril	gleam
Lucy	parallel	repeal	glen
lumber	selection	sale	plough
lunch	telegraph	wail	slant

1. Alice sent a telegram to tell her family of her arrival.
2. Walter went to Toledo to play golf.
3. The company built a new kind of elevator.
4. Alfred illustrated the book with pictures of lambs.
5. The salesman persuaded him to replace his telescope.

r [r]

Initial	Medial	Final	Blends
radio	apron	actor*	brace
refrain	barrel	alter	bracelet
refresh	bedroom	boar	break
regarding	ceremony	door	confront
remove	Dorothy	floor	crow
rhyme	embarrass	error	crusade
ribbon	ferry	explore	crush
rifle	horrid	hare	draft
ripe	Irish	horror	dried
robber	jury	pure	frail
runner	marine	peer	Fred
rural	mirror	rare	grab
rust	operate	sore	graceful
rustle	seriously	spear	pray
Ruth	terrific	traitor	proof

1. Fred went after the robber with a rifle.
2. The argument finally ended in agreement.
3. Because he was careless, he broke the mirror that he borrowed.
4. Ralph fixed the radio
5. Ruth lived in a rustic house in a rural area.

th[θ]

Initial	Medial	Final
thankful	Athens	bath
Thanksgiving	author	both
theater	birthday	cloth
thicket	breathless	depth
thirst	cathedral	doth
thirteen	earthquake	Edith
thorn	enthusiasm	hath

* The final r's in these words may not be articulated in certain areas such as New England.

th [θ]

Initial	Medial	Blends
thorough	faithful	hearth
threat	monthly	henceforth
thrill	northeast	mirth
throne	overthrow	ninth
thrust	overthrown	path
thumb	southwest	seventh
thunder	sympathy	wrath

1. At Thanksgiving time they gave thanks for their food.
2. Timothy took thirteen of his friends to the theater.
3. On his seventh birthday, both he and his sister went to the Cathedral.
4. He gave his car a thorough examination monthly.
5. Edith found the path that led to the northeast corner of the island.

th [ð]

Initial	Medial	Blends
than	altogether	bathe
that	bother	smooth
theirs	farther	soothe
themselves	feather	clothe
thereafter	furthermore	
therein	grandfather	
thereof	grandmother	
thereupon	heathen	
they'll	neither	
they're	other	
they've	smoothly	
therewith	unworthy	

1. They sailed their boat smoothly.
2. They wear feathers in their hats.
3. They decided not to bother going farther.
4. That day neither the grandmother nor the grandfather wanted to bathe their dog.
5. Thereafter, they asked their grandson to bathe him.

Another means of drill is playing a game similar to bingo in which children place beans on cards that contain ten or more pictures. The teacher, who has a duplicate set of pictures, shuffles them, holding up first one, then another picture. The child who has the picture of the object that the teacher holds up on his card says its name. Several children with particular sound difficulties can play this game, since the teacher gives them cards with pictures of words that contain their particular sound difficulties. The child who fills his card first calls "Word" and wins the game.

A bus route which involves towns with sounds with which the children have difficulty can be arranged. The bus carries a driver who drives the bus and a hostess who explains the points of interest enroute. A small toy bus travels over the route, which is drawn on the blackboard or on a large sheet of paper. The driver may either chug, chug [tʃʌg|tʃʌg], or bur, bur [bɝ|bɝ], or si, si [si|si] along while the hostess takes care of the passenger. The driver stops, calls the towns, and assists the passengers on and off the bus. If the *chug, chug, bur, bur,* or *si, si* is incorrect, the inspector sends the bus to the garage to be fixed. When the teacher drives, he occasionally says the sound incorrectly so that the children have training in recognizing the incorrect sound.

Another game that children like to play is one for which the teacher has collected pictures of objects the names of which contain the difficult sound. As the child closes his eyes tightly, he puts his finger on one of the pictures which have been arranged on the table. After the teacher has told him about the article, the child guesses what it is. For example, the teacher might say to a child in the first grade, "This is something you eat with." After the child guesses a dish, the teacher might respond with, "You often eat ice cream with it." In all probability the child would then guess *a spoon*. The child then becomes the leader. The teacher closes his eyes and the child tells him about the article to which he is pointing.

When the child works with a correctionist, he may well keep his words, phrases, and sentences in a notebook. These he may show to the teacher who may help him and who on occasion will remind him, "Johnny, there's a word you can say now. Try it again." The teacher will not interrupt a flow of speech in which the child is interested. The teacher's correction will be easy, natural, and casual. No child is able to watch his speech constantly and always incorporate the right sound into words. This process takes time.

Teaching the Child to Carry the Correction Over Into Everyday Speech

When the child incorporates the sound into words easily, he is ready to begin the transfer to his everyday speech. His teacher, correctionist, and parents need to provide as many speaking situations as possible. At this stage the teacher is as important as the correctionist, for she can set up situations wherein the child has many speaking and reading opportunities to incorporate his newly acquired sounds. She tells him that he must think before he makes the sound and that if he makes it inaccurately, the members of the group will wait while he says the word again. After the activity has occurred, she will commend him on his acceptable pronunciations and show him a list of phrases where he did not make the sound acceptably. Sometimes the teacher will ask the correctionist to work on some words and phrases which occur frequently in the classroom work. For instance, one child, working on *s* and at the same time, preparing a report comparing a small town in the suburbs to New York City, needed to pronounce these words: subway, station, supermarket, stores, suburbs, schools, snow, small, success, house, miss, bus, stop, and smooth. Consequently, the correctionist helped the child to say these particular words acceptably. Since the child was excited about her research, it also proved a good topic of conversation in the correction session. The classroom work helped to motivate the improvement.

Creative activities, including both puppetry and creative drama, encourage children to talk. To give practice in certain sounds, the correctionist may use these activities in a therapy session and the teacher may use them in reinforcing work taught by the correctionist. For the puppet play or the creative drama the teacher or correctionist can create a situation or use a story which will involve particular sounds. For example, in guiding a dramatic activity the teacher may suggest articles to build a story which contain many s's: a silver scepter, an evening dress, and a sled. Or she may recommend that the children dramatize Eleanor Estes' *A Hundred Dresses* (Harcourt, 1944). Or the picture she supplies as motivation for their play may have a sad, wistful child as its focal point.

McIntyre and McWilliams (53) explain the use of creative drama in speech correction—describing how children used a story of Sammy Snake and his sisters Sally and Sara. They show how in the playing of the story the four steps suggested for articulatory correction by Van Riper (isolation, stimulation, identification, and discrimination) take place. A study done by McIntyre (52) cited on page 142 gives evidence that creative activities do have a remedial effect on consonantal articulatory disorders.

Other situations for just plain talk arise spontaneously. The teacher takes advantage of these opportunities to promote oral communication. Chapter 8 suggests many speaking experiences for all children.

Parental Help

Recent studies seem to indicate that parents can help improve children's articulatory difficulties provided speech therapists give them training. Tufts and Holliday (64) selected three groups of ten children each. One group received no speech therapy; a second group received group speech therapy by a trained speech therapist; the third group received speech therapy from their mothers who had in turn received instruction in methods of handling articulatory therapy. Group 1 showed no significant improvement during the seven-month period but both groups 2 and 3 did. Between these two groups there was no significant difference. In a study by Sommers and others (59), where they matched two groups of children with functional articulatory problems, the parents of children in one group received intensive training in helping their children at home whereas the parents of the other group received no training. The data in this study reveal a trend which suggests that the simultaneous training of parents and children with functional articulatory problems may result in more rapid improvement of articulation than would be the case if the parents received no training. Egbert (46) studied 31 pairs of children with articulatory disorders: one group who had made superior progress and one who had made below average progress. The mothers of the more successful group had received meaningful and clear information from speech therapists, had utilized desirable techniques in home speech lessons and desirable methods of motivating their children to correct faulty speech patterns, and had encouraged their children in development of objective attitudes toward speech problems. On the other hand, significantly more mothers of children who made below average progress had used undesirable methods in motivating their children to correct faulty speech patterns and had tended to dominate their children through administering frequent and injudicious punishment, maintaining overly high or unrealistic standards, and an atmosphere of overprotection and oversupervision.

These studies point to the need for involving parents of children with articulatory defects in the school program of speech therapy. Conferences or courses may be set up with the teacher, correctionist, and parents participating. At these meetings topics for discussion might well include attitudes of adults toward speech defects, what the parent and teacher can do for the speech defective child both by way of motivation and correcting his difficulty, and how to handle the handicapped child. Such conferences promote an understanding of the child and his handicap and establish consistency in approach to him and his problems.

We have indicated one set of steps in correcting an articulatory difficulty and noted how the correctionist and teacher cooperate to bring about improvement in the child's articulation. Other correctionists and teachers will cooperate differently, for various procedures for correction exist. The Remedial Procedures Subcommittee of the Research Committee of the American Speech and Hearing Association (42, p. 62) reports on procedures used most frequently in articulation therapy. The values listed represent percentages of clinicians indicating frequency of use:

	Frequency of Use	
Procedure	*Often*	*Sometimes*
Auditory discriminating training	88	8
Ear training	85	10
Mirror observation and practice	75	22
Speech sound games	75	19
Sound drills (word lists, sentences, rhymes)	66	27
Parent guidance	59	29
Imitation	50	29

The Story of Jackie, A Child with an Articulatory Defect

Jackie was a little boy with an articulatory defect whom the teachers, correctionist, and the school psychologist helped. Because the reports of his teachers were very much alike, because he was a child with an articulatory defect for which no cause could be readily assigned, and because he was an unusually interesting child, we have chosen to tell about him, his scholastic progress, and his program of speech correction.

Jackie went to a private school located in a small Eastern industrial town about twenty-five miles from a large city for all ten years of his elementary school history. The school, one with good facilities, had classes of about twenty-five students with well-trained teachers. The part-time services of a psychologist and a speech correctionist were available. In Jackie's early school years, he was examined by the school doctor.

In the following pages, we shall tell about his school history, his academic progress during his elementary school career, and the reactions of his teachers to him as a student and as a personality. The report of his school history is based on the boy's cumulative record. Each of the teachers wrote three reports during the school year and a summary at the end. We have summarized these reports. Second, we have explained the kind of home he lives in and have described his parents. Third, we have included the essential material from the report of the psychologist. Fourth, we have given the necessary information from his health record. Last, we have summarized the reports of the two correctionists who worked with Jackie.

School History

Jackie entered kindergarten at 5 years, 2 months, where he adjusted easily and well to other children, and enjoyed his classmates and his teacher. His teacher called him a "likable child." He talked often and at great length. He liked to talk. Although many children have articulatory difficulties in kindergarten, his was particularly noticeable to the teacher. His classmates understood what he said readily and seemingly did not notice his speech difficulty. The kindergarten teacher also noted that he was "slow, pokey, and easygoing." She remarked on his poor work in general and particularly on his inferior hand work.

From kindergarten, Jackie went into first grade. At the end of the year the first-grade teacher felt that he might better remain in first grade another year. Although he got along well with other youngsters, he seemed immature for his age in his ability to cope with work problems. His reading score was zero. At first, he was not sure that he wanted to leave his own group, but then changed his mind. He, therefore, repeated first grade. During the two years in the first grade he had many absences, mostly because of colds and childhood diseases. But from the second grade on he was never absent more than five days a year and was never tardy.

As Jackie progressed through school, the reports of different teachers show many likenesses. In general, they agree that his personality is a pleasant, easy-going one. He quite obviously is a child well liked by his peers and by his teachers. Four of the teachers note that he is an easy-going child. All the teachers commend his "good attitude," and his ability to get along with other children. Five of them specifically mention his pleasant and likable personality. Others indicate positive traits such as "dependability," "cooperativeness," "good ability to work," and "good adjustment to people." Interestingly enough, negative traits are almost completely absent. One teacher mentions untidiness and a second notes that unless reminded he tends to be sloppy. Three complain about his "messy" or "sloppy" handwriting. A third indicates that he tends to be careless, a fourth that he needs to be reminded of responsibilities. Obviously the teachers agree that he is a pleasant child who gets along well with others.

Seven of the teachers note that he likes to talk although they express the idea in different ways. Several write, "He likes to share experiences." Another notes, "He enjoys talking to and with members of his group." A third, "He is eager to take part in discussion." A fourth, "He comes early just to talk. He likes to talk." Several indicate that his speech difficulty does not seem to hinder his talking. The report of the correctionist contains this statement, made by Jackie when he was eight: "I don't like to talk to people I don't know. They don't listen hard enough to understand me."

The reports agree that Jackie is a poor student. Five teachers indicate that in general his work is poor. Four of them believe he does not do as well as he can. On the other hand, two note that although he works slowly, he works hard. In each grade his scholastic achievement was reported as well below the average of his classmates and somewhat below the national average. In the eighth grade, he achieved an overall 7.9 on the Stanford Achievement Test. His poorest work, except for one grade, was in spelling. His best work throughout the grades was in science. He also usually attained scores above the national average on national science tests. His next best work was in the area of social studies. Here he did fairly well both in classwork and in national objective tests. Reports of the teachers on his reading ability show inconsistency. His reading scores on national tests varied. In some grades, he made a year's progress in reading, doing about as well as the average child would do. Except for one instance, he did not do as well in reading tests on word meaning or vocabulary as he did on comprehension. He scored from 4 months to 1 year, 8 months higher on comprehension than he did on vocabulary. His work in language usage or English was well below his work in reading and almost as poor as his spelling. Teachers report an inability to organize his thoughts. One writes, for example, "He has difficulty learning to leave out extraneous details in his reports." Another, "He is learning to stick to his subject better." In general, Jackie was not a good student.

Home Environment

His parents are hard-working people who are most cooperative and who want to do what they can for their two children. The mother works with Jackie with his spelling at home. She comes to school gladly when asked. Once in a while, she also comes voluntarily, always apologetic for taking the teacher's time; she apologizes in spite of the fact that on each visit the teachers have tried hard to make her feel welcome. She is a high-strung person who has had two serious operations, one while Jackie was in second grade and one while he was in the fourth grade.

Both parents completed the eighth grade, but left high school in their sophomore years. Both speak English; both use acceptable speech. The father is American-born and the mother was born in Poland. The father first worked as a laborer and later as a mechanic in a factory. They own their own home in a middle-class neighborhood where homes are not too expensive.

Both the mother and father enjoy Jackie. Several teachers note that his parents are interested in him and are understanding of his problems. The father takes Jackie fishing and hunting. As a small child, Jackie enjoyed telling tall tales of these expeditions. Because he had a delightful imagination, the tales were exciting and creative.

In a conference with the parents regarding Jackie's future at the time he was in the eighth grade, his parents indicated that they would like him to take up such work as carpentry or masonry. In an occupational interest inventory, his score was very high (90th percentile) in the mechanical area which includes such occupations as maintenance, machine operation, construction work, repairing, and designing. His next highest level of interest was in the natural area including farming and ranching, raising and caring for animals, gardening, lumbering, forestry, raising and taking care of fish or game. His lowest level was in the personal-social field which includes domestic and personal service, teaching, social service, and law and law enforcement. His next lowest was in the area of business, which includes selling and buying, bookkeeping, shipping, distribution, training and supervision, management, and control. In the areas of science and the arts, he showed about average interest. Jackie himself thought he might like to be a farmer or a carpenter. He thought he would prefer being a farmer.

While he was in the eighth grade, he delivered papers for the news dealer and articles for one of the local merchants. He said that he delivered papers just because it was a job. He remarked that a lot of people were fussy about where their papers were placed. He did not enjoy taking care of the accounts of who paid for their newspapers. In fact, he asked the help of a teacher in working out a better system. He said that he enjoyed talking with his customers. Most of them, he felt, were very nice people.

Report of the Psychologist

The school psychologist reported somewhat above normal intelligence, an I.Q. of 113. He tested the child with a nonlanguage test because of his speech difficulty. This test was given when Jackie was in first grade. During the second grade, the correctionist tested him with the Terman Revision of the Binet Simon Test. On this test, he achieved an I.Q. of 118. The psychologist's reports of personality tests showed no outstanding deviation, although Jackie did show some sibling rivalry. Jackie's sister was five years younger than he.

Medical Report

Jackie appeared to be a healthy youngster, somewhat bigger than the average child. Before entrance to school, he did not have any of the childhood diseases except measles. When he was in first grade, he had chicken pox, mumps, and many colds. From second grade on he missed almost no school because of illness. The report of the doctor indicated no physical difficulties. His hearing, measured by both group and individual audiometric tests, was normal. He received a group hearing test each year and was given an individual one in second grade.

Motor Development

Information on this aspect is not complete. As a child in kindergarten, he rode a scooter easily and built a farm with blocks nicely. But when he cut paper or put puzzles together, he was somewhat awkward and clumsy. He seemed to run as well as the other youngsters in his class. He rode a two-wheeler when he was seven. His writing, however, was likely to be badly formed unless he was especially admonished to be careful.

Report of the Speech Correctionist

Jackie was first examined in the second half of the first grade, but he received no speech help there. He did receive speech help in the second grade, third grade, fourth grade, sixth grade, seventh grade, and eighth grade.

His first examination revealed a mechanism that was normal in all respects except for a teeth structure where the molars did not come together properly. This structure might cause a distortion of sibilant sounds.

The substitutions he made included the following:

w[w] for *l*[l]	*d*[d] for *v*[v]
h[h] for *w*[w] and	*t*[t] for *th*[θ]
r[r]	*d*[d] for *th*[ð]
t[t] for *k*[k]	*t*[t] for *s*[s], *sh*(ʃ), and *ch* [tʃ]
d[d] for *g*[g]	*d*[d] for *zh*[ʒ] and *j*[dʒ]
t[t] for *f*[f]	

All his vowel and diphthong sounds were accurate.

For example, when a first grader he said, "I went titing wid my Dad. Me and him, we taught ten bid batt." (I went fishing with my Dad. Me and him—we caught ten big bass.) Another sample of his speech is: "We wat way up de twit to tut dee." (We walked way up the creek to shoot deer.) In response to what creek, he said, "De twit dat dod pat my hout up de hoad." (The creek that goes past my house up the road.)

In the first interview, he talked freely and happily with the correctionist. He told about his fishing and hunting trips with his Dad. Many of the incidents were imaginary but quite delightful. Because he had visited a farm recently, he talked about what he saw and did there. He played with the available toys. He put a jigsaw puzzle together, handled it rather well, and enjoyed working with it.

As the correctionist examined him, she found that he could make some of the sounds by repeating nonsense syllables after her. For example, he repeated accurately: *fee*[fi], *vee*[vi], *aith*[eθ], and *thee*[ði]. He did have a semblance of an *s*[s], *sh*[ʃ], *ch*[tʃ], and *j*[dʒ] when repeating nonsense syllables. He did not repeat *kay*[ke], *gay*[ge] but said *tay*[te], *day*[de]. He did badly on a test to discriminate between sounds.

SPEECH TRAINING IN SECOND GRADE. In the second grade, he began his speech work. He was given a second test to find out about his ability to discriminate between sounds. Again he did not do well. Ear training was begun. This training was fun for him and he seemed to enjoy it and to grasp the principles unusually quickly. He played the games eagerly and his next test showed marked improvement. His third test late in the year showed regression. His ability to discriminate between sounds showed wide discrepancies on different days. His poor days seemed to coincide with times when he had not had enough sleep. As a small child, he obviously did not get enough sleep. His family had difficulty getting him to bed some days. On other days, his mother and father kept him out late at meetings in a neighboring town.

In second grade, he learned to make *f*[f], *v*[v], *th*[θ], and *th*[ð] in nonsense syllables and to incorporate them into words and everyday speech. The correctionist attacked *f*[f], *v*[v], *th*[θ], and *th*[ð], first, because for him these sounds were the easiest to make. The correctionist reported that he was a delight to work with, for he loved to talk and to use his new sound in words. Although his power to concentrate varied from day to day, he found pleasure in the work. Once in a while he asked to bring one of his classmates with him. On many occasions he shared his speech help experiences with his classmates.

While in this grade, he was to give a report on weaving at the end of a unit on wool. The children planned to invite members of their families. He wrote the report, and took it to the correctionist, who helped him rewrite it, substituting words he could say accurately. He was proud to practice reading the report to the class. The day he was to read it, however, his mother went to the hospital, and his aunt, who was taking care of the family, was too busy to come to school. At first, he thought he wouldn't read it. Finally, he asked his teacher whether he could invite the correctionist to be his family for that day. Although he was disappointed not to have his mother there and although he was worried about her, he read his account well with pride and joy.

The classroom teacher reported to the correctionist words he needed to learn how to pronounce. The teacher in turn went over the word lists compiled by the correctionist in the child's notebook. The teacher encouraged him to incorporate the newly learned sounds in speech. She was a teacher of infinite patience, and understanding of and good-feeling toward children.

SPEECH TRAINING IN THE THIRD GRADE. His speech work in the third grade was begun in November. The correctionist and he continued work on ear training. During this year he learned to make the sounds k[k], g[g], s[s], sh[ʃ], ch[tʃ], and j[dʒ]. In the sibilants, lateral emission was obvious. The correctionist, however, preferred to wait until later to help the child control the sibilant sounds, since they were at least recognizable. Work on l and r was begun. At the end of the year he could make these sounds in nonsense syllables. Although he now could make all the sounds, he did not always incorporate them into his speech. During this grade he again was particularly fortunate in having a teacher who encouraged him to do his very best and who was particularly understanding of him and his problems. She was able to give him many opportunities to feel successful.

Speech Training in the Fourth Grade

In the fourth grade ear training was still continued. A report of the correctionist indicates, "A test on sound discrimination was given four weeks apart and showed wide discrepancy in ability to discriminate between sounds." During this year, the correctionist concentrated on r[r] and l[l]. The correctionist notes: "His s[s], sh[ʃ] are still poor. His r and l he can make accurately. In blends, such as pl[pl], bl[bl], pr[pr], br[br], sl[sl], and tr[tr], the r[r] and l[l] tend to be poor. He still does not consistently incorporate his new sounds in words." Until the fourth grade all the teachers complained that they could not understand what he said and that frequently the other children translated for him. This teacher understood him from the first day he was in her class. The teacher was particularly helpful in giving him opportunities to succeed in speaking situations.

Speech Training in the Fifth- and Sixth-Grades

In the fifth grade, no speech help was available for Jackie. In the sixth grade, he was again given ear training. Here he was working with a different correctionist. She noted that preliminary ear training to improve his ability to discriminate, analyze, and synthesize sound sequences had occupied a major part of Jackie's time in speech help. His response was such as to indicate that his difficulties were the result of poor training. In this grade he was taught a type of compensatory mechanics for his particular mouth deformity in teaching the s[s] and sh[ʃ]. He was also given training on bl[bl], pl[pl], br[br], pr[pr], and sl[sl].

Speech Training in the Seventh- and Eighth-Grades

In the seventh grade, his difficulty with blends was largely eradicated. His phonetic discrimination became more accurate.

Progress in teaching an acceptable *s* and *sh* continued to be slow. In this grade, however, his speech was such that an adult said, "Why, there's nothing wrong with that child's speech. He sounds all right to me." There was no report for the eighth grade.

Comments on Jackie's Progress

Several factors are noteworthy. Jackie's largest gain in reading was made between the fourth and fifth grades. It was at the end of the fourth grade that his speech showed the greatest amount of improvement. The success of his speech work depended on his ability to concentrate and this ability varied from day to day. He did not move forward steadily in his ability to speak. His test scores in academic subjects showed the same kind of progress and at times retrogression.

Jackie's story is particularly interesting, because his environment at home and at school, his own adjustment, and his intelligence seem conducive to at least average ability in speech. Attempts to form a hypothesis as to the possible organic cause were unavailing. His motor coordination may have been poor for tasks that needed fine, exact coordination. At one point, it was felt that his difficulty might be one of perception. A neurologist's examination indicated that he felt that this was not the cause of the difficulty.

A conclusion that can be drawn rather readily is that his speech work should have started in kindergarten rather than in second grade. His teachers felt that if the speech work had been started earlier, his spelling and reading would not have been as difficult for him.

Another interesting aspect is that Jackie remained an alive, outgoing child who got along well with his peers and adults. It appeared that his speech difficulty did not affect his relationships with others. That he did accept his defect and that his classmates also did so are a credit to his teachers and to his family. One time an adult in his neighborhood said, "Jackie's stupid—the way he talks." A small friend of his, overhearing, said, "Ah, he's good at a lot of things." One day Jackie brought to school a small stool that he had built to show his classmates and teacher. When he showed it to the correctionist, she remarked, "I couldn't make that." Jackie replied, "Well, everybody can't do everything. Lotta things I can't do—like spelling."

Jackie's progress in learning to make all the sounds was not rapid. But he finally learned to speak so that his difficulties were not apparent to his listeners. That he did learn to speak well is in a large part due to the help given him by his elementary school teachers and the speech therapists. They accepted him as he was, encouraged him to speak well, and to participate in a variety of experiences.

Bibliography of Children's Books Which Provide Practice Material for the Indicated Sounds

t[t]	3, 4, 12, 16, 21, 23, 33
d[d]	3, 4, 5, 12, 16, 21, 23, 33
k[k]	5, 11, 12, 25, 26, 30, 32, 40
g[g]	6, 12, 25, 32, 40
p[p]	20, 33
b[b]	8, 20, 33
s[s]	1, 4, 7, 9, 15, 17, 20, 29, 36, 38, 39, 41
z[z]	4, 16, 22
ng[ŋ]	22, 24
sh[ʃ]	3, 5, 12
ch[tʃ]	3, 7, 17, 20, 33, 41
j[dʒ]	5, 14, 21, 30, 33, 35, 38
f[f]	14, 20, 24, 30, 32, 33
v[v]	24, 32, 33
th[θ]	11, 16
th[ð]	11, 16
l[l]	8, 10, 13, 16, 20, 22, 28, 30, 41
r[r]	16, 17, 18, 20, 24, 28, 30, 33, 38
All sounds	19, 26, 27, 34, 37, 39

New York: Lothrop, Lee and Shepard, 1949. A tale of a doll long hidden in the attic now placed under a Christmas tree.)

30. PARKER, BERTHA MORRIS, *Fall is Here*. Evanston, Ill.: Row, Peterson, 1953. (Contains a picture dictionary at end. An explanation of fall—its flowers, berries, wild life, weather, harvest of fruit and vegetables.)

31. ———, *Winter is Here*. Evanston, Ill.: Row, Peterson, 1948. (An explanation of winter—its snow, weather, trees, birds, animals, sky, stars, and sleighriding. Includes a picture dictionary.)

32. READ, HELEN S., *Mr. Brown's Grocery Store*. New York: Scribner, 1929. (An explanation of the operation of a grocery store—where groceries come from and how they are sold. Tells about children playing store.)

33. REED, MARY (ed.), *Counting Rhymes*. New York: Simon and Schuster, 1946. (Rhymes having to do with numbers.)

34. SALAFF, ALICE, *Words are Funny*. Garden City, N.Y.: Doubleday, 1952. (A book of riddles including word games and puzzle rhymes.)

35. SAWYER, RUTH, *Journey Cake, Ho!* New York: Viking, 1953. (How Journey Cake became a Johnny Cake.)

36. ———, *Roller Skates*. New York: Viking, 1936. (Exploration of New York City on roller skates.)

37. SEATTER, MINNIS, *Romp in Rhythm*. Cincinnati, Ohio: Willis Music Co., 1944. (For kindergartners.)

38. SLOBODKIN, LOIS, *Clear the Track*. New York: Macmillan, 1945. (A story of playing at traveling.)

39. STEINER, CHARLOTTE, *Charlotte Steiner's A B C*. Garden City, N.Y.: Garden City Books, 1946. (An A B C book.)

40. TRESSELT, ALVIN, *Autumn Harvest*. New York: Lothrop, Lee and Shepard, 1951. (Description of autumn with its harvest time, Hallowe'en, and Thanksgiving.)

41. ———, *Sun Up*. New York: Lothrop, Lee and Shepard, 1949. (The description of the day with sun, wind, rain, and night.)

References and Suggested Readings

42. American Speech and Hearing Association Research Committee. "Public School Speech and Hearing Services." *The Journal of Speech and Hearing Disorders,* Monograph Supplement 8 (July 1961.)

43. BERRY, M., and J. EISENSON, *Speech Disorders: Principles and Practices of Therapy.* New York: Appleton-Century-Crofts, 1956, Chapters 6, 7. (Includes carefully planned drill material.)

44. BLACK, M. E., and R. A. S. LUDWIG, "Analysis of the Games Technic." *Journal of Speech and Hearing Disorders,* **XXI** (June 1956), 183-187. (Gives criteria for using games in treatment of articulatory difficulties.)

45. CYPREANSEN, L., J. H. WILEY, and L. T. LAASE, *Speech Development, Improvement and Correction.* New York: Ronald Press, 1959.

46. EGBERT, J. H., *The Effect of Certain Home Influences on the Progress of Children in a Speech Therapy Program.* Ph.D. thesis (Stanford University, 1955).

47. GOTT, S. R., and R. MILISEN, *"Functional Articulatory Disorders."* Education, **LXXX** (April 1960), 468-470. (Tells how classroom teacher can help the child with an articulatory disorder.)

48. HAHN, E., "Communication in the Therapy Session: A Point of View." *Journal of Speech and Hearing Disorders,* **XXV** (February 1960), 18-23.

49. JOHNSON, W. *et al, Speech Handicapped School Children.* (Rev. ed.) New York: Harper and Bros., 1956. (Describes retraining and states the responsibility of the classroom teacher in retraining.)

50. LLOYD, G. W., and S. AINSWORTH, "The Classroom Teacher's Activities and Attitudes Relating to Speech Correction." *Journal of Speech and Hearing Disorders,* **XIX** (June 1954), 244-249.

51. McINTYRE, B. M., "The Effect of Creative Activities on the Articulation of Children with Speech Disorders." *ASHA,* **I** (November 1959), 80.

52. ———, *The Effect of a Program of Creative Activities Upon the Consonant Articulation Skills of Adolescent and Pre-Adolescent Children with Speech Disorders.* Ph.D. Dissertation (University of Pittsburgh, 1957).

53. ———, and B. J. McWILLIAMS, "Creative Dramatics in Speech Correction." *Journal of Speech and Hearing Disorders,* **XXIV** (August 1959), 275-279.

54. MADER, J. B., "The Relative Frequency of Occurrence of English Consonant Sounds in Words in the Speech of Children in Grades One, Two and Three." *Speech Monographs,* **XXI** (November 1954).

55. MAWHINNEY, C. K., "To Isolate or Not to Isolate in Speech Ther-

apy." *Exceptional Child,* **XXV** (1959), 247-255. (Presents the case for teaching the sound in isolation. Shows how processes of speaking and reading are different.)

56. Parish, M. H., "Defects of Speech." *Instructor,* **LIV** (September 1945), 22. (Includes suggestions for games for work with articulatory defects.)

57. Parks, M., "The Classroom Teacher and Speech Correction." *Quarterly Journal of Speech,* **XXVIII** (December 1942), 471-477.

58. Smith, M. B., "A Clinician's Story." *Quarterly Journal of Speech,* **XXX** (February 1946), 63-66.

59. Sommers, R. K., S. P. Shilling, C. D. Paul, F. G. Copetas, D. C. Bowser, and C. J. McClintock. "Training Parents of Children with Functional Misarticulation." *Journal of Speech and Hearing Research,* **II** (September 1959), 258-265.

60. Templin, M. G., *Certain Language Skills in Children.* Minneapolis: University of Minnesota Press, 1957.

61. ———, "A Study of the Sound Discrimination Ability of Elementary School Pupils." *Journal of Speech Disorders,* **VIII** (June 1943), 127-132.

62. Thorndike, E. L., and I. Lorge, *The Teacher's Word Book of 30,000 Words.* New York: Bureau of Publications, Teachers College, Columbia University, 1944.

63. Travis, L. E., *Handbook of Speech Pathology,* New York: Appleton-Century-Crofts, 1957.

64. Tufts, L. C., and A. R. Holliday, "Effectiveness of Trained Parents as Speech Therapists." *Journal of Speech and Hearing Disorders,* **XXIV** (November 1959), 395-396.

65. Van Riper, C., *Speech Correction: Principles and Methods.* Englewood Cliffs, N.J.: Prentice-Hall, 1954, Chapter 7.

66. ———, and J. V. Irwin, *Voice and Articulation.* Englewood Cliffs, N.J.: Prentice-Hall, 1958.

67. West, R., M. Ansberry, and A. Carr, *The Rehabilitation of Speech.* New York: Harper and Bros., 1957.

Materials and Games for Sound Discrimination and Drill

68. Abney, L., and D. Miniace, *This Way to Better Speech.* Yonkers, N.Y.: World, 1940. (Includes a simple exposition of how sounds are made, followed by sentences and jingles. Usable for children in the second or third grade.)

69. ARNOLD, G., *The Goodspeaker Family*. G. Arnold, 4926 Culmore Dr., Houston 21, Texas, 1959. (Gives basic foundation of speaking for young children.)

70. ———, *Practice Manual for the Correction of Speech Sounds*. G. Arnold, 4926 Culmore Dr., Houston 21, Texas, 1959. (Contains articulation test, word lists, and sentences for consonants and blends and conversational activities for carry-over. For upper grades and high school.)

71. ———, *Teaching Speech Sound Series*. G. Arnold, 4926 Culmore Dr., Houston 21, Texas, 1960. (Set of cards which contains consonants in various positions, blends, vowels, and diphthongs.)

72. ———, *Speech is Fun*. G. Arnold, 4926 Culmore Dr., Houston 21, Texas, 1959. (Materials for testing, sound stimulation, and discrimination. For young children.)

73. BAKER, P., *A Primer of Sounds*. Boston: Expression Co., 1941.

74. BARROWS, S., and K. HALL, *Games and Jingles for Speech Development*. Magnolia, Mass.: Expression Co., 1936.

75. BRYNGELSON, B., *Speech Correction Through Listening*. Chicago: Scott, Foresman, 1959. (Suggests activities for correction of articulatory difficulties.)

76. BRYNGELSON, B., and E. GLASPEY, *Speech Improvement Cards*. Chicago: Scott, Foresman, 1941. (A set of cards with colored pictures. One group is for testing; the second group is for remedial work and includes cards where the names of objects in pictures contain specific sounds.)

77. CASE, I. M., and S. T. BARROWS, *Speech Drills for Children in the Form of Play*. Magnolia, Mass.: Expression Co., 1929. (Describes games for speech drill that are fun for children in the primary grades.)

78. DOLCH, E., *Take*. Champaign, Ill.: Garrard Publishing Co. (Game for matching sounds in beginning, middle, and ends of words.)

79. FAIRBANKS, G., *Voice and Articulation Drillbook*. New York: Harper and Bros., 1960.

80. FITZSIMMONS, R. M., and A. T. MURPHY, *Let's Play Hide and Seek*. (Rev. ed.), Magnolia, Mass.: Expression Company, 1959. (Provides practice designed to help the young child with articulation. Spiral bound book.)

81. ———, *Guess Who*. Magnolia, Mass.: Expression Co., 1959. (Presents riddles utilizing sounds said inaccurately. For younger children.)

82. Lloyd, A. M. L., *Rocket Race*. Talk Along Products, Box 444, Monterey, California. (Sound game drill.)

83. Matthews, J., E. J. Burgi, J. W. Birch, and E. R. Phillips Wade. *The Best Speech Series*. Stanwix House, 3020 Chartiers Ave., Pittsburgh, Pa., 1959. (Contains 64 pages of pictures, stories, and games designed to motivate the child to hear and say sounds accurately.)

84. Pollock, M. P., and M. S. Pollock, *The Clown Family Speech Book*. Springfield, Ill.: Charles C. Thomas, 1960. (Contains material for developing articulation in children.)

85. Schoolfield, L. D., *Better Speech and Reading*. Magnolia, Mass.: Expression Co. (Provides material for drill for consonant and vowel sounds. For use in Grades 1 to 6.)

86. Stoddard, C. B., *Sounds for Little Folks*. Magnolia, Mass.: Expression Co., 1940. (Contains drill for children who have not learned to read.)

87. Thomas, C. K., *Handbook of Speech Improvement*. New York: Ronald Press, 1956.

88. Wolf, F. W., and G. A. Kelder, *Sounds I Say, Book I*. Moravia, N.Y.: Chronicle Guidance Publications, 1959. (Includes material for work on sounds.)

89. Wood, A. E., *The Jingle Book for Speech Correction*. New York: E. P. Dutton, 1934.

90. ———, *Sound Games: Speech Correction for the Very Young*. New York: E. P. Dutton, 1948.

91. Word Games—Ideal Speech Materials, 6218 South Albany, Chicago 29, Illinois.

92. Yoakum, D., "Speech Games for Children." *Quarterly Journal of Speech*, **XXX** (February 1944), 85-87.

Problems

1. Visit a school or clinic where you may observe a specialist working with a child with an articulatory difficulty. Indicate how you can reinforce in the classroom some of the learning that took place in the speech class or clinic.

2. Indicate ways other than those mentioned in this chapter of helping the child to listen to sounds more accurately.

3. Tell how you as a classroom teacher could make use of some of the drill material listed in this chapter.

4. Read one of the children's books listed in this chapter that emphasize particular sounds. Explain how this piece of literature might be used to reinforce learning that has already taken place.

5. Make up a story involving nonsense syllables.

6. Indicate ways you as a classroom teacher could help a child like Jackie (page 250) to speak better.

7. Read and report on one of the following references: 47, 48, 50, 53, 55, 59, 61, or 64.

12

Voice

Disturbances

V OICE disturbances occur far less frequently in school-age children than do defects of articulation. For each school-age child with a vocal disturbance we are likely to find ten to fifteen children with defective articulation. The study of voice disturbances is not important for its total incidence (only two-tenths of 1 percent among school age children) as it is for the possible signficance of a vocal disturbance as a mirror of the child's personality, or the personality of the individual the child is unconsciously imitating. Another reason for appreciating the importance of voice disturbances is that they may be associated with some organic condition that may require medical attention.

Before considering vocal disturbances, we ought first to appreciate the characteristics and potentialities of a normal voice.

Characteristics of a Normal Voice

A normal voice should be able to communicate reliably the feelings and thoughts that the speaker wishes to convey to his listener. When well controlled, the speaker's voice should reveal rather than betray the type and shade of feelings that color his thinking. Through appropriate changes in pitch, force, duration, and quality, a speaker's voice should be able to command attention, maintain interest, and convey changes and emphasis in meaning.

The ability of a speaker to communicate intellectual and affective content will be enhanced if the speaker's voice attracts no attention to itself because of the manner in which it is produced or because of any undesirable characteristics. Vocalization should take place without apparent effort or strain. The acoustic results should be appropriate to the speaking situation. The voice should, in addition, be appropriate to the age and sex of the speaker. Little children may sound like little children, but older ones should not be mistaken for them. Neither should first graders sound like their parents or their teachers.

From the point of view of the listener, a normal and effective voice is one that is pleasant, clear, and readily audible. It should be heard without listener effort, provided, of course, that the listening conditions are not unfavorable for the purpose.

Types of Voice Disturbances

The defects of voice most frequently heard are: (1) inadequate loudness; (2) faulty volume (loudness) control; (3) loudness inappropriate to the speaking situation or speech content; (4) defects of quality, especially nasality and denasality, breathiness, and huskiness; (5) faulty pitch range or too narrow a range of pitch; and (6) inappropriate rate. Each of these will be considered in some detail in our discussion of therapy for voice disturbances.

Causes of Vocal Disturbances

At the outset, it should be pointed out that the *diagnosis of a voice disturbance should be made by a specialist*. Where a physical condition may be the underlying cause, treatment should not be undertaken without medical clearance and approval. Fortunately, even where the cause is physical, treatment may help to prevent aggravation of the disturbance and often may improve the condition as well as the voice.

Vocal disturbances may be present for a variety of reasons. Among the most numerous are: (1) poor physical health; (2) anomalies in the structure or condition of the voice mechanism; (3) pathologies in the neurological control of the mechanism; (4) glandular conditions or other physical conditions that may affect the growth or the tonicity and the responses of the muscles involved in voice production; (5) defects of hearing that impair the individual's ability to respond to and monitor his own voice as it is being produced; (6) disturbances of personality that reflect themselves in voice; (7) the presence of poor models (which the child is imitating) so that he acquires a vocal defect through normal processes of learning; and (8) poor habits of vocalization.

The speech clinician and classroom teacher are most likely to be directly concerned with the last two of the listed reasons. To a lesser degree, defects of hearing may also directly concern them. Vocal disturbances that have a physical basis, as already suggested, are the therapeutic concern of the specialist in speech problems. The teacher, however, is frequently the first to have an opportunity to recognize that something may be wrong which is causing the child to have vocal difficulty, and so has a responsibility for bringing the condition to the attention of the parent and speech specialist.

POOR PHYSICAL HEALTH. Most of us are able to recognize that "something is wrong" with a friend or relative by the way he sounds. Sometimes "what is wrong" may be temporary and a matter of momentary mood; occasionally, it may be physical and a matter of health. The interested and sensitive listener who may be parent, friend, or teacher is often the first to suspect that a speaker may not be well. Voice, because it is a product of the physiological as well as the emotional and intellectual state of the speaker, is the mirror that reflects the speaker's state of health. The expert speaker may, with awareness, control his voice and so succeed in disguising this condition. The school-age child, less practiced in concealment and control, frequently reveals both his affective state and the state of his general physical health through his vocalization.

PHYSICAL ANOMALIES. Perhaps the most frequent cause of all

vocal disturbances is the common cold. When we suffer from a cold, any or all of the following modifications of the voice mechanism may be present. The nasal cavities may be filled with mucous and so prevent adequate reinforcement of voice. The mucous membranes of the nose, throat, and larynx may be inflamed, and so modify the normal resonating activity of the voice mechanism. The vocal bands may themselves be inflamed and swollen, and so prevent normal vocal activity. The general "run-down" condition of the individual may impair normal functioning and control of the voice mechanism. If the cold is accompanied by a persistent cough, the general condition may be aggravated by the vocal abuse that is caused by coughing. Some idea of the effect of a cough may be appreciated from the following abstract of a Science Note from *The New York Times* (10): "When you cough you force air through the windpipe at a speed approaching or exceeding that of sound, which is 732 miles an hour at sea level. . . . By the time the air reaches the level of the Adam's apple, its speed has dwindled to hurricane velocity of about 100 miles per hour. When it blows out of the mouth the air is moving at fifteen miles per hour, a mere zephyr."

Persistent coughing may produce laryngitis. The condition of laryngitis may, however, be caused by vocal abuse not associated with either a cough or a cold. Continued overloud talking, or yelling under conditions of competing noise, may also produce a laryngitis.

Sometimes vocal difficulties are associated with abnormalities of the structure of the larynx. The laryngeal cartilages may, for congenital reasons or through injury, be so constructed that the vocal bands may not be able to approximate normally, or the reinforcement of vocal tones may be impaired because of the change in the size and shape of the larynx. More frequently, the vocal bands may have developed nodules on the inner edges as a result of vocal abuse. Sometimes the vocal bands become thickened because of chronic incorrect vocalization. The effect is usually a voice characterized by low pitch, breathiness, and effort in production. Fortunately, these conditions usually improve through a combination of voice rest and a program of training to modify the incorrect vocal behavior of the speaker. Occasionally the edges of the vocal bands may have slight irregularities which impair normal activity. Any of the conditions described can be determined only through an examination of the larynx by a competent physician. The treatment of these conditions will call for the active cooperation of the classroom teacher. Voice therapy, if it is indicated, is a problem for the speech therapist working in cooperation with the physician.

HEARING LOSS. Because we learn to vocalize as well as to articulate "by ear," hearing loss, especially in the low-pitch ranges, is likely to be manifest in vocal inadequacies. If the hearing loss is appreciable, and of the type that does not permit the child to check on the voice he produces, he may speak in a voice too loud, or not loud enough, for the specific speaking situation. Sometimes the loss may be temporary, and associated with the effects or aftereffects of a cold. Occasionally, as a result of middle-ear involvement, there may be prolonged hearing loss. With proper medical attention, this situation should clear and the vocal disturbance disappear.

GLANDULAR DISTURBANCES. Thyroid gland deficiency is associated with a falling of the basal metabolic rate. Frequently, though not invariably, decrease in metabolic rate is causally associated with sluggish physical and mental activity, and with a general reduction of body tone. This condition is likely to reflect itself in a colorless, poorly modulated voice.

In contrast with thyroid deficiency, the presence of an excess of thyroid hormone generally results in making the individual hyperactive and "nervous." The condition is likely to be reflected in a rapid rate of speech and in a tense, high-pitched voice.

The teacher and therapist who observe what appear to be significant changes in the general activity and mental alertness of a child in association with vocal changes should refer the child to the school nurse or physician for a medical examination to determine the possibility of a glandular involvement. Caution, however, should be exercised that no hasty conclusion be made. Comparable changes in the voice of a child may result from conditions not related to glandular disturbances. Vocal changes may sometimes merely indicate a temporary indisposition on the part of the child.

PUBERTAL CHANGES. With the coming of physical adolescence and associated physiological and growth changes, many children have marked vocal difficulties. These are more likely to be present among boys than among girls. In males, the size and structure of the larynx undergo considerable change, so that boys have to adjust to longer vocal bands as well as a larger larynx. Girls, with a longer and slower pubescent period, and with a smaller amount of laryngeal growth, have less modification and more time for adjustment. The little girl soprano may, during adolescence, become a woman mezzo-soprano or perhaps an alto. The boy soprano may become a tenor or a baritone.

Often the difficulty during puberty is aggravated by problems of social adjustment. The shy youngster may be so embarrassed by his voice "breaks" that he withdraws from his groups or finds excuses for not talking. Some of the difficulties may be related to self-consciousness resulting from a poor skin condition, or an awareness of physical awkwardness. Occasionally overly passive adolescents may try to vocalize within a pitch range determined for them by their parents or older siblings, or other influential members of their environment. In some instances, dependent and infantile boys and girls may try to maintain their preadolescent voices as an aspect of their general wish to continue to be young children. In other instances, both boys and girls may try to show how mature they are by attempting to establish low, deep-pitched voices inconsistent with their amount of laryngeal growth and general physical change.

It should be apparent that the influence of the speech clinician and the classroom teacher in helping the adolescent through his period of voice change can hardly be overestimated. The teacher can ward off taunts and help the adolescent build up his defenses. If the adolescent has prolonged difficulty in arriving at his "new voice," referral to a speech therapist may be of help. If there is reason to believe that psychological problems may be part of the difficulty, referral of the adolescent for proper guidance is in order.

PERSONALITY DISTURBANCES. Few of us question the general observation that the voice is a mirror of the personality. Temporary emotional upsets are likely to be reflected in the speaker's voice. Similarly, chronic emotional disturbances and maladjustments of attitude are likely to be manifest in disorders of voice.

Early in his experience, the classroom teacher may have had to urge some child to "speak up" because of a weak and apologetic voice. Some other child may frequently need to be reminded to "tone down" because his classmates are close to him and shouting is not necessary. Both these children may be revealing attitudes toward their classmates in particular and their environment in general suggestive of a significant degree of maladjustment. So does the child whose voice is a constant whine; so also does the child whose breathless voice and breath-taking rate suggest that he is afraid that someone may interrupt him if he pauses, and that once interrupted he may not be able to resume his talking.

Although the vocal defects briefly described are not important in themselves, they are of importance if they are symptoms of chronic personality maladjustments. Occasionally, the child's voice may be reflecting not his own maladjustment but one of an older member of his environment whom the child is unconsciously imitating. Whatever the case may be for the individual child, appropriate treatment calls for determining and dealing with the underlying cause as well as with the vocal symptoms of the cause. With the young child, the voice symptoms are likely to disappear without direct treatment if the basic personality problem is relieved. The older child, who may have established his vocal traits so that they are fixed and habitual, may need direct treatment for voice even if the personality problem is treated.

IMITATION OF POOR MODELS. The child learns both his language and the manner in which his language is produced by ear. The mother who teaches her child the name of something also teaches him the manner in which the naming is done. If mother shouts, so will the child; if mother speaks as though she were not worthy of the evocation, the child is apt to develop the same tone. As the child grows up, other models become subjects for imitation. Friends, liked or respected adults, who frequent the home, and teachers, when the child is of school age, become likely models. Usually the imitation is unconscious; occasionally a child's urge or need to identify with another person is so strong that the imitation may be conscious. Imitation that begins early may continue into and beyond adolescence.

Often a parent will be aware that there is something wrong with a child's voice but have no awareness that the fault is parent-centered. We have frequently pointed out to complaining parents that they must have children who love them because the children spoke so much like them. And we have frequently suggested to parents that they accept treatment for their own voices as the best device for improving the voices of their children.

Teachers, obviously, have a great responsibility for the voices of their classroom children. If the teacher is liked, the children may imitate him unconsciously or consciously; if he is not liked, he may be mimicked in manner as well as in voice. Before the teacher turns to other sources for his pupils' vocal traits, he should listen to himself or have an objective appraisal of his voice made by a professionally competent person. He may then conclude that the "epidemic of hoarseness" is a tribute to his influence in the classroom and followed his own recovery from laryngitis. He may in some instances have to conclude that his own habit of breathiness, denasality, low pitch, or rapid rate needs attention if he is to hope that the children in his class are to vocalize without these specific defects.

POOR HABITS OF VOCALIZATION. The professional speech therapist often treats persons whose vocal habits are poor and are not apparently associated with any present disturbance of personality or any specific or general physical condition. It is possible, of course, that the faulty vocal habits have outlived the cause of their origin, that in a given instance the speaker is presenting the residual of an adolescent "crush," or a once serious personality maladjustment, or a vocal manner that began with an illness and has persisted long after all physical evidence of illness disappeared. Not infrequently vocal habits may be interpreted as lingering memories of what used to be. If, however, "what used to be" is no longer in need of treatment, the vocal symptoms, or the vocal habits with which the symptoms are associated, may be directly treated. Chief among faulty vocal habits are unsuitable pitch level, inappropriate nasal reinforcement, and poor breath control for speech.

Vocal pitch and vocal range are not to be selected by the individual as he might choose his clothes. Pitch, as we pointed out earlier, is determined by the size, shape, and normal functioning of the vocal bands and the resonating cavities. Each of us is potentially intended for a given "optimum pitch" and range of pitch according to individual vocal equipment. Most of us arrive at this without special instruction by doing "what comes naturally." Some of us make the most of our potential by special motivation or by competent instruction. A few of us succumb to pressures to vocalize in a manner not consistent with nature's intentions for us, and difficulties may arise. One of these pressures is the contemporary one of admiring women's voices that are low-pitched and somewhat breathy in quality. The not infrequent result of employing a voice pitched too low for the physical mechanism is hoarseness. Although there is considerable variability in regard to the consequences of the constant use of a voice pitched too low for the mechanism, there is a growing body of evidence indicating that undesirable physical consequences can frequently be expected. Among these consequences are thickening of the vocal bands and chronic irritation of the larynx.

Boys, as well as men, are not at all exempt from the cultural pressure for the low-pitched voice. Unfortunately, just so many women are born to have soprano voices, and only a few to be altos; so it is that many boys and men are by nature intended to be tenors and high baritones, just as some are to be low baritones and basses.

The result of confusing physical virility with vocal depth is frequently low pitch and poor quality. On occasion, as Williamson (12) has shown, chronic hoarseness results from the attempt to pitch the voice at a level too low for the optimum functioning of the vocal apparatus.

Our emphasis thus far has been on the abnormally low-pitched voice. This does not mean that some persons do not speak at a pitch level too high for their vocal mechanism. Among speakers with inappropriate pitch they are, however, likely to constitute a small minority. Cultural pressures in the United States place a premium on the low-pitched voice and are inclined to penalize the high-pitched voices. Unless there is a strong psychological drive to maintain an abnormally high-pitched voice, the individual is likely to yield in the direction of cultural pressure. Interestingly enough, persons who persist in using an abnormally high pitch are not susceptible to some of the physical changes that are apparently correlated with abnormally low-pitched vocalization. We may appreciate some of the reasons for this by intentionally, but briefly, talking considerably below and then considerably above our normal pitch ranges. In talking at the low end of our range, we will find that it takes appreciably more effort to produce loud voice than within our normal range or at a high pitch. Fatigue is likely to set in quickly, and a feeling of "vocal strain" will follow if vocalization is continued.

Habitual use of pitches much below or above our natural pitch range is often accomplished at the expense of the abuse of the vocal mechanism. We have worked with preschool children who developed nodules on their vocal bands as a result of vocal abuse. Typically, these children were high-pitched screamers. There are always, of course, some individuals who are able to vocalize either above or below normal pitch range without suffering physical consequences. Perhaps these persons are kin to those who do not develop calluses despite poorly fitted shoes, or who do not become sunburned despite what would be overexposure to the sun for most of us. Our only suggestion is that these hardy persons be considered exceptions rather than models for the more susceptible of us to follow. Most of us do better vocalizing within a pitch range suited to our vocal apparatus. How to determine this range will be considered later in our discussion of optimum pitch in the section on Vocal Therapy.

INAPPROPRIATE NASAL REINFORCEMENT. The movements of the soft palate largely determine whether the produced voice is characterized by the presence or absence of nasality. Normally, when vocalization occurs with a relaxed soft palate that permits the stream of breath to enter the nasal cavities, voice is reinforced there and becomes characteristically nasal. Of course, some nasal reinforcement occurs whether or not the soft palate is relaxed or elevated, so that a degree of nasality is likely to be present even when nasality is not the characteristic quality of the produced voice.

The American-English sounds *n, m,* and *ng* are normally produced with a relaxed soft palate and "open nasal cavities." All other sounds of English are normally produced with the soft palate elevated so that the stream of breath is directed and emitted orally. If an individual has a weakened soft palate, he will tend to speak with more than a normal amount of nasal emission, and so have a voice quality characterized by *positive nasality.* The same quality may result from sluggish palatal control and from related activity of the mouth, throat, and nasopharynx in their functions as resonators. Positive nasality may also arise as a result of imitation. The French-speaking child quite properly nasalizes some of his vowels as well as the nasal consonants of his language. The American- or English-speaking child may do the same if he is imitating the speech of a member of his environment who nasalizes more than most American or English speakers do.

Denasality, or an absence of appropriate nasal resonance, occurs when there is too little reinforcement by the nasal resonators. This may result from a blocking within the nasal cavities themselves, or a partial blocking within the area of the nasopharynx. The result is a pinched, flat quality that suggests the voice of a person with a head cold or an allergic condition involving the nasal cavities.

The quality is more than an absence of nasality when it is anticipated in the production of the nasal consonants. It is an overall effect recognizable on sounds that are normally emitted orally. We can produce what approaches a denasal voice by pinching our nostrils in the articulation of such a sentence as "Who is that tall boy with a black coat?" The result, even though the sentence does not contain nasal consonants, should be different in quality if the sentence is articulated without pinched nostrils.

Techniques for recognizing and improving nasal reinforcement will be considered in our discussion of voice therapy.

BREATHING FAULTS.   It is unusual for a physically normal child to breathe incorrectly while speaking unless he has somehow been trained to do so. Such training may be the result of a child's efforts to be obedient to the direction, "Take a real deep breath before you begin to speak," or "Raise your chest high and pull your tummy in before you begin to speak." Occasionally, but really rarely, a child may speak with a too shallow breath, or attempt to speak while inhaling rather than or in addition to exhaling. In such instances investigation is likely to show that we are dealing with an insecure or anxiety-ridden child who is apprehensive that if he stops for a normal breath someone will interrupt him, or he may forget what he has to say and be embarrassed or penalized for his forgetting. The same factors are likely to operate with the child who tries to speak on inhalation as well as exhalation, or the child who forces himself to continue to speak on breath he must strain to emit when the normal "tidal breath" has been expired. We must not, of course, overlook the possibility that in a rare instance we are dealing with a normal child with normal psychological dynamisms, imitating a member of his environment whose breathing habits for speech are faulty.

We are inclined to agree with Gray and Wise (5, p. 153) that it is probably of little importance whether the person's breathing is predominantly abdominal or diaphragmatic, predominantly thoracic, or predominantly medial (characterized by activity about the base of the sternum). Most persons not specifically trained to exaggerate the activity of one part of the thoracic mechanism are likely to do pretty well in coordinated participation of all parts of their respiratory mechanism. For the rare individual who does not have adequate breath for normal speech purposes, attention may be directed to the emphasis on either diaphragmatic action and control, thoracic action, or medial action. Our own preference is for diaphragmatic (abdominal) control because it is easy, effective, and readily discernible. The individual may be directed to breathe while speaking as he or she is likely to breathe when relaxed, unless tightly girdled or belted. On inspiration of breath the abdominal area will be noted to move upward if the person is lying down, or forward if the person is sitting up or standing. On expiration, the abdominal area should pull in. A gradual, controlled pulling in of the abdominal muscles helps to bring about an upward movement of the diaphragm and so to produce a well-sustained, steady vocal tone if the action takes place during vocalization.

It is probably best to minimize or to eliminate entirely breathing characterized by action of the upper chest (clavicular breathing). Such breathing frequently results in a strained humping of the chest and shoulders, and so interferes with easy breath flow. In this awkward and strained position, which is associated with neck and throat tension, proper reinforcement of tone in the resonating cavities becomes difficult so that voice production becomes unnecessarily effortful. It is apparently also more difficult to obtain an adequate supply of breath with "clavicular breathing" so that the speaker finds it necessary to pause for breath more often than with abdominal, thoracic, or medial breathing.

Generally, we do not consider it either advisable or necessary to stress manner of breathing. As a practical matter, we have found that it is usually possible to modify and improve breath use for vocalization without direct attention to the individual's breathing activity. Correction of posture and attention to the initiation and maintenance of proper vocal tones are usually sufficient and effective.

Therapy for Voice Disturbances

The classroom teacher who suspects that one of his students has a voice disturbance should first make certain that he is not imposing a personal preference. Second, the teacher should be certain that no physical condition requiring medical attention is present before any treatment is undertaken. It follows also that if a psychological problem underlies the voice defect, the problem and the child rather than the defect should be treated. With these precautions in mind, the classroom teacher with an understanding of voice production may be of real help to those children with defects of quality, pitch, or loudness of voice. The classroom teacher, as well as the speech correctionist, will also do well to bear in mind that despite the best of teachings, not all defects are fully remediable. Sometimes the most apparent defect resists specific improvement, but overall improvement may still be attained if other, not so readily apparent, aspects of voice and speech are trained to the fullest extent. For example, a child with a weakened, soft palate may necessarily speak with characteristic nasal quality. If this child is helped to articulate clearly, but not pedantically, and to have a wide and flexible pitch range reflective of changes in thought and feeling, the overall impression is likely to be favorable despite the persistence of nasality. Similarly, a child with a high-pitched voice, especially if the child is a boy, may not be able to do much about lowering his fundamental pitch if he is one intended by nature to have a high pitch. Such a child can still be helped if he learns to make full use of his pitch range, and can produce voice that is readily audible and is meaningfully emphatic according to speech content. With these points in mind, several specific suggestions for dealing with particular aspects of vocal deficiency may be considered.

Pitch Level and Range

As indicated earlier, appropriate pitch for an individual should be determined by factors other than either the listener's or speaker's liking for a given pitch range. The other factors are anatomic, including the length and mass of the individual's vocal bands, the relationship of vocal bands to the laryngeal structure, and the size and shape of the other resonating cavities. We are aware that pitch varies inversely as the length and directly as the tension of the vibrating body. Changes in length and tension enable the speaker to produce a range of normal or natural pitches that comprise a physically appropriate pitch range. The production of vocal tones consistent with the intellectual and affective content of speech comprises an appropriate pitch range for speaking.

The natural or "optimum" *pitch* is that pitch level at which an individual is able to vocalize most efficiently. This is the level at which good quality, loudness, and ease of production are found. For most persons, natural or optimum pitch level is about one-fourth to one-third above the lowest level within the range of pitch levels at which vocalization can occur. It can be found by having the individual intone as low as he can and then having him raise his level a step at a time until he reaches falsetto. If twelve levels are produced, it is likely that level three or four will be the optimum pitch. It helps considerably to use a piano and to match pitch levels with those of the piano in finding total pitch range.

If the child's habitual pitch is found to be more than one level below or above his natural level, it is advisable to train him to initiate voice on his natural level. The same advice, of course, holds for adults. It is well to remember, however, that young growing children have changes in their natural pitch as laryngeal growth takes place. After physiological adolescence, growth changes are not so great, and natural pitch should become pretty well stabilized.

The determination of natural pitch is a point of departure in the production of an adequate and effective pitch range. For most persons, voice will be best produced in that part of the pitch range between the natural pitch and one-third below the highest pitch. Thus, for a child with a fifteen-level range, pitch levels from five to ten are likely to be produced with good quality and with ease. With training, the child can learn to initiate voice for usual conversational purposes on his natural pitch level, and to use several levels above it for variety, emphasis, and appropriate feeling or affect. There is no objection to the use of a level or two below natural level if the child has a fairly wide range. If the range is narrow, it is probably best to avoid dropping more than one level below natural pitch. The danger of dropping two levels below natural pitch for a person with a narrow pitch range is that effortful, breathy voice may be produced which may be harmful to the speaker.

Breathiness

Vocal quality characterized by breathiness results from air "leakage" between vocal bands during voice production. The ultimate of breathiness is intentionally whispered speech. Voiceless consonants are, of course, breathy, and appropriately so. Vowels, however, and voiced consonants should be produced without any obvious breathiness.

Breathiness may result from overrelaxed vocalization with associated partial approximation of the vocal bands. If a person's voice is pitched too low in terms of his natural pitch range, the tension of the vocal bands will be less than optimum, and the voice is likely to be breathy. If a person is suffering from laryngitis, attempts at vocalization are frequently associated with pain because of contact between swollen vocal bands. A similar condition may be associated with growths on the inner edges of the bands. To avoid or reduce the pain, the speaker is likely to keep his vocal bands in a partially approximated position, and so will speak with breathiness. Figure 8 shows the position of the vocal bands when they are not sufficiently approximated for good voice production, and yet too closely approximated for purposes of normal breathing.

Sometimes a breathy voice is associated with shyness or timidity. A child who speaks quietly because he is afraid to speak aloud may not bring his vocal bands close enough to vocalize without excessive breathiness. Occasionally a "good" but not necessarily timid

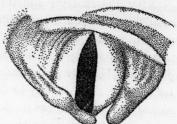

Figure 8. Diagram, adapted from a high-speed photograph, showing vocal bands not sufficiently, approximated for good voice production, and too closely approximated for normal breathing.

Courtesy Bell Telephone Company Laboratories, New York

child will imitate a teacher's low voice used by him to keep his class quiet. Such a child, in his attempt to speak "low and quiet" may also speak breathily.

There are several reasons for children to avoid breathy voice quality. First, the breathy voice is frequently too low in pitch, and vocalization becomes effortful and unpleasant. Second, breathiness is wasteful in terms of length of phrase in speaking. The child, or the adult for that matter, who speaks with excessive breathiness will need to pause for inhalation more often than would otherwise be necessary. In his attempts to establish normal phrasing, he may speak on residual breath, and his speech efforts will sound strained and be strained.

To overcome breathiness it is frequently necessary to have the child become aware of the difference between a breathy and normal voice quality. This may be done by having the child place his hand in front of his mouth while saying a sentence such as "The lamb's name is Annie." Normally, such a sentence, which has no voiceless or plosive consonants, should be produced with little or no breath being felt on the hand. The child should then be directed to "feel" the breath of a sentence such as "Polly wants three crackers," which has both stop plosive and voiceless fricative sounds and is therefore appropriately breathy. If there is no distinct difference in the child's vocalization, another child whose voice is not breathy should be asked to speak the two sentences and the breathy-voiced child directed to hold his hand about six inches in front of the second child's mouth.

After the concepts and the feeling of breathiness and non-breathiness are established, other techniques may be employed to establish normal vocalization. A very simple and often effective technique is simply to direct the child to speak as if breath were precious and to have just as little breath come out as possible. Then, for contrast, the child may be directed to be as breathy as possible, so that the difference can be clearly appreciated.

Another helpful technique is to have the child intone a vowel such as [i] (ee) and to hold the vowel as long as comfortable on a single breath. The vowel [i], because it is relatively tense and high-pitched, is likely to be produced with a minimum of breathiness even by the child who is inclined to be breathy. If this is done successfully, the child may then be directed to intone [a] (ah) and to maintain the sound until he begins to become breathy, or until he needs to inhale. Then he should repeat the effort with a reduced loudness but without obvious breathiness. In this way the child can learn how "quietly" he may speak without becoming breathy. The same technique may be used with a change in pitch rather than loudness so that the child may learn at which pitch level he becomes breathy, and so avoid that pitch level.

Other recommended exercises include saying as much of the alphabet as possible or counting as long as is comfortable on a single breath. When quantity of production becomes the objective, the child is spontaneously likely to conserve breath. As soon as possible, of course, he should be given an opportunity to apply what he has learned in his exercises to reading aloud and conversational speech. Although he should not be interrupted in his normal speaking efforts because of breathiness, the therapist should work out a system of signals to tell the child, when he has concluded his effort, whether he has been successful in his control of breathiness. The teacher, working with the therapist, may apply this approach in the classroom situation.

Nasality

Positive or excessive nasality as a characteristic voice quality, as we pointed out earlier, is associated with a relaxed soft palate during the act of vocalization. In the absence of specific anomaly involving the palate,[1] nasality may occur either because of generally slow or sluggish palatal action or because of specific "retarded" action of the soft palate after the articulation of appropriately nasal sounds. If there is generally sluggish soft palate action, speech as a whole is likely to sound nasal. If there is a limited failure of the soft palate to be elevated quickly immediately following the production of a nasal consonant, the sound or sounds produced after the nasal are likely to be partially nasalized. In the latter case, words such as *me, many,* and *among* are produced as though all the sounds were nasal.

In some children, nasality is associated with an apparent attitude of indifference to their environment. These children seem to have an "I don't care" attitude and seem unwilling to speak in particular or to act in general with sufficient energy to elevate their soft palates to avoid nasality.

Children who have had their adenoids removed change frequently from having markedly denasal voices to having characteristically nasal voices. This change can be appreciated when we realize that when enlarged adenoids are present, a child does not need to elevate his soft palate very much to obstruct the opening to the nasal cavity. After the removal of the adenoidal tissue, the habit of partial elevation of the soft palate may persist, and nasality may then occur during the production of all speech sounds.

Regardless of the cause of nasality, if therapy is in order it should begin with giving the child awareness of how a nasal voice sounds and, if the child is capable of such understanding, how nasality occurs. The child can easily learn to recognize nasality by having him listen to his teacher intentionally nasalize a sentence such as *The sailor shouted "All aboard!"* or *This is the house that Jack built* and then listening to the same sentences spoken without intentional nasality. Both of these sentences, incidentally, contain no nasal consonants and so provide no temptation to nasalize because of proximity of a sound to a nasal consonant.

[1] See chapter 15 for a discussion of cleft palate speech.

The child inclined toward nasality may also learn how it feels to be nasal by pinching his nostrils while uttering either of the above exercise sentences. If pressure is felt or if there is a feeling of stuffiness in the nose, it means that breath has entered the nasal cavities that should have been emitted through the mouth. Other sentences that may be used for establishing physical awareness of inappropriate nasality include:

> I would like to go to the big city.
> Please take care of the dog.
> The cat chased the bird up the tree.
> Polly likes to eat.
> Joe hopped to the store.
> Peg played jacks.

The same sentences may be used to help the child *see* his nasality. This can be accomplished by placing a cold hand mirror under the child's nostrils while he repeats one of the sentences having no nasal consonants. Clouding of the mirror by the warm air that escapes from the nostrils is visual evidence of positive and inappropriate nasality.

Once awareness is present in a child not organically involved and he is motivated to overcome his nasality, the following techniques may be employed:

RAISING THE SOFT PALATE. Have the child stand before a mirror and yawn with his mouth wide open. The child should be directed to note that his soft palate tends to lift up. He should learn how this feels as well as how it looks for the soft palate to elevate.

The child may be directed to blow up a previously stretched balloon. Even if he fails to blow the balloon to a large size, he should feel the action of the soft palate in his attempt.

The child may be directed to say [ɑ] (ah) while holding his nose. All sound should come through the mouth, and no stuffiness should be felt. Then the child should be permitted to produce a nasalized [ɑ]. The process should be repeated with other vowel sounds and with such words as *boy, girl, tree, tall, go,* and *bread,* and short phrases such as *go away, pretty girl, big boy,* and *a slice of bread.* If the child is old enough to understand the difference between nasal and nonnasal sounds, he should be encouraged to make up his own list of words and phrases for practice.

EAR TRAINING. The child can be helped to distinguish between appropriate and inappropriate nasality by listening to appropriate articulation of the following pairs of words:

moo	two	an	at
me	bee	wing	wig
my	by	I'm	I'll
no	go	in	it
may	pay	aim	ape

It may also help if the therapist informs the child that occasionally words in the second column will be intentionally nasalized and the child is to signal when he becomes aware of such nasalization. The therapist with good control, who can turn nasality off and on at will, may go beyond single words to pairs of phrases and sentences.

If a recorder and playback are available, ready use may be made of such an instrument in helping the child to recognize his own nasality. A sentence or two may be recorded by the nasal child and the same material by another child without the defect. The child "in training" may then hear the difference in voice quality between himself and a peer. Later, recordings may be used to help the child recognize improvement in exercises and for parts of readings or conversation. Many children enjoy a chance to do intentionally what they are seeking to improve. Permission "to do the wrong thing" should be given so that the child may practice and so gain voluntary control over nasality. The same approach, of course, is also relevant for other aspects of voice therapy as well as for the improvement of articulation.

GENERAL ARTICULATORY ACTIVITY. Often the child who speaks nasally will also be one whose overall articulatory activity lacks precision and clearness. For this child, in the interest of improving articulation in general as well as nasality in particular, more precise and energetic articulatory activity is recommended. With increased activity of the lips and tongue, there will also be a reflexive increase in energetic activity of the soft palate. The child should also be instructed to direct all nonnasal sounds through his mouth and to increase the feeling of front-of-the-mouth activity. Words and phrases such as the following might be used in drill work and incorporated into practice sentences and conversational speech.

two	do
treat	tweet
pooh	boo
chew	food
tuck	buck
see	saw
lick	tick
bing	bang
come along	sing a song
take some tea	beat the drum
red rose	don't trip
all aboard	pickled peppers
leave the boat	hit the deck
stay away	broken bones

Denasality

Some children speak as though they have either chronically stuffed noses or enlarged adenoids that block the entrance of sound into the nasal cavities. These children need to be helped to become aware of adequate nasal resonance when it is required.

Humming with lips relatively relaxed so that a sensation of tickling is experienced is a recommended technique for establishing nasal resonance. Another useful device is the intentional lengthening of nasal consonants. The child may be instructed to hum and then follow the hum with a vowel. Specifically, the exercise might proceed as follows:

1. Hum gently on a sustained breath, first with the sound *m*,

then *n*, and then [ŋ] (*ng*). Repeat each hum three or four times.

2. Begin a hum and then blend with a vowel.

3. Prolong an initial nasal sound and blend with a vowel as in *mmm-a*, and *nnn-oo*.

4. Begin with a lengthened nasal, blend with a vowel, and end with a lengthened nasal as in *mmmannn, nnnoonnn*.

Other exercises might include articulating such words as *me, my, moo, may, meal, nail, now, new, never, nice, sing, long*, and *running* with intentional lengthening of the nasal consonants.

Sentences incorporating words with more than a usual number of nasal consonants should be made up and conversation with such words and sentences should be practiced. Whenever possible, the child should be encouraged to make up words and sentences so that he may have the pleasure of creative activity as well as practice.

Inappropriate Loudness

Most children whose speech patterns are a result of identification with normal adults speak loud enough to be heard. Those who speak with inadequate loudness or with voice louder than the occasion demands reflect either their own personalities or the personalities of the adults with whom they identify. Only in the rarest instances is there an organic basis for either a weak or an overloud voice. The comparatively rare organic causes include hearing loss, weakness of the muscles of the larynx, and weakness of the muscles involved in respiration. Furthermore, it is extremely unlikely that the carrying power of the voice is significantly related to the individual's breath capacity or the manner in which he breathes while speaking. As Van Riper and Irwin (11, p. 258) emphasize, "So long as sufficient air pressure is engendered below the vocal folds, it does not matter how it is created, at least so far as adequate loudness is concerned. But we must have a greater air pressure to have louder speech." In the absence of organic pathology, the will to be heard is sufficient to supply the energy to provide for the necessary pressure below the vocal folds so that they are closed firmly, held together firmly for an appropriate length of time, and then blown apart from their occluded (approximated) position to produce a vocal tone loud enough to be easily heard.

Occasionally we find children who because of poor posture, or from anxiety, get in the way of their own efforts of effective breathing for speech. A child with a "caved-in" abdominal area may not be able to breathe comfortably and deeply enough for purposes of speech. Obviously, the slump and the associated cave-in need to be corrected. Similarly, any other postural defect which interferes with adequate air-intake and easy control of breath output needs to be corrected. Such correction might well be directed to emphasizing the need for the abdominal area to be relaxed and to "push out" in inhalation and to contract and "pull in" gradually in controlled exhalation.

Another fault found in some children is the attempt to vocalize and speak during inhalation. This fault, in the absence of neuropathology, is usually a result of an anxious effort to continue talking when the child's breath supply has been expended. The creation of awareness of what the child is doing can be established by directing him to do intentionally what he is doing unconsciously. Such a child is also likely to gain from breathing exercises that emphasize abdominal control of outgoing breath.

The Overloud Voice

Aside from the possibility of a hearing loss which prevents proper monitoring of the voice as it is being produced, the overloud voice is likely to be a product of imitation or an aspect of the personality of the speaker. Our experience as clinicians suggests that most children who speak too loudly are either imitating their parents or competing with their siblings for attention from their parents. We have had parents come to us with complaints about their children's loud voices. They presented their complaints in our offices in voices loud enough to reach the last row of a 40-row auditorium without electrical amplification. The research of Paul (9) supports our impression that children of overloud speaking parents speak more loudly than do children of softer-speaking parents. Moses (8), talking as a psychoanalyst interested in voice problems, points out that, on the one hand, fearful people speak fearfully (in voices not loud enough to be heard easily) and that the voice of authority, in our culture, on the other hand, tends to be a loud voice. Certainly, we tend to associate aggression and assertiveness with loud voice.

The Weak Voice

In the absence of organic involvement, we may assume that a weak voice is a reflection either of a timid personality or of the reaction of the individual to a given speaking situation. Most children who are unsure of themselves, or of what they have to say, tend to talk with a weak voice. The voice, regardless of the particular speech content, is also saying "Maybe if I don't talk loudly I won't be noticed, or what I have to say won't be heard, and I will be left alone." Occasionally, however, the weak voice may be the result of imitation, and the inadequate loudness has become habitual. The reproduction of such a voice on a playback is a necessary first step in the modification of this manner of voice production.

Treatment for Inappropriate Loudness

Except for children whose hearing difficulty impairs their ability to monitor their voices, or who have some other organic basis for either their weak or overloud voice, an adequately loud voice should be attainable for all children. Treatment should include the following aspects: (1) an assessment of the voices of the members of the family and other key persons in the child's environment; (2) an evaluation of the personality and adjustment factors that may be associated with the child's manner of vocalization; (3) an evaluation of the specific situations (e.g., the child's voice in the classroom compared with his voice in play activity) that may be associated

with inadequate voice; (4) an evaluation of the overall characteristics of the child's voice, in addition to the degree of loudness; and
(5) an objectification of the voice through recording and playback
so that the child may hear himself approximately as others hear him.

In many instances, children who have been brought to our clinic
for their voice problems have been treated through their parents.
We have permitted parents to hear their recorded voices and invited
them to accept treatment—*in the interest of their child*. Sometimes
we accepted the child for treatment only if the parent or parents
accepted concurrent voice therapy. Occasionally, we have encouraged parents to subdue a sibling just enough to give the child concerned a fair chance in the vocal competition. Occasionally, we have
had to advise counseling for the parents while the child, *after
medical clearance,* was undergoing symptom treatment.

In instances where we felt that an adjustment problem was basic
to the voice difficulty, we have recommended treatment by a qualified psychotherapist. Whenever possible, we prefer that the choice
of a psychotherapist be made with the help of the family physician.
Occasionally we have found that a child's voice problem was limited
to the classroom. For reasons that developed out of the relationship
between a child and a teacher—and sometimes it is a previous
rather than a present teacher—the child had become anxiously concerned about his adequacy as a student. Obviously, in such instances, treatment should be directed at the improvement of the
child-to-school relationship rather than to the vocal symptoms.

When, after investigation, we are convinced that there is nothing
organically or emotionally wrong with the child who is speaking
either not loudly enough or too loudly, direct treatment of the
symptoms is in order. As we suggested earlier, an overall evaluation of the vocal characteristics of the child is then undertaken. Our
experience suggests that the weak voice is often also a breathy
voice, and one likely to be too low in pitch. Often, but not always,
we find that the loud voice is apt to be too high in pitch. The first
order of the procedure for correcting degree of loudness is to determine the child's normal pitch range and his optimum pitch. When

these are determined (see pages 282-284), the speech clinician should help the child to become aware of them, to initiate voice habitually at optimum pitch, and to vocalize within the optimum pitch range. Breathiness, if it is found to be present, should be treated by procedures indicated on pages 284-286.

Ordinarily, after the procedures outlined and after the child has been made aware of the loudness level of his voice through playback, adequate loudness is attained. Occasionally, however, old habits are maintained and the child's voice, though appropriate in pitch and not characterized by breathiness, is still not appropriate in loudness. If it continues to be weak, procedures such as those listed below should be productive of improvement.

1. Record successively the voice of the weak-voiced child and a peer with adequate voice. Have the child make the comparisons and rerecord until clinician and child are satisfied with the result.

2. If available, employ visual feedback apparatus so that the child may see when his voice is at the proper level. Most tape recorders are equipped with "magic eyes" which may be so employed. An oscilloscope may serve both to impress the child and to provide him with a basis for visual monitoring. A simpler and more readily available apparatus, though perhaps not quite so impressive, is the raised hand and approving look of the teacher or clinician when the child's voice is at a proper level and the lowered (thumb-down) hand and disappointed (but *not* disapproving) look when the voice level is not loud enough.

3. Emphasis on clarity of articulation with lengthening of the vowels and nasal consonants is often of considerable help. Support for this procedure may be found in the investigation of House and Fairbanks (6) that overall intelligibility *decreased markedly* when the experimental subjects spoke at reduced loudness levels. By emphasizing clarity of articulation, the child is likely to use greater energy not only for articulatory activity but also for the accompanying respiratory behavior while speaking. The result is a reflexive increase in air pressure below the vocal folds, and a louder voice.

4. The game of *competitive speaking* or "Who can talk loudest

in the group without shouting?" may be employed as motivation and play. It may be of help if some of the competitors are encouraged at the beginning of the game to give the weak-voiced participant a chance to be heard. Later on, the erstwhile weak-voiced member should be permitted free and open competition.

5. The need for the child to adjust his voice level to the listener in terms of distance between listener and speaker may need emphasis. A teacher may bring about such an adjustment by asking a child a question when he is standing close to the child and then intentionally moving away from him. Another technique is to have the child stand in front of the room and speak just loud enough to be heard by his classmates in the first third of the room, then in the second third as well, and finally throughout the room. This procedure impresses the child with the need to change his voice level according to the number of listeners and the distance between himself and the furthest listener.

6. Pretended situations, such as announcing the arrival of a train or plane, giving orders to a military group, or speaking in a crowded and noisy place (a train station or a plane waiting room), can also be useful to help the child to be heard under difficult situations. Artificially competitive noise situations, such as speaking against a masking noise or buzzing noise, may also be used. If these techniques are employed, *care must be exercised that the optimum pitch range is maintained*. We would not want a child to speak loudly at the expense of vocal nodules.

Control of Breath for Speaking

As indicated earlier in our discussion of breathing faults, difficulty in breathing is not a frequent cause of vocal difficulty for the otherwise normal child. We should be alert to see that the children do not attempt to vocalize while inhaling. Vocalization should occur on an easy, controlled exhalation of breath. Because only a rare and occasional child will attempt vocalization on inhalation, we recommend that the teacher who has such a child in his class arrange for him to be given corrective instruction on an individual basis. It is better for most children to do their breathing while speaking without special awareness or consciousness of the action involved.

If a child shows throat or laryngeal effort in speaking, attention might be directed to abdominal control for expiration. Usually such attention serves to distract the child from excessive tension in the upper part of the respiratory mechanism. Other therapeutic suggestions relative to breathing faults were indicated earlier (see pages 280-281 and 284-286, BREATHING FAULTS.)

Review of Principles for Correcting Voice Defects

1. *Medical clearance is a must* for any child who presents a voice problem and for whom vocal therapy is contemplated. A child who develops a vocal disturbance should be examined by a physician and, if at all possible, by a throat specialist for the detection and treatment of possible physical pathology before consideration is given to voice training.

2. When a child's vocal defects seem to be associated with personality disturbances, referral to a competent counselor or psychotherapist is in order. It should not be overlooked, however, that poor vocal habits may persist after the initial cause is no longer present. This principle holds for vocal defects of both physical and psychological origin.

3. Often vocal defects are temporary and of short duration and call for patience and understanding rather than active treatment.

4. A voice is a product of the mechanism that produces it. The mechanism belongs to the individual, and the product should be consistent with its features. Neither the professional speech clinician nor the teacher, nor any other person who may influence the child, has a right to decide what kind of voice the child should have. Fundamentally, this decision was made by the way the child was physically endowed. The objective of vocal therapy is to help the child to make the best possible use of his vocal endowment.

5. The classroom teacher, especially if he is respected and liked, has a personal responsibility that his own voice be free of undesirable traits which his children may imitate.

6. Vocal habits, both good and bad, tend to persist. Considerable motivation is necessary to help a child to wish to change his defective voice and to maintain vigilance that changes are maintained.

7. The child with a vocal defect should be helped to become aware of what his defect is like acoustically, and how it feels. He needs to be aware of how his voice sounds and feels when it is at its best. Objective attitudes and objective listening to his own voice and comparing his own voice with others by listening to "on-the-spot" recordings are of help.

8. Often a "negative" approach is helpful. By creating awareness of the nature of the undesirable vocal traits and how they are produced, voluntary control may be established. Thus a child, by intentionally *doing what is wrong,* learns to know what he is doing, and so becomes conscious of what he should not do. By contrast, awareness must be created of the "right way" to produce voice and to replace the undesirable characteristic with a desirable one.

References and Suggested Readings

1. ANDERSON, V. A., *Training the Speaking Voice.* (2nd ed.) New York: Oxford University Press, 1961, Chapters 2-5. (A clear exposition of the voice mechanism and principles and techniques for voice improvement. Excellent practice materials for the teacher and clinician.)

2. BERRY, M. F. and J. EISENSON, *Speech Disorders: Principles and Practices of Therapy.* New York: Appleton-Century-Crofts, 1956, Chapters 9 and 10. (These chapters include a more advanced and technical consideration of voice disturbances and their treatment than will be found in most of the other suggested readings.)

3. EISENSON, J., *The Improvement of Voice and Diction.* New York: Macmillan, 1958, Chapters 2-9. (These chapters include a discussion of the voice mechanism and expositions of techniques and procedures for voice improvement. The principles are applicable to school-age children. Practice materials may be used with the older children.)

4. FAIRBANKS, G., *Voice and Articulation Drillbook*. (2nd ed.) New York: Harper and Bros., 1960, Chapters 10-15. (A clear and concise exposition of the vocal aspects of speech. Includes practice materials. Especially recommended is Chapter 11, which discusses techniques for determining one's natural pitch level.)

5. GRAY, G. W., and C. M. WISE, *The Bases of Speech*. New York: Harper and Bros., 1959, Chapter 3. (An advanced consideration of the physiological basis for voice production.)

6. HOUSE, A., and G. FAIRBANKS, "The Influence of Consonantal Environment upon the Secondary Acoustical Characteristics of Vowels." *Journal of Acoustical Society of America,* **XXV** (1953), 105-113.

7. JOHNSON, W. (ed.), *Speech Handicapped School Children*. (Rev. ed.) New York: Harper and Bros., 1956, Chapter 4. (The material on disorders of voice is written by James F. Curtis. It presents a scientific orientation to the understanding of the vocal mechanism as an instrument for producing sound. Includes a discussion of the most frequent voice problems in school-age children.)

8. MOSES, P. J., *The Voice of Neurosis*. New York: Grune and Stratton, 1954. (A psychiatrist's approach to persons with voice problems.)

9. PAUL, J. E., *An Investigation of Parent-Child Relationships in Speech: Intensity and Duration*. Ph.D. thesis (Purdue University, 1951).

10. "Science Notes." *The New York Times,* April 17, 1955.

11. VAN RIPER, C., and J. V. IRWIN, *Voice and Articulation*. Englewood Cliffs, N.J.: Prentice-Hall, 1958, Chapters 7-13. (The chapters explain voice production and problems related to voice disturbances. Good upper-level material.)

12. WILLIAMSON, A. B., "Diagnosis and Treatment of Seventy-Two Cases of Hoarse Voice." *Quarterly Journal of Speech,* **XXXI** (1945), 189-202.

Problems

1. What are the characteristics of a normal, effective voice?

2. What is the percentage of voice disturbances in children compared with articulatory defects?

3. Why is puberty a period of frequent vocal disturbance?

4. Listen to a radio "soap opera" program. What are the vocal characteristics of the "hero"? Why are you able to recognize the "villain" even before you have him identified by the contents of the script?

5. What is the role of identification in the formation of poor vocal habits?

6. What is nasality? How do you distinguish the characteristics from denasality? When you have a cold are you more likely to be nasal or denasal? Why?

7. Why is it important for voice cases to be given medical clearance before undertaking therapy? If you are not certain of your answer, read A. B. Williamson, "Diagnosis and Treatment of Seventy-Two Cases of Hoarse Voice," *Quarterly Journal of Speech,* **XXXI** (1945), 189-202.

8. What is the danger involved in high-pitched screaming? (Read D. K. Wilson's "Children with Vocal Nodules," *Journal of Speech and Hearing Disorders,* **26** (1961), 19-25, for some pertinent material on the question.)

13

Stuttering

General Observations

WITH THE incidence of stuttering close to 1 percent among school-age children, it is likely that almost every classroom teacher, and certainly every speech clinician, with more than a year or two of experience has had some dealings with a stutterer. The more experienced clinicians and teachers may have made several observations about stutterers, if not about stuttering. They may have become satisfied as to what the cause of stuttering might be, and possibly what to do about the stutterers *if time permitted*. Usually, time did not permit them to put tentative conclusions to the test of actual trial. Nevertheless, all classroom teachers, whether or not they are assisted by clinicians, are likely to have to do something about their own stutterers, even if they cannot do as much as they might wish.

Among some of the observations made by experienced teachers and clinicians, which have been put to the test, are the following:

1. There are more stutterers among boys than among girls. Research on the incidence of stuttering shows a ratio of two to ten males for each female stutterer. Probably an average ratio is four male stutterers to each female stutterer.

2. The severity of stuttering tends to be greater among boys than among girls.

3. Stuttering tends to last longer for boys than for girls.

4. No stutterer, regardless of the severity of his difficulty, stutters at all times. Almost all stutterers have times when their speech is relatively if not "completely" free of significant hesitancies, blocks, repetitions, or prolongations. In group-speaking situations, and in singing, stutterers are likely to do about as well as other children.

5. Stuttering is more likely to begin in the nursery, kindergarten, and primary grades than in the secondary grades. It is comparatively rare for a child to begin stuttering after age fourteen or fifteen.

6. Many young children in the kindergarten and first grade seem to have been on the verge of stuttering without becoming stutterers. They were hesitant and repetitious, but apparently had no awareness of their manner of speaking. By the time these children reached the age of eight or nine, their speech seemed to be "normal" again.

The observations we have just noted are among the relatively few generalizations or "facts" accepted by students of stuttering. Beyond these, there is considerable difference as to the cause of stuttering, and the choice of treatment. We will not attempt to resolve these differences. Instead, we will present several of the more prevalent points of view, and suggest what the classroom teacher can safely do about children who are considered stutterers. We shall also suggest therapeutic approaches that are widely used with considerable success by speech clinicians in and out of school settings.

The Nature of Stuttering

From the point of view of overt speech behavior, stuttered speech is characterized by hesitancies, blocks, repetitions, and/or prolongations of sounds in excess of normal. These may be referred to as dysfluencies. Because many young children of preschool and primary school age have so-called dysfluencies which, according to occasion, may occur in as much as 10 percent of utterance, we should be liberal in our concept of normal. In addition to dysfluencies, the stutterer's voice is likely to be somewhat tense and narrow in pitch range and in modulation. Most children who regard themselves as stutterers also entertain feelings of anxiety and apprehension about some speaking situations or about communicative speaking in general.

Primary Stuttering

Many speech therapists distinguish between two types of stuttering. When the speech symptoms are limited to repetitions, hesitancies, and prolongations, and when these occur without any evidence that the child is aware of them, or does anything to avoid speaking, the child may be characterized as a primary stutterer. Van Riper (21, p. 351) adds another criterion for primary stuttering. He reserves the term for the dysfluencies of speech which appear under conditions when most children speak with comparative fluency. According to Van Riper, if a child speaks with nonfluencies (dysfluencies) so often that the speech calls attention to itself and significantly interferes with communication, the child is a primary stutterer rather than a "normally nonfluent child." This distinction is accepted by the authors of this text.

Secondary Stuttering

If speech dysfluencies become associated with facial grimaces, tics, or other forms of spasmic movements either of the articulatory mechanism or of other parts of the body not ordinarily directly concerned with speech production, we have secondary stuttering. It is usually assumed that the nonlinguistic associates of stuttering arise initially as an effort on the part of the speaker either to delay, distract, or avoid speech, or as a device to "break through" a block that occurs, or which it is feared may occur, in the speech effort. When nonlinguistic, overt, accessory activity takes place, we may assume that the stutterer has become aware of his hesitations, repetitions, blocks, and/or prolongations, and is doing something in an attempt to modify what takes place in his speech, or what he anticipates may take place.

The stutterer with secondary symptoms, in contrast with the primary stutterer, is aware of the nature of his speech. He has begun to respond to himself as an atypical speaker, if not an atypical person. His accessory movements reveal both apprehension of what he may do and struggle against doing it. Sometimes the struggle against doing it precedes the actual articulatory and vocal effort. At other times the struggle seems to interrupt the effort. Usually, at least at the outset, the struggle behavior seems to help the stutterer to begin his speech effort or to resume his interrupted effort. Unfortunately, the accessory movements tend to become incorporated in the overall pattern of the stuttering. In time they constitute merely another factor that the stutterer must try to modify in his fight against stuttering.

Frequently the breathing of the secondary stutterer shows marked irregularity. Sometimes the stutterer takes a deep breath and then expires most of it before beginning to speak. This, in our judgment, is a breathing mannerism that many stutterers are taught by poorly informed adults who confuse stuttering symptoms with stuttering cause. Occasionally, a stutterer attempts to talk while inhaling. Often stutterers interrupt their speaking to inhale before there is any physiological or speech need to do so. Many stutterers modify the normal inspiration-expiration ratio (a short period of inhalation followed by a considerably longer period for exhalation) so that their inhalation-exhalation ratio is about one to one.

Associated Speech Defects

We have already mentioned that stutterers frequently have defective voices which are usually characterized by tension and narrow pitch range. In many cases, also, articulatory defects are present. Sound substitutions among young children, and lisping and lalling, occur more frequently among stutterers than is normal. Often enough to be significant, the histories of stutterers reveal that their speech onset was somewhat slower than for nonstutterers who were not clearly delayed-speech children. It is probably no chance coincidence that recent studies strongly suggest marked similarities in the family background of stutterers, delayed-speech children, and children with defective articulation. For all these groups, the attitudes of the parents appear to be marked by unrealistically high expectations for speech as well as for social behavior in general. This observation, of course, does not mean that in every instance the parents of a stutterer are demanding, unrealistic, high-aspiring persons. It does mean that these attitudes are found more often in parents of stutterers than among parents of children who do not stutter, so that the possibility of a relationship between the two cannot be overlooked.

Before closing this section and going to other aspects of the problem of stuttering we might pause for the definitions of primary and secondary stuttering.

Primary Stuttering is speech characterized by repetitions, prolongations, and/or hesitations that take place without apparent awareness or anxiety, and without evidence of special effort or struggle behavior on the part of the child. It is different from the normal dysfluencies that are present in young children because they occur more frequently and in conditions and situations when most young children are relatively fluent.

Secondary Stuttering is speech characterized by the occurrence of more than normal repetitions, prolongation, and/or hesitation associated with some form of struggle behavior or accessory, spasmic activity. From the point of view of the speaker, awareness, apprehension, and anxiety are associated either with specific speech situations or with communicative speaking in general.

For varying reasons, some authorities do not accept the terms or the implications of *primary* and *secondary* stuttering. Johnson believes that the early dysfluencies of children are normal, however frequently and under what circumstances they occur, and does not regard the dysfluencies (disfluencies) as a first or primary stage of stuttering. His recent investigations reveal, however, that "For the 'stutterers' the median number of repetitions that involved either words or syllables was approximately six per hundred words, and for the 'non-stutterers' the median number was between one and two per hundred words. The median numbers of all other kinds of disfluency were about seven for the clinical group and five for the control group per hundred words." (14, p. 135).

Bloodstein also argues against the use of the terms primary and secondary stuttering. On the basis of his clinical experience, he suggests four developmental phases or overlapping stages for stuttering but cautions that in some instances individual children who are regarded as stutterers may skip whole phases. The first three phases are considered by Bloodstein to be most differentiating. The phases are characterized as follows:

Phase 1. The child's difficulty is usually episodic with repetitions the chief characteristic. *Prolongations, forcings, and hard contacts* and various associated symptoms ordinarily found among advanced stutterers may also be present.

Phase 2. The child's difficulty becomes increasingly chronic, though it may fluctuate considerably in severity. Most of the "stutterings" occur on the major parts of speech. The child now thinks of himself as a stutterer but apparently does not avoid opportunities to speak and ". . . has little or no concern about his stuttering except in severe cases or at moments of unusual difficulty."

Phase 3. The child's difficulties in speaking have begun to become *situational* in that he has more difficulties, and anticipation of difficulties, in some situations than in others. The stutterer has now an elaborately developed symptomology including devices for postponement, starting, and release. Despite these, he apparently continues to be comfortable about speaking, or at least does not avoid opportunities to speak. Toward the close of phase 3, there begins to be evidence of emotional reactions to his stuttering and, in this respect, signals the fourth stage.

Phase 4. The individual, who may now be quite "grown up" is sensitive about his speech. Many young children, however, may show this sensitivity shortly after the onset of their difficulty. In many instances the individual blocks and is apprehensive that he will block if required to talk. Nevertheless, in most play activities and in noncommunicative speaking the stutterer is likely to be free of his speech difficulties.

Conditions Associated with Stuttering

We indicated earlier that no stutterer, regardless of the severity of his stuttering, stutters every time he speaks. Even severe secondary stutterers are often free of stuttering, and sometimes even free of anxiety that they may stutter. Parents of stutterers, teachers, and even the stutterers themselves may be aware that they can engage in choral activity without stuttering, that they can talk aloud to themselves with normal fluency, and that they can usually talk to pets or other animals without difficulty. Many stutterers can talk fluently while playing, especially if the talk is on a nonsense level. Some stutterers can talk normally to younger persons and a few can talk to a selected peer or even an adult without difficulty or with less than usual difficulty. Stuttering, then, may be regarded as a situational problem. We have suggested some situations conducive to relatively free-from-stuttering speech. Are there any general situations conducive to stuttering? Recent research suggests an affirmative answer.

Brown (6), in several studies, found that stutterers tend to have verbal cues or indicators that are related to increased stuttering. These include: initial words in sentences; longer words in sentences; more nouns, verbs, and adverbs than other parts of speech; and accented syllables within words.

Eisenson and Horowitz (9) found that stutterers had increased difficulty with reading material as the intellectual significance of the material was increased.

Eisenson and Wells (10) found that stutterers had increased

difficulty when they were shifted from choral reading with normal speakers to solo reading and were responsible for communicating what they were reading aloud.

All the above studies and others available in the literature strongly suggest that there are two factors or situations conducive to increased stuttering. These are: (1) awareness that what is to be spoken has intellectual content; and (2) awareness of communicative responsibility for the speech content. It is not surprising, therefore, that Bloodstein (3), in what might be considered a converse study, found that adolescent and adult stutterers as a group reported that their stuttering was reduced or absent when they felt no need to make a favorable impression and when they did not feel individually responsible for their utterance. This, as we pointed out earlier, is in line with the observations of most teachers who have observed stutterers in their periods of fluency and periods of relative difficulty.

Beyond these linguistic and environmental situations, which tend to be related to the incidence of stuttering, there are other factors which apparently influence speech control. Most stutterers have increased difficulty when they are fatigued. Stutterers tend to stutter more when they expect to stutter than when such expectancy does not exist. On an individual basis some stutterers expect to stutter in special situations or with specific persons more than they do in other situations or with other persons. By and large, these expectancies tend to be confirmed by actual experience. Even when other speech and associated stuttering manifestations are not present, stutterers experience feelings of apprehension and anxiety because of their anticipation of stuttering. The result is that they respond to themselves as if they had stuttered even though the listener-observer may have seen no external evidence of stuttered speech.

The last point suggests an aspect of stuttering that is deserving of consideration. Although what the listener-observer hears and sees may be important in the evaluation of stuttering, much goes on *within the stutterer that cannot be evaluated by anyone but the stutterer*. How he feels about himself when he anticipates the need for speech is important. How much effort and anxiety does the stutterer entertain when he succeeds in controlling his stuttering? Does the stutterer feel better when his speech seems normally fluent than when he hesitates, blocks, repeats, or prolongs his utterances? These are subjective aspects of stuttering of extreme importance to the individual stutterer even though they do not readily affect the response of the listener. If we appreciate this, we can begin to understand why some adolescents and adults who seem to speak without any of the speech and associated mannerisms of stuttering nevertheless regard themselves as stutterers. They do so, we may conclude, because they feel like stutterers, even though they do not overtly behave like stutterers.

Theoretic Points of View as to the Causes of Stuttering

Theories as to why people stutter are numerous and diverse in their points of view. Many theories once influential, if not dominating, have become reduced in importance, not because they have been disproved or discredited but because their proponents have ceased proposing them or have changed their minds. The attempt in this chapter will be to present several current points of view. This will be done with responsible awareness that we are not including many other points of view which, in a larger or more specialized text, might well be included. The points of view which will be considered in this chapter may be broadly classified along the following lines:

1. Stuttering is a constitutional problem. There are physical reasons that predispose a person to stuttering or that make him a stutterer.

2. Stuttering is essentially a learned form of behavior that may happen to anyone.

3. Stuttering is a manifestation of an underlying personality disorder.

Stuttering as a Constitutional Problem

The proponents of the theoretic position[1] that there is a constitutional predisposition to stuttering point to research studies to support their stand. Some of the findings suggest that as a group stutterers' familial histories include the following as occurring more often than in the population as a whole: (1) more stutterers; (2) more left-handedness; (3) more twins; (4) later onset of speech; and (5) higher incidence of prolonged fevers that might affect the nervous system.

Although the theorists are not unanimous as to the specific constitutional factors associated with stuttering, there is general agreement among them that the stutterer is somehow predisposed to his disorder. Some believe that if the child is fortunate and escapes environmental pressures or tensions, he may safely pass without stuttering through the developmental stage when language behavior is established. If, however, conditions are less fortunate, and either illness or emotional disturbance upsets the child during the speech-development stage, stuttering is likely to result. In other words, constitutional factors provide a subsoil for stuttering. Stuttering itself is a product associated with the subsoil and the specific environmental, physical, or psychological factors that tend to nurture it.

An interesting point of view along this line is held by Travis (20). According to Travis, the child who becomes a stutterer starts life with a deviant cerebral mechanism that tends to prolong infantile behavior and so makes for difficulty in adjustment. The stutterer, in his attempts at speaking, is not successful in inhibiting infantile impulses or speech mannerisms. Childish wishes, hates, and fears force their way into the stutterer's expression and become part of the characteristics of stuttering. The stutterer, as he grows older, is torn between the forces that urge infantile expression and the fears of the consequences of such expression. Travis regards

[1] See bibliography at the end of chapter for specific readings on each of the theoretic positions.

the stutterer's speech as an unhappy compromise between his drive to express himself and his fear of revealing himself.

Stuttering as a Learned Form of Behavior

The proponents of the point of view that stuttering is a learned form of behavior are, as we might expect, opposed to believing that stutterers as a group are significantly different constitutionally in any way from nonstutterers. Instead, children who stutter are considered to be essentially normal children in regard to heredity, physical development, health history, psychological traits, intelligence, or any other single factor about which the first group of theorists we have discussed finds important differences. Johnson (13), a leading proponent of "normality of the stutterer" school, holds that stuttering is a *speech disturbance which can happen to anyone*. How stuttering has its onset and how it becomes established as a reaction to some but not all speaking situations are explained through principles of learning that apply to behavior in general as well as to stuttering in particular.

The early stages of stuttering are explained as resulting from a misevaluation of the dysfluencies normal in young children. Young children of preschool age and in the early primary grades are inclined to be repetitious and hesitant when they talk as well as in other forms of behavior. Parents, teachers, or other adults, who mistake these dysfluencies for stuttering symptoms, and who show concern or anxiety about them, are likely to transmit this attitude to the child. When a child becomes aware of adult anxiety and permits it to affect him, he may approach a speaking situation with an attitude of apprehension. It is not the hesitation or repetition but ". . . the stutterer's anxiety and strain, the fear and the effort with which he pauses or says *uh,* repeats sounds or prolongs them, that serve to distinguish him from the so-called normal speaker" (12, p. 451).

In another publication (14, p. 138) Johnson explains that:

The problem called stuttering begins, then, when the child's speech is felt, usually by the mother, to be not as smooth or as fluent as it ought to be. There seems as a rule to be a quality of puzzlement mixed with slight apprehension and dread about the mother's feelings. She uses the only name she knows for what she thinks must be the matter with her youngster's speech, and that word is "stuttering"—or, if she has grown up in England or certain other parts of the world, "stammering."

... She may not be sure of herself at first in deciding that her child is stuttering, but her use of the word crystallizes her feelings and serves to focus her attention on the hesitations in the speech of her child.

Johnson emphasizes that the mother's feelings and apprehensions tend to become apparent to the child and in time the child "takes from the mother the feelings she has about his speech."

Stuttering, then, may be considered to be a specific anxiety reaction associated with speaking situations. But stuttering and its consequences seem to be unpleasant and apparently more penalizing than rewarding. Normally, behavior that persists is behavior somehow rewarded. Are there any rewards or pleasant aftereffects in stuttering? There are, if we look for them. One of the possible rewards is attention a child may receive that may not otherwise be available to him. The stutterer may learn to enjoy the intensity of reaction and the disturbance he causes by his speech. If he needs these more than he does normal speech, stuttering is likely to persist. In the classroom, the stutterer may be excused from recitations or win sympathy that he may learn to enjoy. He may become a "special child" and be loath to give up that status. Until he is ready to do so, the child who begins to stutter through no fault of his own is likely to continue to stutter. Unfortunately, when the penalties of stuttering begin to exceed the rewards, the habits and attitudes of the stutterer may persist, and many stutterers need help in overcoming them. A few, however, seem able to stop without outside help. These children may have taken an accounting of the assets and liabilities associated with stuttering and have reached a conclusion that became translated into self-modified behavior. Certainly many experienced teachers know youngsters who stuttered in the early grades and who became normal speakers in later grades without outside help.

For those who do not or cannot stop, a theoretic explanation for the continuance of stuttering can be made along these lines: The stutterer continues to fear that he will stutter in a given situation, or on a given word. He becomes tense and apprehensive in anticipation of the situation or word. If, with great effort, he finally manages to speak despite the initial tension and anxiety, he brings about a momentary reduction in the anxiety-tension state. This brief period of relief may be sufficiently pleasurable to reinforce and to perpetuate not only the stuttering but also the entire attitude and pattern of behavior associated with it.

Stuttering as a Manifestation of a Personality Disorder

Earlier, in discussing the point of view of Travis, we pointed out that he felt that stutterers were maladjusted persons who became so because of initial constitutional differences. There are many psychologists and psychoanalysts who emphasize the maladjustment and do not appear to be concerned with the possibility that stutterers are constitutionally different from normal speakers. They regard stuttering as a manifestation of personality disorder and are inclined to agree that the stutterer speaks as he does because of some psychological need that is better satisfied through stuttering than through normal speech. Stutterers are likely to be characterized as infantile, compulsive, dependent, ambivalent, regressive, anxious, insecure, withdrawn, or by some other adjective or combination of adjectives consistent with the specific theoretic formulation or bias of the theorizer. For example, the psychoanalyst Coriat (7) looks upon stutterers as ". . . infants who have compulsively retained the original equivalents of nursing and biting." The equivalents we might note are the specific oral characteristics of the stutterer, the way in which he repeats, hesitates, blocks, or prolongs on the sounds he utters or stops himself from uttering.

Glauber also looks upon stuttering as an expression of an underlying personality involvement associated primarily with an "arrest in ego maturation." According to Glauber, "The fixation is manifested in the speech symptoms and in the total personality" (8, p. 93).

Theorists who believe that stuttering is a manifestation of a personality disorder are able to point to a large number of studies to support their own positions.[2] The results of many of these studies strongly suggest that adolescents and adults who stutter are, on the whole, not as well adjusted as nonstutterers. We might add, however, that seldom do the studies provide evidence to indicate whether the stuttering is the cause of or is caused by the maladjustment. The possibility that the stuttering preceded the maladjustment must be considered by those who look objectively on the overall problem of the stutterer and his stuttering.

Multiple Origin Viewpoints

The points of view we have just presented each sought to explain stuttering as having a single cause. Obviously, theories inconsistent with one another cannot all be correct at all times. There is a possibility, however, that each of the theories, and the theorists, is correct at some times—often enough, we would gather, to satisfy himself, but not often enough to persuade those holding opposing or even supplementary viewpoints. Before leaving the discussion of theories as to the cause of stuttering we will consider two points of view of practicing speech therapists who currently believe that stuttering may have multiple causes. Why any given individual stutters can best be estimated by his individual clinical history and the cause that seems most likely to fit his case.

Stuttering as a Manifestation of Perseveration

Eisenson believes that persons tend to persist in a given mode of behavior even when such behavior is not appropriate when they

[2] See Murphy and FitzSimons (17) for a detailed discussion of the position that stuttering is an expression of underlying personality dynamics.

are confronted with conditions which call for more rapid change than they are capable of making. The tendency for an individual to resist change, and for a mental or motor process to dominate behavior after the situation which originally evoked it is no longer present, is termed *perseveration*. The perseverating phenomenon is normal for all of us. Most often we experience it when tired, sleepy, or under conditions of pressure or tension. We do the same thing or feel the same way even when we are able to recognize that the cause for the doing or feeling has ceased to exist. So, minutes after we have gotten off a bicycle we may still feel that we are riding on it. When tired, and we are required to talk, we tend to repeat utterances more often than the intellectual aspect of the situation requires. If we do not become anxious or apprehensive about our normal inclination to perseverate, we are not likely to fear recurring or similar situations because we have perseverated. There are, however, physiological and psychological conditions conducive to more than a normal amount of perseverative behavior. Among these conditions are brain damage, lowered vitality, the aftereffects of physical or mental shock, and emotional tension and anxiety.

According to Eisenson (8), if an individual is required or feels that he is required to speak under a condition conducive to perseverative behavior, the perseveration will be manifest in speech. Unfortunately, the awareness of blocked or repetitive tendencies in speech may increase the individual's apprehension about his speaking and so aggravate the condition initially responsible for the speech perseveration. The result is a generalized reaction toward speaking that transforms what might otherwise be hesitation, block, repetition, or prolongation (perseverating manifestations) into stuttering.

Speech conditions which are associated with a feeling of responsibility are more likely to be associated with perseverative speech than speech devoid of responsibility. Communicative language content is also associated with perseveration in speaking. Persons who find themselves pressed by their environment, or by their own inner compulsions, to speak intellectually when they have nothing to say, or are not completely prepared to say what they would like, are likely to perseverate in speech. In general, these are speech situations productive of some degree of anxiety.

It is also possible that some persons with an atypical neurological mechanism are unable to respond with spoken language as rapidly as some speech situations require. In such situations, and for such persons, perseveration in speech tends to occur. These may be the persons with a constitutional predisposition to stuttering in particular and perseveration in general.

In summary, according to Eisenson, stuttering as a manifestation of perseveration may take place whenever the speaker finds himself inadequate or unequal to the demands of the speaking situation. The perseverating tendency may have a physiological cause, a psychological cause, or a combination of both.

Van Riper's Eclectic Viewpoint

Van Riper (21) holds that stuttering may arise from one of several or a combination of causes. Speech difficulty that may become stuttering is likely to begin when the child is between two and four years of age. This is a developmental period when most children are having some trouble in becoming fluent. Dysfluencies are characteristic of the speech of most if not all children in the two- to four-year age group. Unfortunately, at this crucial period, most children are also likely to be exposed to an influence that Van Riper terms fluency disruptors. These disruptors include competition from adults who can outspeak their children or pay no attention to them when the children try to speak. They can also exercise authority to interrupt their children with their own interruptions or silence them by looks or by words. Fortunately, most children are hardy enough to survive the negative influences on their speech attempts. A few are not and are likely to be among those who eventually become stutterers. The stutterers, according to Van Riper, may be distinguished from the more fortunate children in any one or more of the following:

1. Their speech environments may have an excess of influences that constitute fluency disruptors.

2. They may have abnormally low-frustration tolerance.

3. They may be those with a constitutional predisposition to prolonged dysfluency or to stuttering.

4. They may have parents whose backgrounds cause them to misevaluate dysfluent speech as stuttering and evidence anxiety when they hear nonfluent speech.

5. They may because of an underlying emotional conflict speak with an excess of dysfluencies.

The above are some more or less specific causes that may be associated with the development of stuttering. For the most part, however, there is a general cause for stuttering that emanates from our culture and its pressure for early linguistic proficiency. Our culture stresses language learning and articulatory proficiency at an age too early for many children. Pressured, consciously or unconsciously, by their parents, to speak in conventional phrases and sentences, some children fail in their fluency attempts and become young stutterers. Usually the onset of stuttering is slow and gradual. Occasionally, however, stuttering is triggered or precipitated by a sudden traumatic incident too intense for ready recovery.

If a child repeats, hesitates, or is nonfluent so frequently that his speech calls attention to itself and markedly interferes with communication, then our society tends to call him a stutterer and so do we. However, if these symptoms comprise the total of his abnormality and occur automatically and without evidence of self-awareness, avoidance, or struggle, and they appear in situations where most children are fluent, then we would insist that he be diagnosed as a *primary stutterer* . . . (21, p. 351).

Stuttering passes from its primary to secondary stage when the child becomes aware of his dysfluent speech and attempts to modify, avoid, or struggle against it. At this stage accessory movements are likely to become associated with the oral speech effort.

The distinctions made by Van Riper and shared by the authors of this book have important implications for therapy that will be considered later.

Therapy for Stutterers

Although the burden of therapy for stutterers is one which should be carried by the professional speech therapist, the classroom teacher is necessarily an important member of the therapeutic team. In the discussion that follows, we will consider the objectives of therapy for the primary stutterer and the secondary stutterer as well as the specific role of the classroom teacher in regard to each.

Objectives for the Primary Stutterer

In characterizing the primary stutterer we emphasized that his dysfluencies, even though excessive, occur without evidence either of awareness or special effort in speaking. Emphasis in the treatment of the primary stutterer is to prevent him from becoming aware that his speech is in any way different from that of others around him and a cause for concern. Awareness of difference, whether it be of speech or any other form of behavior, arises from observed reactions. A young child will have no way of knowing that his speech is atypical unless some person important to him says or does something to direct his attention to the difference. The child who is dysfluent is not likely to compare himself with other children until after some older person has made or suggested a comparison. Dysfluencies become something for the child to be concerned about only after he has responded to another person's concern. To prevent awareness and concern, we must somehow control the reactions of persons who may show and so create awareness. Essentially, therefore, the primary stutterer is to be treated through his parents if he is not of school age. If he is of school age, teachers as well as parents become the recipients of direct treatment. The primary stutterers should be given no direct speech therapy or any other form of therapy that he can relate to his speech. Nothing should be done or said to the child that suggests that his speech is in any way in need of change. If the primary stutterer is to be involved in therapy, it is only to permit the trained therapist to observe what possible pressures exist in the child's environment which disturb his speech. For this purpose, a permissive play group is recommended. In a play group it is possible for a therapist to observe conditions conducive to increased dysfluency. The therapist's observations are, of course, later discussed with the parents with a view toward modification of comparable home conditions so that pressure and excessive dysfluencies can be reduced, or, if possible, eliminated. Some of these specific aspects of treatment, and some of the information to be given to the parents of the primary stutterer, or of the child believed by his parents to be a stutterer, will now be considered. Many of these aspects, incidentally, are also relevant for the classroom teacher.

Distinguishing Between Dysfluency and Primary Stuttering

Often parents are unduly sensitized about stuttering because of their own family history. One or both of the parents may have stuttered or still be stuttering. Older children or relatives may be stutterers. Perhaps the parents are being pressured by their own parents to "do something" about the child's speech. The parents, understandably concerned, are "doing something" about what they believe to be stuttering.

A first step in the direction of treatment of the parents is to determine whether the child's dysfluencies are within the limits of normal or, in terms of incidence and situation, in excess of normal. Are we, in other words, dealing with normal dysfluency or primary stuttering? Information is obtained from the parents' description and, if possible, imitation of the child's dysfluencies. The parents are asked to recall when dysfluencies most often occur and when they are least likely to occur. The child's speech should be observed when talking to his parents, with a special note made as to whether there is any difference in ease of speaking when the response is made to the mother or to the father. The child should also be observed in a play situation when he is away from his parents as well as in their presence. If the total observed speech behavior adds up to normal speech flow—normal ease of speech—this should be stated and explained to the parents. We have found that parents are frequently able to understand and accept hesitancies and repetitions in speech when these are compared with hesitant and repetitious nonspeech behavior. We are usually able to get from parents their observations that not only their child but most children repeat activities when at play, that young children enjoy hearing the same song or the same story repeated many times. We try to make parents realize the normality of repetitions in all aspects of a young child's behavior so that repetition does not seem abnormal when it occurs in speech.

We have found effective the technique of recording and playing back part of the interview held with the parents about the child. In listening to the playback, parents are able to hear their own hesitations and repetitions as well as those of the interviewer. If they do not consider themselves stutterers, the parents are then able to compare their own speech with that of their child in regard to the incidence of dysfluencies. If the parents are disturbed about their own dysfluent speech, they should be assured that few if any persons are always fluent, except possibly when they are reproducing memorized material. Even actors, it might be pointed out, have occasional dysfluencies, so that nonprofessional speakers should certainly be permitted some of their own.

Nothing in the interview with the parents should suggest, by words or manner, that the parents were either foolish or over-anxious or in any way exercised poor judgment in coming for help about their child's speech. We believe that parents have a right, if not an obligation, to be concerned. We also believe that each child has his own right not to be concerned about all things that may concern his parents. The child's dysfluencies, if they are normal in frequency and not excessive for the situation, are among things about which the child should not be concerned. We think that parents are usually able to appreciate that most dysfluencies are normal.

Furthermore, we point out that the difference between normal dysfluency and stuttering may lie in the matter of awareness and anxiety that young children not indifferent to their parents may get from them. We indicate that frequently stuttering is the sum of dysfluency plus awareness plus anxiety, while dysfluency alone is developmentally normal speech behavior.

Information About Language Development and Speech Functions

Many parents become anxious about their children's speech because they are either uninformed or misinformed about how speech and language develop in children. They are likely to have some vague notions that children begin to talk somewhere about the time that they begin to walk. Most parents have heard about children who talked reasonably plainly at one year of age and may show disappointment if their own children seem slower. We believe that properly informed parents are likely to be less anxious parents, and so, either in an interview situation or in a larger parent group situation, we inform the parents about the normal expectancies in regard to language development, speech proficiency, and the function served by speech. Among the points we emphasize for parents are the following:[3]

1. Every child has his own rate and pattern of language and speech development just as he has his own rate and pattern of physical growth and motor development. A slower than "normal" developmental pattern does not necessarily mean that the child is retarded.

2. Language and speech development are related to some factors over which the child has no control. These include the position and number of children in the family, the linguistic ability and intelligence of the parents, the child's sex, and the appropriateness of motivation and stimulation for the child to talk. A first child tends

[3] The teacher or clinician might at this point review Chapter 7 on the Development of Language in Children.

to begin to talk earlier than a second, and a second earlier than a third. Girls, by and large, talk somewhat earlier and more proficiently than boys. The child who is urged to talk too soon may be more delayed in beginning than the child who begins to talk when he is ready and needs to talk.

3. Attentive and available parents are much more helpful for the development of speech than either anxious or nonavailable parents.

4. Language is not likely to be used unless its use is associated with pleasure.

5. Children should enjoy making sounds before sounds are used as words. Even after children begin to use words they continue to enjoy making sounds even when they have nothing to communicate.

6. Many children do not establish articulatory (speech sound) proficiency until they are almost eight years of age. A young child is entitled to lisp, hesitate, and repeat without being corrected except by good example.

7. Children must hear good speech if they are to become good speakers.

8. Fluency does not become established all at once. Most preschool children are dysfluent some of the time, and many of them are dysfluent much of the time. Dysfluencies up to 10 percent of utterance are not in themselves abnormal. They have been found to occur considerably more frequently among children who are just beginning to speak.

9. Absence of speech fluency becomes important and a matter for concern when it is associated with specific recurring situations or events. Parents should note whether the child becomes increasingly dysfluent when frustrated, when fatigued, or when talking to particular persons. If the child's dysfluencies increase sharply in these situations, control of them, if possible, is recommended. Control may take place either by avoiding the situation or by doing nothing that requires the child to communicate in these situations. By communicating we mean having to answer questions that call for precise answers. Nothing, however, should be done to give the child a feeling that he is not to speak if he wishes to do so.

Parents should also note whether the child becomes increasingly dysfluent when he bids or competes for attention. If this is so, parents should be alert to give the child quick attention when he is normally fluent. This is important so that increased dysfluencies do not result in greater satisfaction than normal fluency.

Parents should know that children do not always want to say something specific or communicative when they talk. They may wish to use words as once they used sounds merely for the sake of the pleasure derived from utterance. Adults also do this when they sing nonsense songs or talk nonsense words to their children.

Parents should be on guard to watch how often they unconsciously or consciously interrupt their children. Interruption may produce frustration, and frustration in turn produces dysfluency. The child who is bought up to silence himself when an adult wishes to talk may interrupt his speech attempts and become hesitant in fear that he may be talking out of turn.

Modification of Reactions to the Child's Dysfluencies

If the child is a primary stutterer or is showing any of the speech characteristics associated with stuttering, it is essential that signs of parental anxiety be kept from him. First, of course, we try to assure the parents that despite our acceptance that the child may be in the first stage of stuttering, the second stage or phase is by no means inevitable. By relieving parental anxiety, we hope to reduce the occurrence of displays of anxiety. Parents are encouraged to listen patiently and without tension when the child speaks. They are instructed not to do or say anything that may be interpreted by the child as a sign that his speech is not acceptable. Among the important *do nots* are the following:

1. Do not permit the child to hear the word stuttering used about his speech.

2. Do not tell the child to speed up, slow down, think before he speaks, start over again, or do anything that makes it necessary for him to think about speaking or to conclude that he is not speaking well.

3. Do not sigh with relief when the child speaks fluently, or look upon him with wide-eyed fear that he may speak dysfluently.

4. Do not show impatience if the child blocks, hesitates, or repeats.

5. Do not ask the child to speak in situations where dysfluencies are likely to occur.

Among the important *positive suggestions* for the parents of the primary stutterer are the following:

1. Establish as calm a home environment as can be achieved. Try to avoid exposing the child to situations that are overexciting, embarrassing, or frustrating.

2. Encourage the child to talk, but do not demand talking in situations where the child is usually fluent and at ease.

3. Listen to your child with as much attention as you would like him to show you when you are talking.

4. Speak to your child in a calm, unhurried manner, but not in a way so exaggerated as to be difficult to imitate.

5. Keep your child in the best possible physical condition and check for possible ailments if he suddenly shows excessive dysfluency.

6. Expect that your child will sometimes begin to say things he cannot finish. If he seems to be groping for a word to complete his thought, offer the word to him. Do not, however, anticipate what he may want to say by completing his thought for him.

7. Do all you can *to make speech behavior pleasurable*. Tell amusing anecdotes and read stories that you know the child enjoys. If you note that at a certain time of day your child has an increase of dysfluencies, try to make that the time in which you read to him. This reading has two results. It removes the opportunity for the practice of dysfluent speech, and with it the possibility that the child may become aware of his dysfluencies. It also affords the child an opportunity to be passively engaged in an enjoyable speech activity.

8. Assure your child, if he asks you whether there is anything wrong with his speech, that you think his speech is just fine. If he tells you that sometimes he has trouble getting words out, make

him understand that everybody has such trouble at some time so that there is nothing to worry about. Avoid overexplaining and overtalking your assurance, or your child, as a wise child, may suspect that you do not really mean what you say.

The Role of the Classroom Teacher

Virtually all that has been outlined or suggested as appropriate attitude and behavior for the parents of the primary stutterer may be applied to the classroom teacher. The problem of primary stuttering is one that the teacher is likely to meet in the nursery and kindergarten grades and in the first two grades of school. In these grades the teacher has an opportunity to observe the pressure situations that are conducive to increased dysfluencies and to control them in the primary stutterer's behalf. The teacher, by being a patient and attentive listener, can help the child considerably. The child who shows signs of primary stuttering should not be corrected in his articulation or have any other aspect of defective speech called to his attention. The teacher should avoid calling upon the child when he is likely to be dysfluent and go out of the way to call upon him when he is likely to speak fluently.

The attitude of calm recommended for the primary stutterer's home should also prevail in the classroom. This applies to all children and to the teacher himself. A teacher, who shows ready anger, ridicules a child for an error, or permits children to ridicule one another, creates an attitude of apprehension. On the other hand, the teacher who accepts error as a normal way of life and indicates that it is better to try even though a mistake may be made, sets a tone which most children will accept with pleasure. If any child responds to a mistake with ridicule, the child should be corrected in a private session.

The teacher should be *generous in his praise of any special abilities shown by the primary stutterer*. If he has no special abilities, praise those which are his chief assets.

If the child has been teased because of his speech, or dubbed a stutterer by his classmates, the teacher should assure him that his classmates are mistaken. The primary stutterer should be told that everyone has the same kind of speech trouble at some time just as all children stumble occasionally when they walk or run. It might help considerably if the teacher, in a not too evident way, does some hesitating or repeating of his own. Beyond this, the teacher should explain to the class that teasing and name-calling are not permitted and that some privilege will be denied to any offending member.

Perhaps the teacher's role can best be summed up in a single directive. Be accepting, permissive, and kind; do only those things to and for the primary stutterer, or any other child in your class, which you would want another teacher to do to and for your own child—or for any child you may love!

Objectives for the Secondary Stutterer

The secondary stutterer, we recall, is aware that his speech is atypical and has reactions to himself and to his environment in terms of his awareness and evaluation of his speech. Therapeutic objectives, therefore, include a modification of the speech pattern as well as a modification of the attitudes that the stutterer has developed toward himself, his speech, and his environment. How much can be done depends upon the professional resources available to the stutterer and his readiness for making use of the resources. In some instances, little more than superficial treatment of speech symptoms can be attempted. Unfortunately, this is not enough for many secondary stutterers, especially for those who have evident personality maladjustments associated with their stuttering. In some settings, psychotherapy as well as speech therapy is available, and more than speech modification can be attempted in a treatment program. When the family of the stutterer has no financial problem, private help can be sought outside of the school.

Where the secondary stutterer shows no evidence of significant maladaptive behavior or of attitudes requiring modifications, treatment may be limited to the speech symptoms. The assessment of what is needed should be made by a psychologist, speech pathologist, or other professional worker trained in personality evaluation. The clinician, we urge, should undertake the assessment of the patient with an objective attitude without assuming either: (1) that every stutterer, by virtue of his stuttering, necessarily has a personality disorder; or (2) that stutterers need treatment only for their speech symptoms to become wholly normal persons.

There is one basic understanding that must be established with the secondary stutterer if treatment, either for stuttering symptoms or for behavioral maladjustments, is to be successful. The stutterer, at the outset, must accept himself as a person who stutters and is in need of treatment. He must not try to conceal his stuttering or fight against the notion that he is a stutterer. When control over stuttering symptoms is established, and attitudes and behavior modified, the once secondary stutterer can then discard his label along with his speech characteristics and associated traits.

Another area of understanding which stutterer and therapist must establish is one of possible gains or values that may have grown out of stuttering. The stutterer must be helped to ask himself, and to answer honestly and objectively, the question, "Am I getting anything out of my stuttering that I don't want to give up?" If the stutterer realizes that his speech may excuse him from social situations he does not enjoy, from running errands when he prefers to be otherwise occupied, or from preparing for daily recitations because he is not called on in school, he will be in a position to weigh the advantages as well as the disadvantages of his speech defect and be prepared for further therapy. When the stutterer ceases to entertain and never uses stuttering as a ready-made alibi for what he might do, or might have been, except for his speech difficulty, then he has traveled a long way toward achieving the objectives of therapy.

Treatment for the Family

Often the parents of the stutterer are in need of counseling if the stutterer is to obtain maximum help from therapy. Earlier we indicated that the stutterer's parental attitudes are frequently characterized by high aspiration, rigidity, and unconscious rejection of the child. If the study of the familial picture shows this to be the case for the individual stutterer, appropriate treatment should be undertaken. Our experience indicates that parental resistance to treatment must be anticipated. Often parents want and expect their children to improve without their active participation in a therapy program. Parents must be made to realize that their participation is essential. The aims of therapy for parents are to give them an understanding about the problem of stuttering in general, their child's stuttering in particular, the relationship of their evaluations and attitudes toward their child's speech, and to reduce their own anxieties and possible guilt feelings about their child's speech difficulty. Parents must be helped to appreciate that stuttering does not disappear all at once. Frequently, in fact, speech becomes apparently worse rather than better in the early stages of treatment.

Speech Goals

The stutterer, as well as his parents, must accept the virtual certainty that stuttering will not stop with the beginning of therapy. The immediate objective for the stutterer is to encourage him to speak more rather than less despite his speech difficulty. While speaking more, the stutterer needs to be helped to take an objective view of his difficulty so that the following intermediate objectives may be attained:

1. A weakening of the forces and pressures with which his stuttering is associated.

2. Elimination of the secondary, accessory symptoms of stuttering.

3. Modification of the form of stuttering so that relatively easy, effortless dysfluencies replace the specific blocks, marked hesitations, strained prolongations, or repetitions.

4. Modification of the faulty habits directly associated with speaking such as improper breathing, rapid speaking, or excessive tensions of the speech mechanism.

5. Modification of the attitudes of fear, anxiety, or avoidance associated with the need for speaking or that occur after speech is initiated.

Therapeutic Approaches for Symptom Modification and Control: The Role of the Speech Correctionist sKip

Some of the objectives of an overall therapeutic program for stutterers, regardless of the possible etiology for the individual stutterer's difficulty, should include modification with an ultimate hope of elimination of the major speech symptoms manifested by the stutterer. Although the rationale for the use of the specific approach may vary considerably with the theorist or the therapist, a number of approaches are widely used with a considerable degree of success. We shall review those we have used and which have wide application.

NEGATIVE PRACTICE. We have previously referred to the principle of negative practice, an approach in which an individual learns to control a habit he would like to discard by practicing intentionally and purposefully that very habit. For a stutterer this would mean that the therapist will direct him to become aware of his manner of stuttering and to practice one or more of the features of the manner. Thus a stutterer will practice his blocks by imitating his own particular way of blocking. When he learns this technique of self-imitation, he will then be helped to modify his blocks through one or the other approaches we will discuss. Through the technique of negative practice the stutterer is helped to undo by consciously doing what he presumably prefers not to do. This approach may be employed to overcome facial or bodily tics, faulty breathing, or any other mannerism which characterizes the speech behavior of the individual stutterer.

VOLUNTARY STUTTERING. This approach in effect helps the stutterer to learn a new, easier way of stuttering so that he can get on with the business of saying what he has to say with a minimum of blocking or spasm. One technique is to direct the stutterer *voluntarily to repeat* the first sound or the first syllable of each word. At first the stutterer may repeat the sound or syllable two or three times, or as many times as he feels necessary before he can complete the rest of the word. The repetitions should be easy and "nonsticky." The stutterer usually finds it easier to engage in voluntary repetition in material he reads aloud while observing himself in a mirror. With practice, the number of repetitions are reduced to the minimum needed by the stutterer to enable him to feel prepared to move along and to finish his utterance. Finally, the stutterer reduces the repetitions to the sounds of the words on which he anticipates he may block. We usually proceed with the stutterer from reading to paraphrasing and then to a conversation that incorporates the words that carried the key ideas in material previously read. Ultimately, the technique of voluntary repetition is applied in free conversation. This technique is particularly useful in group sessions in which stutterers observe how successful the members of their group are in their efforts at voluntary, easy repetition. A good repetition (easy and "nonsticky") is given a positive value; an involuntary repetition earns a minus score.

Prolongation or the intentional *lengthening* of initial sounds that are capable of being lengthened (vowels, diphthongs, and continuant consonants) is another approach to voluntary stuttering. The lengthened sound must be produced in an easy, relaxed manner. The stutterer must use the lengthened sound production as a preparatory set to move into the next sound and so to complete his utterance. The modifications from reading to free speaking may follow the sequence suggested for voluntary repetition.

EASY ARTICULATION. Though clarity of diction may suffer somewhat, many stutterers find it helpful to learn a relatively lax, "nonsticky" manner of articulation. This is especially helpful in the production of stop-plosive sounds. With reduced articulatory tension it may become possible for some stutterers to move from sound to sound without abrupt pauses which suggest mild spasms.

ARTICULATORY PANTOMIMING. Some stutterers need to be convinced that there are no real difficult sounds but only "bogey sounds" that the individual has somehow come to believe are diffi-cult for him. For such stutterers, initial pantomiming of words or phrases—going through the articulatory activity without uttering the words aloud—may be of considerable help. After pantomiming, the stutterer is directed to add voice and to speak (read or engage in free conversation) what had previously been pantomimed. In the second phase, ease of articulation and moving through the utterance are stressed.

FAKE STUTTERING. A useful group technique is to have a stutterer imitate a speech feature of another stutterer. Many can do this with considerable success. For those who can, a feeling of control is achieved. Such control may then be used to imitate speech free or relatively free of stuttering mannerisms.

Ultimate Objectives for the Stutterer

We should like to be able to recommend that a legitimate, ulti-mate objective for each secondary stutterer is the establishment of normal speech and a well-adjusted personality. Such a recom-mended objective, however, cannot be made in the light of our experience with many stutterers. Perhaps a more reasonable and more moderate objective may be speech relatively free of the more severe characteristics of stuttering and a relatively normal adjust-ment. We should not expect a stutterer, not even one who is having psychotherapy, to become better adjusted than most of his peers because most of his peers have some traits that can stand improve-ment.

Many stutterers are able to free themselves of significant speech symptoms. Some, however, continue to have some dysfluency symp-toms under conditions of fatigue, ill health, or stress. For some, also, it is possible that more than normal dysfluency is likely to persist on a constitutional basis. For these, the acceptance of dys-fluency without accompanying apprehension and struggle behavior may be all that can be accomplished. If this attitude can be estab-lished, the characteristics of stuttered speech that arise from anxiety

and apprehension are removed, and the overall occurrence of dysfluencies is, therefore, reduced.

The Role of the Classroom Teacher

The task of helping the secondary stutterer toward better speech
and the improvement of his adjustment problems are, as we have
indicated, primarily for the speech therapist and not for the classroom teacher. There are, however, a number of ways the classroom
teacher can be of appreciable help to the stutterer in his improvement program.

The teacher should make note of the class situations that appear
to be conducive to stuttering. Unless the child volunteers, he should
not be called upon to speak in these situations. If he does speak, the
stutterer should not be stopped regardless of the severity of his
difficulty. If at all possible, however, the stutterer should be called
upon for short replies rather than for ones that require lengthy
explanations.

If many children are to be called on during a recitation period,
the teacher should call upon the stutterer early. Waiting induces
anxiety and anxiety an increase in stuttering. The stutterer should
know that participation is expected, but that he will not have to
wait anxiously for the moment of active participation.

The teacher should also note the conditions or situations when
the stutterer is likely to have least difficulty with speaking and call
upon him when these situations are present. For example, if a
stutterer can recite memorized poetry without difficulty, he should
be given an opportunity to recite. If he can read aloud much better
than he can recite impromptu, he should be called upon to read
aloud.

The teacher can get considerable information from the stutterer
as to both easy and difficult speech situations. In most instances,
an understanding can be reached with the stutterer as to his participation in class recitations. We recommend a basic principle to
be followed in regard to oral recitations: If the stutterer is exempt

from any oral activity, he must compensate by some other form of activity. This may call for additional written work done at home, or for board work done in class. Exemption without compensation gives stuttering a positive value that may be difficult to surrender. The teacher should not become a partner to the creation of gains to be derived from stuttering; neither, of course, should the teacher become part of any classroom attitude that inflicts punishment on the stutterer because of his stuttering.

The teacher should try to reward the stutterer for his fluent speech, but to do so without readily apparent fuss. "Very good, Johnny" is much better than a lengthy response of praise because Johnny has been fluent. If the teacher looks pleased, Johnny is likely to get the idea even without a verbalization of the pleasure. There is a very real danger that a remark intended as a verbal reward may actually backfire and become an implied penalty. For example, "You spoke very well, Johnny" may be interpreted to mean that in most instances Johnny does not speak well, hence the need to point out the occasions when speech is good. As a general procedure, the teacher should try to avoid directing attention to good speech as well as to poor speech. The nature and form of the reward should depend upon the intellectual and emotional maturity of the child. Rewards should be given for good speech as for any other worthwhile performance. They should come quickly and inconspicuously.

The teacher should help to create a classroom atmosphere which will encourage the stutterer to talk. Such an atmosphere exists when any child, whether he stutters, has no defect in speech, or has some form of defective speech other than stuttering feels free to volunteer to speak without fear of penalty or criticism. It may help to explain to the stutterer's classmates, *at a time when the stutterer is out of the classroom,* how they can be of help. Nothing said to the classmates should suggest that the stutterer is in need of pity or excessive sympathy. Instead, the teacher should emphasize that what the stutterer needs is a group of patient listeners when he talks and opportunities to talk. If the stutterer is excused from any recitations, his classmates should be informed that he is doing other work to make up for it. In this way the classmates will not feel resentful that the stutterer is a privileged member of the group. Rather they will feel that he is a member of their group who has a problem that all are helping to solve by their understanding.

Some of the therapeutic approaches included in this chapter are incorporated in the student-clinician report of a group therapy session with seven young adolescents. This session was conducted by a demonstration teacher of speech correction on the staff of Queens College.

Report on a Speech Therapy Session for a Group of Stutterers

Place: Queens College
Group: Five boys and two girls between ages 12 to 14.
Assignment: Speaking before a group.

The atmosphere in the class was extremely relaxed and permissive. Although the children did not wander, they were permitted to talk, even while the instructor was speaking. The boys especially were vociferous members of the group. They joked, laughed, and one boy used "unacceptable" language for which he was not reprimanded. As the children talked to each other, I heard little of the symptoms associated with stuttering such as blocking, repetition, or uncontrolled prolongation.

The therapist motivated the lesson by showing a picture of an embarrassed man leaving a board meeting. The story they told about this picture could be as fantastic as they wished it to be, but it must have a beginning, middle, and end. After this initial warming-up period, the instructor gave each child a picture of his own about which he could make up a story.

The activity permitted the children to change pitch for the different characters they would tell about and to use different rates of speech to add color to their stories. Before they began, the therapist emphasized that they could stutter all they wanted or needed to, but that they should "bounce" on the repetitions or use an easy, relaxed prolongation on sounds they thought might be troublesome.

The enthusiasm over the pictures and the informal atmosphere helped these children speak with confidence before an audience. The therapist called the most severe stutterer first. He spoke extremely rapidly and repeated syllables, but he was able to finish his story with a smile. As a group, they were free from secondary characteristics of stuttering such as tics, twitchings, or hand movements. They were not hard to listen to, for all had learned to relax and stutter without extreme tenseness and fear.

After relating their stories, an evaluation period followed. Each member of the group was asked how he felt about his performance. Those who seemed particularly anxious were praised highly on one or two fine points in their delivery. Generally, it was pointed out that most members of the class spoke too fast and did not pause often enough or long enough to formulate their thoughts before beginning to verbalize them.

After the evaluation, the class was broken up into groups of two to three children per instructor. In the smaller groups the students were able to converse freely on a subject of their own choice. One group was interested in baseball; another talked about a newly launched satellite. The therapist used this interest to show the reason for proper pausing and to encourage the student to pause without fear or apprehension that while doing so another speaker would become impatient and take over the conversation.

References and Suggested Readings

1. BERRY, M. F., "Twinning in Stuttering Families." *Human Biology,* **IX**, 3 (1939), 329-346.

2. BERRY, M., and J. EISENSON, *Speech Disorders: Principles and Practices of Therapy.* New York: Appleton-Century-Crofts, 1956, Chapters 11, 12, 13.

3. BLOODSTEIN, O., "A Rating Scale Study of Conditions under Which Stuttering is Reduced." *Journal of Speech and Hearing Disorders,* **XV** (1950), 29-36.

4. BLOODSTEIN, O., "The Development of Stuttering: II. Developmental Phases." *Journal of Speech and Hearing Disorders,* **XXV** (November 1960), 366-376).

5. BLOODSTEIN, O., *A Handbook on Stuttering for Professional Workers.* Chicago: National Society for Crippled Children and Adults, 1959.

6. BROWN, S. F., "The Loci of Stuttering in the Speech Sounds." *Journal of Speech Disorders,* **X** (1945), 181-192.

7. CORIAT, I. H., "The Psychoanalytic Conception of Stuttering." *The Nervous Child,* **II** (1943), 167-171.

8. EISENSON, J. (ed.), *Stuttering: A Symposium*. New York: Harper and Brothers, 1958. (Six points of view are presented on the nature of stuttering with therapies consistent with the theoretic positions. The contributors are O. Bloodstein, J. Eisenson, I. P. Glauber, J. Sheehan, C. Van Riper, and R. West.)

9. EISENSON, J., and E. HOROWITZ, "The Influence of Propositionality on Stuttering." *Journal of Speech Disorders,* **X** (1945), 193-198.

10. EISENSON, J., and C. WELLS, "A Study of the Influence of Communicative Responsibility in a Choral Reading Speech Situation for Stutterers." *Journal of Speech Disorders,* **VII** (1942), 259-262.

11. HAHN, E., *Stuttering: Significant Theories and Therapies.* Stanford: Stanford University Press, 1956.

12. JOHNSON, W., *People in Quandaries.* New York: Harper and Brothers, 1946, Chapter 17.

13. JOHNSON, W. (ed.), *Speech Handicapped School Children* (Rev. ed.) New York: Harper and Brothers, 1956, Chapter 5.

14. JOHNSON, W., *Stuttering and What You Can Do About It.* Minneapolis: University of Minnesota Press, 1961. (The author summarizes recent research on stuttering and explains, in relatively simple language, the therapeutic implications of the research.)

15. KARLIN, I. W., "Stuttering: The Problem Today." *Journal of the American Medical Association,* **CXLIII** (1950), 732-736.

16. MONCUR, J. P., "Parental Domination in Stuttering." *Journal of Speech and Hearing Disorders,* **XVII** (1952), 155-164.

17. MURPHY, A. T., and R. M. FITZSIMONS, *Stuttering and Personality Dynamics.* New York: Ronald Press, 1960. (The thesis of this book is that stuttering speech is a symptom of deep-seated personal difficulties. The stutterer can be helped only through an understanding of his special problems as a person.)

18. ORTON, S., *Reading, Writing and Speech Problems in Children.* New York: W. W. Norton, 1937.

19. SHEEHAN, J. G., "Theory and Treatment of Stuttering as an Approach-Avoidance Conflict." *Journal of Psychology,* **XXXVI** (1953), 27-49. (See also reference 8, 123-166.)

20. TRAVIS, L. E., "My Present Thinking on Stuttering." *Western Speech,* **X** (1946), 3-5.

21. VAN RIPER, C., *Speech Correction: Principles and Methods.* (3rd ed.) Englewood Cliffs, N.J.: Prentice-Hall, 1954, Chapter 9.

22. WEST, R., S. NELSON, and M. F. BERRY, "The Heredity of Stuttering." *Quarterly Journal of Speech,* **XXV**, 1 (1939), 23-30.

23. WISCHNER, G. J., "Stuttering Behavior and Learning: A Preliminary Theoretic Formulation." *Journal of Speech and Hearing Disorders,* **XII** (1950), 324-335.

Special Reading List for Parents

ANONYMOUS, "We Made Our Child Stutter." *Parents' Magazine,* **XXXVIII** (April 1949), 131-132.

EISENSON, J., "Has Your Child a Speech Difficulty?" *Parents' Magazine,* (October 1954).

JOHNSON, W., "An Open Letter to the Mother of a Stuttering Child." Distributed by the National Society for Crippled Children and Adults, 2023 W. Ogden Avenue, Chicago, Illinois.

JOHNSON, W., *Stuttering and What You Can Do About It.* Minneapolis: University of Minnesota Press, 1961.

VAN RIPER, C., *Stuttering* (1948). Distributed by the National Society for Crippled Children and Adults, 2023 W. Ogden Avenue, Chicago, Illinois.

Problems

1. What is the approximate percentage of incidence of stuttering among school children? Does this percentage agree with the number diagnosed as stutterers in your school? Does the ratio of boy to girl stutterers conform with the ratio of the population at large?

2. How do you distinguish between primary and secondary stuttering?

3. Read Chapter 5, of W. Johnson, *Speech Handicapped School Children* (New York: Harper and Brothers, 1956) and Chapter 9, of C. Van Riper, *Speech Correction: Principles and Practice* (Englewood Cliffs, N.J.: Prentice-Hall, 3rd ed., 1954). Do these writers agree on the meanings of the terms *normal nonfluency* and *primary stuttering?*

4. Observe a stutterer in your school. Note the situations conducive to his stuttering. Can any of these be controlled by the classroom teacher? What can most teachers do to be of positive help to the stutterer?

5. Does your speech ever resemble that of a stutterer? How is it the same? How is it significantly different?

6. Read J. P. Moncur, "Environmental Factors Differentiating Stuttering Children from Non-Stuttering Children," (*Speech Monographs*),

XVIII (1951), 312-326), and K. S. Wood, "Parental Maladjustments and Functional Articulatory Defects in Children," (*Journal of Speech Disorders,* **XI** (December 1946), 255-275). Are there any common factors in the home backgrounds of stutterers and children with articulatory defects? Is there any basis in these studies for a thesis that "whether a child becomes a stutterer or one who has articulatory difficulty may depend largely on his age and stage of speech development?"

7. What common environmental factors have you observed or been able to determine among stutterers you have known?

8. What gains may a stutterer obtain in school by virtue of his speech? What can you do to avoid the establishment of such gains, or to replace them if they are present?

9. How does Bloodstein's position on the onset of stuttering differ from that of Johnson? What is your own observation as to how stuttering may begin?

10. What is the evidence for and against the assumption that there is a "stuttering personality?"

14

Speech and

Impaired

Hearing

In this and the two following chapters we shall consider the speech and language difficulties of three groups of children with organic involvements. The groups are those with hearing impairments, those with facial clefts (cleft lip and palate), and those who have incurred brain damage. Of these groups the classroom teacher who is not in the field of special education is most likely to be concerned with children who have facial clefts and those with relatively slight hearing loss. Severely deaf children and brain-damaged children who have related motor and sensory deficits are usually the concern of the teacher of special education in a specialized class or in a specialized school. The child with brain damage and without readily apparent motor or sensory deficit may well be a member of a regular class, and often a problem and puzzle to himself and to his teachers. The reasons for this will be considered in some detail in the chapter on Brain Damage.

Hearing Impairment

Know the definition for this

Classification and Incidence

Although "functional" definitions of hearing loss will be presented in this section, it is essential to appreciate that the effect of hearing loss is variable. In some instances, what might be regarded as a relatively small amount of hearing loss may be associated with greater impairment of hearing in particular and adjustment in general than a measurably greater amount of hearing loss for other persons. Even among persons born with severe hearing loss, some are able to make considerably better use of a small amount of residual hearing than others. With these reservations in mind, "practical" definitions will be offered.[1]

The *deaf* are those for whom the sense of hearing is so impaired as to have precluded normal acquisition of language learning. Somewhat more broadly, the deaf are those for whom the capacity to hear is so limited as to be considered nonfunctioning for the ordinary purposes of life. Children who are deaf are (1) either not able to learn speech through the avenue of hearing; or (2) if their hearing impairment was acquired shortly after "natural" speech was learned, then lost their speaking ability.

The deaf may be divided into two subgroups according to onset of impairment. The *congenitally deaf* are those who are born without hearing. The *adventitiously deaf* are those who were born with hearing sufficient for the acquisition of speech but later, as a result of illness or accident, suffered severe hearing impairment.

The *hard-of-hearing* are those for whom the sense of hearing, although defective, is functional with or without a hearing aid. Hard-of-hearing children, although frequently with considerable defect, learned to speak essentially through the avenue of hearing.

The criterion for the distinction between the deaf and the hard-

[1] The reader interested in definitions, concepts, and implications of impaired hearing is urged to read the chapter by Lee Meyerson, "A Psychology of Impaired Hearing," in W. M. Cruickshank (ed.), *Psychology of Exceptional Children and Youth* (Englewood Cliffs, N.J.: Prentice-Hall, 1955).

of-hearing is *the manner of learning to speak*. The deaf include those who require special instruction to learn to speak. The hard-of-hearing are those who learned to speak in the normal, developmental manner of hearing children.

Most deaf children are educated in special schools, and many in residential schools. Most hard-of-hearing children are educated in "regular" schools and usually attend classes with hearing children.

Estimates of the incidence of impaired hearing in the school population vary from about 5 to 10 percent. Usually the percentage is higher among children in the middle and upper grades. The reason for this is the high incidence of upper respiratory diseases and adenoidal involvements in young children. These conditions are productive of temporary hearing loss which, fortunately, improves with proper medical treatment. Glorig (8) reports that 3 percent of a male population between the ages of ten through nineteen were found to have a hearing loss of 15 decibels or more. This figure is based on a sample of approximately 400,000. Davis and Silverman (5, p. 416) recognize that there is considerable variability in estimates of hearing loss. They say, "Our best estimate is that 5 percent of schoolage children have hearing levels outside the range of normal . . . and that from one to two of every ten in this group require special educational attention."

Measurement of Hearing Loss

Hearing loss is objectively measured in terms of decibels. A decibel is a unit of power or physical intensity. From our point of view, we may consider a decibel the minimum unit of intensity necessary for us to appreciate a difference between the loudness of sounds.

The pure-tone audiometer is widely used as an objective instrument for measuring possible hearing loss. The pure-tone audiometer is an electrical instrument designed to produce a number of tones of discrete or individual frequencies at intensity levels that can be controlled. Most modern pure-tone audiometers cover the

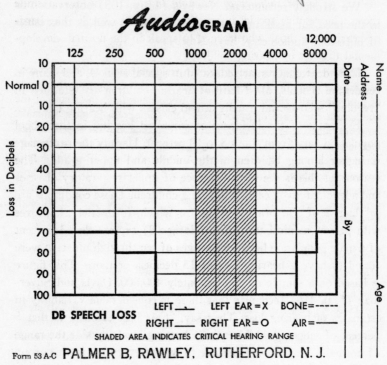

Figure 9. An audiogram form.

frequency range between approximately 125 and 12,000 cycles per second. Many audiologists in their examinations, however, do not consider it necessary to go beyond 8,000 cycles. On a pure-tone audiometer the weakest sound that can normally be heard is considered as zero decibels.

Losses are measured in terms of the normal threshold of hearing for tones at specified pitch levels and are stated in decibels. The following tables suggest how we would evaluate the results of a pure-tone audiometric examination. We should always bear in mind, however, that many factors other than the "objective" amount of hearing loss enter into the effect of the loss for the given individual.

We strongly recommend Newby's (13, p. 105) observation as to the need for assessing functional hearing as well as the results of pure-tone audiometry. Says Newby:

Thus we see that the audiogram can yield important information concerning the rehabilitative needs of patients. In this connection, the degree of loss, especially through the speech frequencies, and the shape of the audiogram curve are of importance. The audiogram is most valuable, however, when it is combined with the results of clinical speech audiometric tests, which measure directly a patient's ability to hear and understand speech. After all, the measure of the handicap of a hearing loss is how one's communicative ability is affected. Whereas predictions of how communication is affected can be made from the pure-tone audiogram, actual measures of the communicative ability can be derived through speech audiometry.

Hearing Loss and Implications

Decibel Loss	Degree of Severity	Implications
0–15	Normal hearing range	
15–20	Very slight loss	Rarely recognized. Detected only by periodic audiometric examinations
20–40	Slight loss	Should have supplementary lip reading
40–60	Moderate loss	Should use a hearing aid where recommended. Should receive auditory training, lip reading, and speech help
60–75	Severe	Cannot follow ordinary conversation. Needs intensive lip or speech reading, a hearing aid where helpful, speech help, and auditory training
80–100	Very severe	Without hearing aid appears deaf. Rarely progresses normally in the public school

Identification Audiometry

Identification audiometry is a term to signify the application of appropriate hearing test procedures leading to an initial discovery

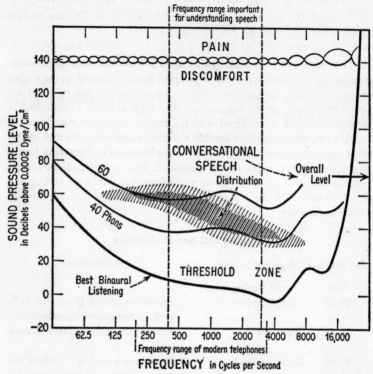

From Davis and Silverman, *Hearing and Deafness,* Holt, Rinehart, and Winston, 1960, p. 52.

Figure 10. The speech area. Speech is a mixture of complex tones, wide band noise, and transients. Both the intensities and the frequencies of speech sounds change continually and rapidly. It is difficult to measure them and logically impossible to plot them precisely in terms of sound pressure levels.

of a hearing loss. (See "Identification Audiometry," *Journal of Speech and Hearing Disorders,* Monograph Supplement, Number 9, September 1961, 9-20). In the ordinary school situations, a screening test rather than a complete audiometric examination is likely to be given as the first step in the evaluation of a child's hearing. Probably the most widely used screening device is the phonograph test. Recorded voice is played back and listened to through earphones, either by a single child or by a group of children. The usual recording is of a sequence of numbers which "fade-out" at the end of the sequence. The results provide information *under the conditions of testing* about the intensity levels at or above which a selected speech sample—a sequence of numbers—can be heard. Unfortunately, as Newby (13, p. 193) points out, a fading-numbers test is not an accurate indicator of a child's ability to hear normal running speech. The test does have a merit as a rough screening device that permits relatively quick assessment of the hearing of many children.

Another technique that permits screening of children on a group basis is the Massachusetts Hearing Test.[2] This is a pure-tone rather than a speech hearing test which was devised to permit screening testing of as many as forty children at one time at three critical frequencies within the range of normal speech. The usual frequencies tested are 500, 4,000, and 6,000 cycles. Each of these frequencies is presented at sensation (loudness) levels of 20, 25, and 30 decibels, respectively. Responses are ordinarily entered on a prepared test blank and consist of a "Yes" or "No" to indicate whether the child who is being examined does or does not hear the spurt of pure-tone sound produced by the test instrument. An audiometrist signals the individual child or children when the response to the sound is expected. According to a prearranged plan, the audiometrist may not always present a tone and signal for a response. Through this procedure some "No" responses are expected and such entries should appear on each test blank.

Another approach for screening employing pure-tone audiometry is the *sweep test*. This testing is done with a pure-tone audiometer, and results are obtained in a very few minutes. In *sweep testing* the dial is set at a critical point, with allowances made for the room and the "free-floating" noise in the surroundings. The most usual setting is 15 decibels. The examiner then "sweeps" through the frequency range. The child is instructed to signal whether or not he hears the tone produced at each frequency.

[2]This and other testing techniques especially suitable in the school situation are described in some detail in Chapter 8 of H. Newby's *Audiology* (New York: Appleton-Century-Crofts, 1958).

As the name suggests, screening tests have as their purpose the singling out of individuals who may have significant losses of hearing at the time of the testing. Final evaluations should include more thorough individual pure-tone testing as well as speech through speech audiometry. In addition, of course, an otological examination should be routine.

In many public schools the responsibility for discovering hearing loss among the children has become an integral part of the overall health conservation program. The development of this aspect of the detection and treatment of children's health needs received considerable impetus from the availability of instruments and techniques for assessing hearing loss that can easily be used in school settings.

School hearing conservation programs have two fundamental purposes. The first is the earliest possible detection of hearing loss so that children, whenever possible, may be referred for medical treatment in the hope that in many instances permanent hearing impairment may be prevented. The second is to provide for the special needs—educational, speech, and audiological—for children whose hearing may not be directly subject to improvement but who can be helped to conserve and make maximum use of their hearing capacities.

Responsibility for the actual assessment of hearing loss varies considerably among school systems. Many large school districts conduct their own hearing testing and conservation programs. Some smaller school districts may contract for hearing services with professional agencies or audiology clinics associated with colleges or universities. In some school districts audiologists or audiometrists are engaged whose responsibilities include the assessment of the children's hearing throughout the grades.[3] In many

---

[3] As of 1961, 28 state health departments employed one or more speech and hearing consultants as part of their programs ("Identification Audiometry," *Journal of Speech and Hearing Disorders, Monograph Supplement 9,* September 1961, p. 6). In 35 states, departments of public instruction are charged with responsibility for health examinations, including hearing testing, for the children enrolled in the public schools (*ibid.,* p. 46).

schools, including those in which there are organized audiological services, the detection of possible hearing loss continues to be the responsibility of the classroom teacher or the school nurse. The nurse may note a child's difficulty in hearing in her routine examination of the children. The classroom teacher, however, has a daily opportunity to detect whether a child, habitually or occasionally, seems to have difficulty in hearing. The child who frequently misunderstands directions, or who asks that questions directed to him be repeated, or who looks blankly at the teacher talking to him or to the class should be checked for possible hearing loss. The teacher should also watch for the child who seems to hear only when spoken to from one side of the room but fails to hear what is said when spoken to from the opposite side. Some children unconsciously turn their heads to favor the better ear. If these habits and manifestations are associated with poor articulation and with voice production inappropriate in quality and loudness, hearing loss should be suspected. Additional significant signs are poor coordination, poor balance, occasional dizziness, and complaints of earaches and of running ears. A child suspected of hearing loss should be referred to the school physician for further examination. If the school has no physician, the possibility of the child's hearing loss should be discussed with the principal and, of course, with the parents, and then referred to a physician.

Therapy for the Child with A Hearing Impairment

Hearing Aids

Many children whose hearing losses range from moderate to severe are able to get considerable help from a properly fitted hearing aid. The decision whether a hearing aid is needed should be made by the otologist, a medical specialist. The actual fitting of the hearing aid may be done either by the otologist or a properly trained audiologist.[4] Although many individual factors enter into the use-

---

[4] Many college and university clinics, as well as hospitals, provide services for the selection of hearing aids.

fulness of hearing aids, experience indicates that for children hearing aids are usually indicated when the hearing loss is between 35 and 75 decibels in the pitch range most important for speech. This range is roughly between 200 and 4,000 cycles. On many audiometers the measurements would range from 256 through 4,096 cycles. For children with more severe hearing losses, exceeding 75 decibels in the pitch range, the help to be derived from a hearing aid is limited. In some instances, only the awareness that there is noise and activity about is made available to the user. This, however, may be important in preventing the child from feeling isolated by inner silence if a hearing aid is not used. To be able to anticipate that someone is about to enter a house because a doorbell ring is heard is often considerably better than to be caught by surprise, or to fail to answer a doorbell because it is not heard.

If a hearing aid is indicated, training in its care and proper use is in order. Such training may be provided by the otologist or by the audiologist associated with a hospital, college, or university speech and hearing clinic.

It is important to appreciate that a hearing aid does not serve to give the user normal hearing in the same sense that properly fitted eyeglasses give most users essentially the equivalent of normal vision. The hearing instrument is, as its name suggests, only an aid. It helps the user to make more complete use of the amount of hearing he has. If the hearing loss is moderate rather than severe, and the individual learns the proper use of his aid, he can approach normal hearing. If, in addition, he learns lip reading and is attentive to his speaker, he comes closer to a complete understanding of oral speech. For the severely deaf, lip reading is of greater importance than for those with moderate hearing loss. The hearing instrument has more limited use, but together with lip reading it can still be a significant aid.

Speech and Hearing Therapy

Proper medical attention may help many children as well as adults to conserve whatever hearing they have. Proper speech and listening training should help them to make the maximum use of their hearing and to conserve the quality and intelligibility of their speech.

The school-age child with a moderate or greater hearing loss and with skill in lip reading is often able to continue his education in a class with normally hearing children. This should be the desired goal for all children with hearing loss. We may be encouraged by the recent accomplishment reported by Wedenberg (10) to the effect that two young children who had 99 percent bilateral loss of hearing were nevertheless able to learn to speak spontaneously and to interpret speech through their ears after several years of intensive auditory training.

The hearing therapist helps the child to make maximal use of his residual hearing as well as of his hearing aid, if one is used. In addition, the child is made aware of all the aspects of sound production so that tactile as well as auditory and visible cues are recognized and utilized. In this way the child not only becomes more completely responsive to how other persons speak, but also responds to his own speech with greater awareness. The result is better articulation, better voice, and improved intelligibility. In working with the school child, specific instruction is correlated with academic subject matter. The vocabulary of a new subject is introduced and becomes the core of the speech and hearing instruction.

The Role of the Classroom Teacher

As indicated earlier in our discussion of hearing loss as a cause of delayed speech, the classroom teacher can do much to help the child with impaired hearing to live with others successfully. He can help the child to attain a sense of social competence and to accept the fact that he can live normally in his school environment. The hard-of-hearing child is apt to withdraw from others, to live within himself. The teacher can draw him into group living. By giving him duties and helping him to accept responsibilities, the child can be made to feel that he is a necessary member of a group whose participation is important to himself and to his classmates. Again, as with other handicapped children, the teacher can help the child with a hearing loss to accept it and himself and to minimize its potentially impairing influences.

The teacher can aid the child in developing language abilities by encouraging him to converse with others, by motivating him to use speech and to take his part in the classroom activities. He can make sure that the child's experiences are fairly broad in nature. In addition, the teacher can encourage him to take part in playground activities and to read widely.

The teacher can help the child to appreciate and understand what goes on in the classroom in several ways: (1) by making sure he is seated where he can best see and hear the speakers in the room; (2) by permitting the child to move around the room as he finds it necessary in terms of his hearing; (3) by making certain that the light is on the speaker's face so that the child can see the face; (4) by speaking naturally but clearly and perhaps somewhat louder than might otherwise be necessary when the child with a hearing loss is at a distance from him; (5) by using gestures normally so that they will help the child in the understanding of language. (One hard-of-hearing child said, "Miss Wilson is easy to understand; she talks with her face and her hands."); (6) by emphasizing what he is teaching by writing on the blackboard; and (7) by remembering to watch the child for signs of lack of comprehension and recalling that when repetition does not help, rephrasing the material often does.

References and Suggested Readings

1. ASHA Committee on Legislation, "The Need for Adequately Trained Speech Pathologists and Audiologists," *ASHA* (December 1959), 138-139. (Article includes estimates of incidence of types of speech defects, including those associated with impaired hearing.)

2. BAKWIN, R. M., "The Deaf Child." *Journal of Pediatrics,* **XXXVI** (May 1950), 668-682. (Gives the incidence and etiology of deafness

and describes the mental functioning, personality traits, and school and occupational achievement of the deaf.)

3. BERRY, M. F., and J. EISENSON, *Speech Disorders: Principles and Practices of Therapy.* New York: Appleton-Century-Crofts, 1956, Chapter 19. (Discusses types of hearing loss, speech symptoms, and treatment.)

4. DARLEY, F. L. (ed.), "Identification Audiometry." *Journal of Speech and Hearing Disorders,* Monograph Supplement 9 (September 1961).

5. DAVIS, H., and S. R. SILVERMAN, *Hearing and Deafness.* (Rev. ed.) New York: Holt, Rinehart, and Winston, 1960. (A survey and exposition of hearing problems. Excellent research lucidly explained.)

6. DiCARLO, L. M., "Program for Children with Impaired Hearing." *Elementary School Journal,* **XLIX** (November 1948), 160-167. (Describes how children with impaired hearing may be educated with normal hearing children. Includes sound advice to teachers.)

7. GARDNER, W. H., "History and Present Status of the Education of the Hard of Hearing." *Journal of Speech Disorders,* **VIII** (September 1943) 227-237. (Historical notes on the treatment of the hard of hearing in schools. Indicates the relationship of school departments relative to the hard of hearing.)

8. GLORIG, A., "Hearing Conservation Past and Future." *Proceedings of the Working Conference on Health Aspects of Hearing Conservation,* Supplement to the Transactions of the American Academy of Opthalmology and Otolaryngology (November-December 1959), 24-33.

9. JOHNSON, W. *et al., Speech Handicapped School Children,* New York: Harper and Brothers, 1956, Chapter 8. (Discusses the hearing mechanism, testing, types of hearing problems, lip reading, and hearing aids.)

10. KEASTER, J., and G. HOVERSTEN, *Suggestions to the Parents of a Deaf Child.* American Academy of Ophthalmology and Otolaryngology, 1958. (Direct and clearly stated information intended for parents of deaf children. Emphasizes approaches for preparing the deaf child, and the parents, for communication.)

11. MILLER, E., "A Public School Program for Hard of Hearing Children." *Journal of Speech and Hearing Disorders,* **XIII** (September 1948), 256-259. (Discusses the segregation of the hard of hearing and deaf child, the adjustment of the deaf child, the responsibilities

of the classroom teacher, speech conservation program, and vocational and educational placement.)

12. MYKLEBUST, H., *The Psychology of Deafness.* New York: Grune and Stratton, 1960. (A study in depth of the psychological aspects of deafness.)

13. NEWBY, H., *Audiology.* New York: Appleton-Century-Crofts, 1958. (Chapter 8 is devoted to the special problem of public school audiometry.)

14. SPRUNT, J. W., and F. W. FINGER, "Auditory Deficiency and Academic Achievement." *Journal of Speech and Hearing Disorders,* **XIV** (March 1949), 26-32. (Studies the relationship of hearing loss and academic achievement.)

15. VAN RIPER, C., *Speech Correction: Principles and Methods.* Englewood Cliffs, N.J.: Prentice-Hall, 1954. Chapter 13. (Describes hearing tests, the characteristics of deaf and hard-of-hearing children. Tells about helping the acoustically defective child in school.)

16. WEDENBURG, E., "Auditory Training of Deaf and Hard of Hearing Children." *Acta Oto-Laryngologica,* Supplementum **XCIV**, Stockholm (1951).

Problems

1. Why are we not able to assess the effects of hearing loss solely in terms of the percentage of loss below normal hearing?

2. Distinguish between the deaf and the hard-of-hearing.

3. What are the most frequently used nonobjective techniques for determining the existence of hearing loss?

4. Define or explain each of the following: (*a*) decibel, (*b*) pure-tone audiometer, (*c*) audiogram, (*d*) sweep test, (*e*) hearing aid, (*f*) residual hearing.

5. Does a hearing aid give the same assistance to its user as properly fitted glasses do for most persons with visual defects? Justify your answer.

6. What specifically can the classroom teacher do for the child known to have a hearing loss?

7. What does the term *identification audiometry* mean? Describe three techniques used in identification audiometry.

8. Why does Newby (see reference 13) recommend testing for functional hearing, as well as pure-tone audiometry, in the assessment of a possible hearing loss?

15

Cleft
Palace

Read

A FACIAL CLEFT[1] is any opening in the oral cavity, lips, or nasal cavity which may be caused either by developmental failure (prebirth), or accident or disease at or following birth. The vast majority of facial clefts are developmental failures. That is, during the embryonic state of the fetus, there was a failure of parts of the facial area to fuse and develop normally. Facial clefts may involve the palate as a whole, or be limited to parts of the hard or soft palate. Clefts may also involve the upper gum ridge (alveolar process), the upper lip, and one or both of the nares (the passageway from the nostril to the nasal cavity). Extensive clefts may involve any two or more of the parts of the oral cavity or upper lip. An insufficient palate, though not technically an oral cleft, is believed to be associated with the anomaly. An insufficient palate is one which does not have a normal amount of soft palate. The uvula may be missing or be shortened, and part of the soft palate anterior to the uvula may be smaller than is normal.

Although the specific cause of congenital facial cleft is not known, there is little doubt that heredity plays an important role in its etiology. Other factors that may be associated with congenital

---

[1] We are using the term *facial cleft* to comprise what is frequently included in the terms *cleft lip* and *cleft palate*.

facial clefts are believed to be the diet and health of the mother and intrauterine pressure on the developing fetus.

Incidence

The incidence of facial cleft varies somewhat according to geographic distribution. Surveys record ranges from one in about 600 to one in 1,000 in the population. Probably a moderate estimate is that one child in 750 is born with some form of facial cleft which will require special care and training. Among cleft palate children the liklihood is that there will be more boys than girls (6).

Voice and Articulation Characteristics

From the description of the inadequacy of the mechanism, the speech difficulties are readily discernible. In the speech of the child with a palatal cleft all sounds pass directly into the nasal cavity where normal oral reinforcement is not possible. Therefore, all the vowel sounds are nasalized and most of the consonants have nasal characteristics. For example, *b, d,* and *g* take on the characteristics of *m, n,* and *ng* [ŋ]. Other articulatory difficulties are obvious. The plosive sounds *p, b, t, d, k,* and *g* are defective because they are emitted nasally rather than orally. The fricatives *f, v, s, z, sh, zh, th,* and *th* are also defective, since the air stream coming through the mouth cannot be adequately controlled.[2] Because *s* and *z* require the direction of an air stream down a narrow channel, they are likely to be the most seriously affected of the fricative sounds. Other distinctive traits include frequent inhalation and considerable use of the glottal stop, particularly before vowels. The resulting speech of a child with a severe cleft palate condition may be a series of snorting sounds.

Certain facial mannerisms frequently go along with cleft palate.

[2] D. Counihan, ("Articulation Skills of Adolescents and Adults with Cleft Palate," *Journal of Speech Disorders,* **XXV,** May 1960, 181-187) found that a group of 45 cleft-palate speakers between the ages of 13 to 23 misarticulated the sounds *z, s, sh* [ʃ], *ch* [tʃ], and *j* [dʒ] more than 40 percent of the time. The investigation also revealed that more than one-half of the subjects had poorer articulation than the average five-year-old normal child.

Some children seem to engage in nasal twitching; others look as if they are habitually sniffing. The alae, the winglike structures of the nose, constrict; this constriction compensates for the failure of the nasal port to close.

The child with a cleft palate often faces other problems. One of the first that he encounters is a difficulty in feeding. As he grows older, he frequently has a dental condition that needs remedying. His teeth may fail to grow in or they may grow in an irregular alignment. He tends to suffer from colds. His Eustachian tube often becomes infected, and, as a result, a hearing loss may occur. Frequently, his general development is poor.

Another factor deserving study and consideration in determining the therapeutic needs of the cleft palate child is his intellectual development. A carefully conducted control study by Goodstein (3), in which the Wechsler Intelligence Scale for Children was used to assess the intellectual status of cleft palate children and a matched group of children without cleft palate, indicates that there are significant differences in intelligence levels between the two groups. An appreciably larger percentage of the cleft palate children fell in the categories of *dull normal, borderline,* and *mentally defective* intellectual classifications than did the control children.[3] The latter group of children tended to distribute very much according to the expected intellectual classification levels. This study points to the need for the individual assessment of the intelligence of the cleft palate child as well as the related need to adjust the therapeutic program so that the objectives, materials, and rate of progress are realistically geared to the child's intellectual capacity.

Therapy

Surgical

The first step, if possible, is to repair the organism to the extent that it can work adequately in terms of life processes and of speech. The primary goal of the surgery is to give the patient the

---

[3] Though there were more cleft palate children in the lower intellectual classifications, the children were also represented in the upper classification.

best possible functioning of the palate and of the other parts of the oral mechanism which may be involved. A secondary purpose is cosmetic, to give the patient an appearance as nearly normal as possible. Various procedures are used to stop the nasal air lead, to close the cleft, and to lengthen and readjust the muscular tissue. At the same time the adequacy of the muscular action must be retained. There is some difference of opinion as to the best age for performing the various stages of surgery. Many present-day surgeons prefer to postpone the operation until the child is four years of age or older. They object to performing the operation too early because of interference with the normal growth of the palate and the teeth. For example, an early operation may damage the tooth buds outside of the alveolars. Usually the repair of extensive facial clefts requires a series of operations. Since surgical repair of facial clefts is a highly specialized area in medicine, most of the work is done in fairly large medical centers. Surgeons not only must make the oral cavity adequate for the present but they must also predict how future growth will be affected by the surgery.

Prosthetic Appliances

In some cases the surgeon may advise against an operation, for he may wish the child to be older or to be in better health before he operates. The surgeon may feel that the fissure is so great that the available tissue cannot cover it. He may recommend that the child go to a prosthodontist, a dental specialist, for an obturator; this is an apparatus used to take the place of the palate of the individual. It is usually made of plastic and conforms to the arch of the hard palate. An obturator for the entire palate includes a tailpiece for the soft palate and a bulb at the end around which the pharyngeal wall is constricted. The obturator must be fitted carefully. Although it must be tight, it cannot close the passage completely. The back part of the obturator and the throat are closed by the action of the muscles of the upper portion of the throat. Thus, the nasal port is shut off from the oral cavity. The aids should be light and comfortable. They are usually placed in the mouth when the child is young. The prosthodontist makes adjustments as the mouth grows. In some cases, this method of closing the palate is impossible because of the insufficiency and lack of flexibility of the remaining palatal tissues.

Cooperation of All Specialists

The treatment of the child with a facial cleft may require long and continuous cooperation and coordination of services. The speech correctionist, surgeon, orthodontist, psychologist, and prosthodontist must work together carefully and well. They must have a fairly intimate knowledge of one another's goals and their methods of achieving them. The classroom teacher must work with the specialists and understand their work.

Speech Correction

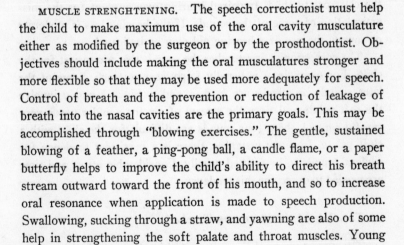

MUSCLE STRENGHTENING. The speech correctionist must help the child to make maximum use of the oral cavity musculature either as modified by the surgeon or by the prosthodontist. Objectives should include making the oral musculatures stronger and more flexible so that they may be used more adequately for speech. Control of breath and the prevention or reduction of leakage of breath into the nasal cavities are the primary goals. This may be accomplished through "blowing exercises." The gentle, sustained blowing of a feather, a ping-pong ball, a candle flame, or a paper butterfly helps to improve the child's ability to direct his breath stream outward toward the front of his mouth, and so to increase oral resonance when application is made to speech production. Swallowing, sucking through a straw, and yawning are also of some help in strengthening the soft palate and throat muscles. Young children may enjoy the interesting noise effects of blowing through the teeth of a comb against which a piece of tissue paper is fixed. A more musical result may be obtained from playing a harmonica.

IMPROVING THE VOCAL QUALITY. Careful ear training and

voice training often reduce the excessive nasality. We are not sure how excessive nasal resonance is produced, although we do know that it occurs when the opening of the nasal cavity is too large as compared with the opening of the mouth cavity. At any rate, the correctionist will strive for a satisfactory acoustic balance of nasal and oral resonance.

CORRECTING ARTICULATORY DEFECTS. Although excessive and inappropriate nasality is the primary problem of most cleft palate children, constant attention should be paid to improving articulation. Recent investigations indicate that cleft palate speakers with intelligible articulation are likely to be judged as having less nasality than do cleft speakers with poorer articulation (7).

The speech correctionist must help the cleft palate child to improve his overall articulatory efforts. Exercises should be directed at increasing the child's mobility and control of jaw, lip, and tongue movements.

In some instances a hearing loss may increase the difficulties of the cleft palate child. Impaired hearing may account for the misarticulation of some of the sounds. If the hearing loss is moderate or severe, the use of a hearing aid may be indicated.

The correctionist first teaches the sounds that are easiest for the child. For example, *h* is usually fairly easy to teach. Some of the later sounds he attacks are *k, g, s,* and *z.* Since *k* and *g* involve the soft palate and since the stream of air for *s* and *z* needs very careful control, these four sounds are difficult for the child with a cleft palate. In many instances, there is a persistent tendency for sibilant sounds to be emitted nasally. Considerable effort and time are needed to overcome this tendency.

The Role of the Classroom Teacher

The classroom teacher must unite his efforts with the correctionist. He realizes that the degree of normalcy of the child's speech will depend on the condition of the mechanism after its repair and on speech training, motivation, intelligence, and interest. At times the teacher is the liaison between the specialist and the home. He and the correctionist advise the parents that the training period for correcting the child's speech may be long and that the work will be hard. They explain to the parents how they can be of assistance to the child.

The teacher helps the child to carry over the work from the correction class into everyday speech. The teacher promotes such activities as creative dramatics in which the child may sell newspapers on the corner or popcorn at the ball game. This activity gives the child practice in the use of the acceptable speech that he is acquiring.

A child with a cleft palate must learn to adjust to his difficulty. The feeling that he has about his difficulty is often more important than the difficulty itself. The attitude of his parents and teachers influences his evaluation of the difficulty. One child with a minor cleft, and who has intelligible speech, may be anxious and concerned, while another with a serious cleft, running from the teeth ridge through to the uvula and with badly distorted speech, may be much less disturbed. The child must feel accepted as he is. When he knows that he is understood and respected, he "feels good." The teacher by accepting him as he is, by helping him succeed, can make him feel adequate. Often the teacher must work hard to help him to achieve a feeling of adequacy because of the effects of his home environment.

Parents sometimes unconsciously reject the child with a facial cleft. They may be a little ashamed of the child. In such instances the teacher's attitude is very important. If the teacher accepts the child as he is, if he promotes satisfactory activity in which the child finds enjoyment and success, the child will be helped to modify his attitudes toward himself.

Other parents are overprotective; they are unduly concerned about the child. As a result of this concern, they may be overly indulgent. The teacher, therefore, may need to compensate for the parents' oversolicitude. The teacher should not let feelings show and should not impose unnecessary limitations. The child with a facial cleft should be expected to perform according to his intellectual capacity. Allowances should be made only on the basis of hazards to health.

References and Suggested Readings

1. ANDERSON, V. A., *Improving the Child's Speech.* New York: Oxford University Press, 1952, 224-233. (Describes the speech of cleft palate children. Suggests treatment.)

2. BERRY, M., and J. EISENSON, *Speech Disorders: Principles and Practices of Therapy.* New York: Appleton-Century-Crofts, 1956, Chapter 14. (Discussion of causes, types, and procedures for overall treatment of cleft-palate children.)

3. GOODSTEIN, L. D., "Intellectual Impairment in Cleft Palate." *Journal of Speech and Hearing Research,* **IV** (September 1961), 287-294.

4. KANTNER, C. E., "Diagnosis and Prognosis in Cleft Palate Speech." *Journal of Speech and Hearing Disorders,* **XIII** (September 1948), 211-222. (Discusses the problems in the examination and diagnosis of a case of cleft palate.)

5. McDONALD, E. T., and H. KOEPP BAKER, "Cleft Palate Speech." *Journal of Speech and Hearing Disorders,* **XVI** (March 1951), 9-19. (Discusses achieving the balance between oral and nasal resonance.)

6. SCHWARTZ, R., "Familial Incidence of Cleft Palate." *Journal of Speech and Hearing Disorders,* **XIX,** 2 (June 1954), 228-238.

7. VAN HATTUM, R. J., "Articulation and Nasality in Cleft Palate Speakers." *Journal of Speech and Hearing Research,* 1 (December 1958), 383-387.

8. VAN RIPER, C., *Speech Correction: Principles and Methods.* Englewood Cliffs, N.J.: Prentice-Hall, 1954, Chapter 10. (Gives causes and incidence. Talks about effects, prosthesis, and speech therapy.)

Problems

1. Define or explain each of the following: (*a*) facial cleft, (*b*) cleft palate, (*c*) Eustachian tube, (*d*) prosthetic device, (*e*) oral surgeon.

2. What are the aspects of overall treatment necessary for most children with facial clefts?

3. Why is the voice of a child with cleft palate characteristically nasal?

4. Why is strengthening of the oral musculature important in the corrective program for a child with cleft palate?

5. Why do many children with cleft palate also have some difficulty with hearing? How does this complicate the problem of speech habilitation?

6. What is the evidence relative to articulatory intelligibility and the subjective evaluation of nasality? (Read reference 7.)

16

Brain

Damage

Cerebral Palsy

W E SHALL use the term *cerebral palsy* to mean that we are dealing with a condition believed to be associated with brain damage. If the brain damage was incurred before or during birth, the term *congenital cerebral palsy* should be used. For the most part, our discussion will be concerned with children whose cerebral palsy condition is congenital. The overall effects of brain damage may include any or all of the following:

1. Motor impairment. The term *palsy* means paralysis. Impairment of parts of the motor apparatus, including that for speech, may be present.

2. Sensory difficulties, often including impaired hearing and vision.

3. Intellectual retardation.

4. Disturbances of behavior and of personality.

5. General learning difficulty.

6. Specific difficulty in learning to speak, read, and write, and to comprehend language, spoken or written.

Figures as to the incidence of cerebral palsy vary considerably according to criteria. They tend to be high, if the individual gathering the data assumes that any of the conditions enumerated above exist, and cannot be attributed to any other cause. The incidence is lower if the investigator demands a clear-cut indication that there is evidence of brain damage. A moderate estimate is that the prevalent rate of cerebral palsy in the United States is from 300 to 350 cases per 100,000 of population. According to the 1959 report of the ASHA Committee on Legislation 0.1 percent of children in the school-age population have defective speech associated with cerebral palsy.

Types of Cerebral Palsy

We shall consider three types of cerebral palsy conditions, with the understanding that the categories are not always clear and completely distinguishable from one another. Mixed types are frequent. The categories to be listed are based on dominant rather than exclusive characteristics.

Athetoid

The chief characteristic of the athetoid is the presence of involuntary, slow, writhing movement. Specific movements may include constant turning of the head, continuous "snake-like" arm activity, and facial grimacing. If the speech apparatus is involved, we are likely to find shallow breathing, poor voice control including whispered, hoarse vocalization, and defects of articulation. In general, speech is likely to be slow and labored.

Spastic

The spastic group includes the largest number of the cerebral palsied. Although all persons diagnosed as "spastic" do not present the same symptoms, in general motor activity is characterized by jerky, labored, uneven movement. For example, when a spastic person moves his arms to reach for an object, the action is likely to be accomplished in a series of sudden jerks which suggest "cogwheel" movement rather than normal easy and evenly flowing movement.

The speech of the spastic is likely to be slow and labored. There is an absence of synergy in articulation resulting from a failure of the muscles involved in sound production to move easily with graded tension from sound to sound. The voice is characterized by poor modulation, sudden changes in pitch, and, frequently, a guttural or breathy voice quality. Perhaps most significant is that the changes that occur in voice are uncontrolled and show only a chance relationship to the meanings the spastic person is attempting to communicate.

Ataxic

The ataxic group is characterized by impairment of the sense of balance, position, and movement. In walking, the ataxic person seems to stagger or to be in constant danger of falling. If the speech musculature is involved, the ataxic is likely to evidence slurring, especially if lengthy phrases are attempted.

Disturbances Related to Cerebral Palsy

Many cerebral-palsied children have multiple handicaps usually associated with the basic brain damage. These handicaps on the physical side include epilepsy and impairments of hearing and vision. Many also show considerable mental retardation even when allowances are made for the inadequacy of the test instruments. In addition, there are often subtle disturbances in perceptual ability such as the ability to recognize and reproduce forms and appreciate spatial relationships. This impairment interferes with their learning potential and with their attempts at adjusting to their physical environment.[1] Another area of difficulty is emotional stability. Many

[1] See Cruickshank's discussion of the multiple-handicapped cerebral palsied child for an explanation of these factors (W. M. Cruickshank (ed.), *Psychology of Exceptional Children and Youth.* Englewood Cliffs, N.J.: Prentice-Hall, 1955, 334-338).

cerebral-palsied children are disturbed children. Some of the disturbances arise out of a reaction to their multiple handicaps. Others arise out of the reactions of the parents and siblings to the cerebral-palsied children and they in turn to their parents and siblings. Perhaps an even greater cause of emotional disturbance may be attributed to the frequent failures in attempts at communication so that quick and chronic frustration may become an established mode of behavior.

Intelligence and Educability

INTELLIGENCE. Until very recently, testing instruments used for estimating the intelligence of cerebral-palsied children have had severe limitations. Most tests used were initially standardized on populations that did not include a significant number of children with motor handicaps or the other handicaps often associated with cerebral palsy. Tested by such instruments, the cerebral-palsied population showed a large incidence of mental retardation. Fortunately, there are now several instruments available that require little or no verbalization and call instead for relatively gross motor actions in the test situations. Such tests enable us to make a more adequate estimate of the intelligence of the cerebral palsied. These tests include the Ammons Full Range Picture Vocabulary Test, the Revised Peabody Vocabulary Test, the Revised Columbia Mental Maturity Scale, and Raven's Progressive Matrices. The results obtained from surveys employing these tests suggest that there is probably less mental retardation among the cerebral palisied than was earlier reported. There is little question, however, that the incidence of mental retardation is considerably greater among the cerebral palsied than among the population at large. Percentages as to the amount of mental retardation range from 25 percent to more than 50 percent.

While becoming aware of the intellectual limitations of many of the cerebral palsied, we should not overlook the important fact that intellectual genius is also present in this physically handicapped group. Taken as a whole, all levels of intellectual capacity are represented among the cerebral palsied as they are among the population at large.

EDUCABILITY. Because many cerebral-palsied children have multiple handicaps, including mental retardation, a large percentage of the children have been classified as uneducable. Many are "trained" in resident institutions rather than in schools. Of late, increasing numbers of cerebral-palsied children are being educated in special classes in regular public schools. Private schools specializing in the treatment of the handicapped are also accepting the cerebral palsied and giving them the benefit of improved understanding and teaching techniques. A majority of cerebral-palsied children have sufficient intellectual capacity for education along with the nonhandicapped in the normal classroom situation. Many of these children, however, will require special attention from the speech correctionist as well as understanding from the classroom teacher.

Therapy for the Cerebral Palsied

The Cerebral Palsy Team

For children with more than minimum or residual cerebral palsy, a program of training calls for the cooperation of a team of professional specialists. Included in the team are the physician, the psychologist, the social worker, the physical therapist, the occupational therapist, the teacher, and the speech correctionist.

The physician or physicians must estimate to what extent the child's neurological involvements may affect his learning. Frequently an orthopedic surgeon is called upon for recommendations as to how classroom equipment or home furnishings are to be constructed or adapted to the child's needs. The orthopedic surgeon's advice is also needed in matters relating to the improvement of motor abilities and the prevention of physical disabilities.

The physical therapist, working with the physician, strives to improve the child's performance in coordination and motor activity. Specific therapeutic measures may be employed which may help the child to learn how to control his speech musculature so that a proper degree of relaxation and synergy of movement is achieved. Such therapy prepares the cerebral-palsied child for the work of the speech therapist.

The occupational therapist functions as an observer of the child's motor activity and trains the child specifically in "occupational" skills. Essentially, the occupational therapist supplements the work of the physical therapist.

The psychologist, through testing and observation, makes an appraisal of the intellectual capacities and the present and potential abilities as well as the disabilities and limitations of the cerebral-palsied child. Recommendations as to the child's educability and type of education are made by the psychologist. Periodic reappraisals are made so that objectives and goals may be changed according to the manner and rate of the child's development.

The social worker investigates the home situation of the cerebral-palsied child. He obtains information about the child's home and the attitudes of the parents and other key members in the household. In addition, the social worker helps to adjust the members of the family to their problem in relationship to the child and in the interest of the child.

The speech therapist evaluates the child's speech problems and trains him to improve his communicative skills. Speech disabilities are found in 50 to 75 percent of the cerebral-palsied children. Some of the disabilities can be considerably improved; others can be modified only slightly. Realistic goals must be established that are consistent with the child's sensory and motor abilities and intellectual capacity. Progress, it must be recognized, is often slow and amounts of improvement are not likely to be discerned on a day-to-day basis.

Speech Therapy

Specific speech therapy for the cerebral-palsied child with speech disabilities must be adapted to the child in terms of his involvements. If a child has a hearing loss, speech sounds must be intensified. This can be accomplished through the using of a speaking tube or through the use of amplification and headset ear phones. For many cerebral-palsied children, an overall program would include the following:

1. Relaxation and voluntary control of the speech musculature. Often much of this work has been accomplished through the training given by the physiotherapist.

2. The establishment of breath control for vocalization and articulation. Many cerebral-palsied children breathe too deeply or too shallowly for purposes of speech. Frequently children attempt to speak on inhaled breath. For most cerebral-palsied children, a normal length of phrase is not to be expected. Short, uninterrupted phrasing is a more modest and more possible achievement. Devices such as blowing through a straw, the "bending" of a candle flame, and the moving of ping-pong balls on flat surfaces and up inclined planes are helpful in establishing breath control.

3. Control of the organs of articulation. Considerable exercise is needed to establish directed and independent action of the tongue and to overcome the frequently present tendency of the cerebral-palsied child to move his jaw as he attempts to move his tongue. Children enjoy such exercises as licking honey from their lips, or reaching for a bit of honey or peanut butter placed on the upper gum ridge. A lollipop held outside the mouth for licking provides a sweet objective for the tip of the tongue. The child should be shown what he does by observing himself and the speech therapist in a mirror.

4. Work on individual speech sounds. The sounds most frequently defective are those that require precise tip of the tongue action. These include *t, d, l, n, r, s,* and *z.* Intense auditory stimulation, even if the child has no significant hearing loss, often helps him to become aware of what he is expected to produce. Sound play, calling for repetition of sounds the child can produce, may give him a feeling of accomplishment in the early stages of speech training. For many children normal proficiency of articulation may

not be expected. The production of "reasonable facsimiles" of sounds so that speech, though defective, is intelligible, is frequently all that we have a right to expect.

5. Incorporation of sounds in words and phrases. Many cerebral-palsied children have considerable difficulty in making the transition from the production of individual sounds to connected speech. Abrupt stops are frequent, especially when words include stop plosive sounds or others that call for rapid articulatory action. The child should be encouraged to keep his sounds moving, to keep his articulation in action, even if there is a resultant lack of precision in the effort as a whole. Articulation must, of course, be coordinated with breathing and vocalization.

The Classroom Teacher's Responsibility for the Cerebral-Palsied Child

Because the cerebral-palsied child may look different, because frequently he is unable to participate in many of the activities of other children, because his family may have been oversolicitous, or may have unconsciously rejected him, he is apt to have difficulty in adjusting to a group. When the teacher accepts his infirmity, is casual about it, but still demands from him standards within his reach and performance within his capabilities, the teacher is doing the child a real service. If the teacher does not let his sympathy show but accepts the child in a friendly fashion with cheerful affection, the child's adjustment is made easier. The child should participate in such regular classroom activities as going on visits. The teacher should consider the cerebral-palsied child just another member of the group who enjoys and likes living with his classmates, and should provide new experiences that give adequate scope for his abilities and energies.

Cerebral-palsied children speak better when relaxed. They do better when they have confidence in themselves and their abilities. As they are anxious or frustrated, they have more difficulty with their speech. When the teacher can help the child to feel that he is making a contribution to group living and that he is accepting, and carrying through responsibilities for successful group living, he is assisted in attaining a feeling of belongingness with his classmates and a feeling of security in this particular environment. The teacher gives him frequent opportunities to relax. At times the teacher or children may make things easy for him physically; for example, his seat may be moved to a particular spot that is more readily accessible for the current activity. Whatever is done should be done in as casual a manner as possible so that no attention is attracted to the activity and the cerebral-palsied child will be able to feel comfortable rather than self-conscious.

Brain Damage Without Apparent Motor Involvement

Many brain-damaged children are not obviously cerebral palsied. Some have such minor motor involvements that they are not suspected of having incurred brain damage until they are of an age when language comprehension and the acquisition of speech is expected. These children, as we indicated earlier, are often problems and puzzles to themselves, their families, and their teachers. The reasons for this perplexing state of affairs should become clear in the discussion that follows.

Dyslogia and Brain Damage

Children who are born with brain damage because of a prenatal condition, or who have incurred brain damage as a result of birth injury or a cerebral pathology before the age at which speech usually begins, are frequently severely retarded in their speech onset and development. Often, even after these children begin to speak, articulation, voice, and vocabulary development are impaired. In very severe cases, usually associated with damage to both hemispheres of the brain, even the comprehension of language may be severely and sometimes completely impaired. It is likely that most of these children who do learn to understand speech also suffer from an appreciable degree of mental deficiency, and others from hearing loss with or without mental deficiency. Our own experience with brain-damaged children leads us to believe that, where hearing loss and mental deficiency are not complicating factors, language learning may be delayed but is usually established by age four or five. In most cases where hearing and intelligence are relatively normal, language is learned and speech, however defective, is usually established by the time the child has reached school age.

The brain-damaged child who fails to develop language is often referred to as aphasic—without speech. The terms *aphasia* and *aphasic* however have meanings that vary considerably with the use and concepts of individual authorities. We prefer, therefore, to refer to the brain-damaged nonspeaking child as *dyslogic* (without words). Following are some critical differences that differentiate the *dyslogic child* from his speaking as well as nonspeaking peers.

1. The dyslogic child has perceptual difficulties related to one or more modalities. He may have difficulty in discriminating visual or auditory patterns even when such patterns are not associated with spoken or written language symbols.

2. The dyslogic child is often slow in developing laterality. At the age of five or even later he may not have established a preferred hand or foot. Associated with this developmental lag is often confusion in directional and spatial orientation.

3. Inconsistency of response is almost a universal characteristic of the dyslogic child. A response made to a situation on one occasion may not be made on a succeeding occasion. A response which may be completely appropriate when first made may simply fail to be made on successive occasions.

4. Morbidity of attention is associated with inconsistency of response. Occasionally the dyslogic child may become completely absorbed with the situation to which he is attending, so that he cannot shift his attention to new situations despite the intensity of a new stimulus. Thus, loud noises may be ignored, or at least are not immediately able to compete for attention with what is already concerning the child.

In contrast with this compulsive and persistent manner of attending to a situation, the dyslogic child may sometimes have such fleeting attention as to seem to be reacting to everything, and adequately to nothing.

5. Associated with inconsistency of response and morbidity of attention is lability of general behavior. The dyslogic child may behave excessively and exhibit uncontrolled emotionality because of seemingly trivial disturbances. If the child is disturbed at all, he is disturbed a great deal. Along with emotional lability there is accompanying hyperactivity. The child may suddenly change from being relatively docile to being active beyond easy control.

6. A characteristic feature of the language development of the dyslogic child, aside from the initial retardation, is uneveness of ability. Even after this child begins to use language, he does not show the expected increments or the "ordered" pattern by which most children increase their linguistic abilities for day-to-day communication. Many dyslogic children learn to say a few words at intervals far apart, but may during these periods have a normal or better than normal increase in their comprehension vocabularies. They may show parallel disparities in learning to read and write. The result may be that even after the children are in the mid-primary grades, their educational achievements are so uneven as to cause considerable concern to their teachers, their parents, and to themselves. They are often painfully slow in achieving an integrated pattern of development with those features which go together and which are ordinarily found together.

The features we considered of the brain-damaged, dyslogic child may be understood in terms of the reduced efficiency of their neurological mechanisms. The overall effects of the cerebral damage is to aggravate any sensory impairments and to minimize their intellectual potential. Functionally, these children do not hear as well as audiometric results would suggest they should be able to hear. Otherwise stated, they do not hear as proficiently as nonbrain-damaged children do with the same amount of "objectively measured" hearing. Similarly, and more generally, they often function considerably below the upper limits of their mental potential. They disturb easily, and have very good cause for such reactions.

The *clinical assessment* of the brain-damaged dyslogic child should be made only by highly competent specialists. This child is not easy to diagnose into a clear-cut category. He often responds or fails to respond in the manner of a deaf child. Sometimes he seems to respond with the slowness and limited understanding of a severely mentally retarded child. Often he behaves as if he were emotionally disturbed. It is essential, therefore, that a team of clinicians, including a physician and, if possible, a neurologist, an audiologist, and psychologist, make the assessment. It may well be that a given child may have brain damage and hearing loss, and his general lability may be a reaction to his own impairments. Even when language learning is proceeding, he, as well as his teachers and parents, may be responding to his uneven abilities with repeated frustration.

Therapeutic approaches for the speech impairments of the preschool dyslogic child are the province of the speech clinician. Other aspects of his training should be for the clinical specialist. If the child has made sufficient progress to be attending grade school, he requires the additional therapy that is a product of understanding and patience. The classroom teacher may help the child to work to his maximum level of ability by motivation that is timed to the child's periods of best effort. The dyslogic child, more than most, needs encouragement, because he is never quite certain what he may expect of himself. In the absence of severe sensory or motor disability, many, if not most, dyslogic children may be helped to achieve at least a normal level of overall proficiency. Care must be exercised that the child not be pushed too hard, or urged too soon, as he begins to acquire language and behave in a world of linguistic symbols. With good timing, and with an educational schedule geared to awareness of his labile inclinations and his intellectual limitations, demands and abilities can be equalized so that proficiencies may develop despite early unevenness in developmental patterns.

References and Suggested Readings

Brain Damage

1. ALTMAN, I., "On the Prevalence of Cerebral Palsy." *Cerebral Palsy Review,* **XVI**; 4 (December 1955), 25.

2. BANGS, T., "Evaluating Children with Language Delay." *Journal of Speech and Hearing Disorders,* **XXVI**; 1 (1961), 6-18.

3. BERRY, M., and J. EISENSON, *Speech Disorders: Principles and Practices of Therapy.* New York: Appleton-Century-Crofts, 1956, Chapters 15-18.

4. CROTHERS, B., and R. S. PAINE, *The Natural History of Cerebral Palsy.* Cambridge: Harvard University Press, 1959. (A review of 1,800 cases of cerebral palsy.)

5. CRUICKSHANK, W. M., and G. M. RAUS, *Cerebral Palsy: Its Individual and Community Problems.* Syracuse: Syracuse University Press, 1955.

6. CRUICKSHANK, W. M., F. A. BENTZEN, F. H. RATZEBURG, and M. T. TANNHAUSER, *A Teaching Method for Brain-Injured and Hyper-Active Children.* Syracuse: Syracuse University Press, 1961. (A discussion in depth of the educational implications of a pilot study with hyperactive brain-damaged children.)

7. DeHIRSCH, K., "Studies in Tachyphemia. IV, Diagnosis of Developmental Language Disorders." *Logos,* **IV**; 1 (1961), 3-9.

8. EISENSON, J., *Examining for Aphasia.* New York: Psychological Corporation, 1954, Chapter 4.

9. KASTEIN, S., and E. P. FOWLER, JR., "Differential Diagnosis of Communication Disorders in Children Referred for Hearing Tests." *American Medical Association Archives of Otolaryngology,* **LX** (1954), 468-477.

10. KIRK, S. A., and J. J. McCARTHY, *The Illinois Test of Psycholinguistic Abilities: An Approach to Differential Diagnosis.* Urbana: University of Illinois, 1961. (As the title indicates, this is a test inventory for diagnosing children with severe delays in one or more aspects of language ability.)

11. MYKLEBUST, H. R., "Aphasia in Children." In TRAVIS, L. E. (ed.), *Speech Pathology.* New York: Appleton-Century-Crofts, 1957, Chapter 16.

12. RUTHERFORD, B., *Give Them a Chance to Talk*. Minneapolis: Burgess Publishing Co., 1948.

13. STRAUSS, A. A., and W. C. KEPHART, *Psychopathology and Education of the Brain-Injured Child*, Vol. II. New York: Grune and Stratton, 1955. (An expanded exposition of differential diagnosis and treatment of brain-injured children.)

14. STROTHER, C., "Realistic Education: Goals for the Cerebral Palsied Child." *Crippled Child*, **XXX** (April 1953), 1-7.

15. TAYLOR, E. M., *Psychological Appraisal of Children with Cerebral Defects*. Cambridge: Harvard University Press, 1959. (A survey of causes, types, and procedures for assessment of the intellectual deficits frequently associated with cerebral palsy.)

16. WESTLAKE, H., and D. RUTHERFORD, *Speech Therapy for the Cerebral Palsied*. National Society for Crippled Children and Adults, 1961. (A clear and illustrated exposition of the problems of assessment and therapy for the speech habilitation of cerebral-palsied children.)

Cerebral Palsy

The following references are for nontechnical materials written so that they may be readily understood by the parents of cerebral-palsied children. They supply information as to what the parents and others in close contact with the cerebral palsied should know and what they can do to help them.

1. GRATKE, J. M., "Help them Help Themselves." Dallas, Tex.: Society for Crippled Children, 1947.

2. HUBER, M., "Letter to the Parents of the Cerebral Palsied Child." *Journal of Speech and Hearing Disorders*, **XV** (June 1950), 154-158.

3. PERLSTEIN, M., *Cerebral Palsy*. National Society for Crippled Children and Adults, 1961. (A booklet in the *Parent Series* in which a medical authority on cerebral palsy answers questions parents might ask about their children.)

4. PHELPS, W. M., "Cerebral Palsy." The Lederle Laboratories (August 1947).

5. STERN, E. M., "Cerebral Palsy." *Woman's Home Companion* (September 1947).

6. United Cerebral Palsy Society, "Seven Essentials in Educational

Planning for Children with Cerebral Palsy." The Society Program Division, Bulletin 2 (February 1955).

7. WEST, J. S., *Congenital Malformations and Birth Injuries*. New York: Association for the Aid of Crippled Children.

8. WISHIK, S., *How to Help Your Handicapped Child*. New York: Public Affairs Committee, Public Affairs Pamphlet No. 219.

9. YAHRAES, H., *Games for Handicapped Children*. New York: Public Affairs Committee, Public Affairs Pamphlet No. 212.

Problems

1. Children now referred to as being *cerebral palsied* were once generally referred to as *spastics*. Why is the term *cerebral palsied* more appropriate than spastic?

2. What are characteristics of the chief types of cerebal palsy conditions?

3. Why are many cerebral-palsied children multiply handicapped? What are the most frequent types of handicaps?

4. Why is it difficult to be certain about the intellectual assessments of cerebral-palsied children?

5. Is it reasonable to believe that all cerebral-palsied children can achieve normal speech? Justify your answer.

6. Can a cerebral palsy condition be acquired by an adult? Justify your answer.

7. What is *dyslogia?* What objections are there to the term *aphasia* when applied to children?

8. What does the term *lability* signify when applied to the brain-damaged child?

9. What does *perceptual dysfunction* imply?

10. Compare the obviously cerebral-palsied child with the dyslogic child. What are the basic similarities? What are the essential differences?

Appendix

AFTER viewing films and listening to recordings in the areas of speech standards, the speech mechanism, and speech defects, we selected a number which we believe are appropriate for an introductory course in speech correction. Our selection in the area of speech defects is limited to materials which involve children and which emphasize speech difficulties found fairly frequently in the school population. Doubtless, there are other excellent films which we have not viewed and which deserve inclusion in an extended list. We believe, however, that our selections are representative of films suitable for students who are taking their first course in speech correction.

Standards of Speech

BETTER DICTION ANYONE? 28 min. 33⅓. Baylor University Book Store, Waco, Texas. (Contains drill material for improving speech—particularly in the Southwest area.)

COMMUNICATING EFFECTIVELY: ARTICULATION AND PRONUNCIATION. Kinescope. 30 min. black and white. Office of Visual Instruction, Extension Division, State University of Iowa, Iowa City, Iowa. (Makes listener aware of articulation and pronunciation errors. Includes examples of inability to produce sounds, substitution, distortion, and omission of sounds.)

DIALECTS. 30 min. black and white. Indiana University (National Educational Television) Audio-Visual Center, Indiana University, Bloomington, Ind. (Explains and demonstrates dialectal differences in standard American English.)

Consonant and Vowel Sounds

ARTICULATORY MOVEMENTS IN THE PRODUCTION OF ENGLISH SPEECH SOUNDS. 22 min. Color. United World Films, 1445 Park Avenue, New York 29, N. Y. (Illustrates the production of consonant speech sounds through animated drawings and the production of vowels through photography.)

THE SOUNDS OF LANGUAGE. 30 min. black and white. Indiana University (National Educational Television) Audio-Visual Center, Indiana University, Bloomington, Ind. (Analyzes and classifies significant sounds of language.)

Anatomy and Physiology

ADVENTURE AND HEARING. 25 min. black and white. Sonotone Corporation, Elmsford, New York. (Shows how the ear functions, how a hearing aid helps, and how an audiometer works.)

EARS AND HEARING. 16 min. black and white. Encyclopedia Britannica Films, 202 East 44th Street, New York City. (Through animated drawings and photography shows the physiology of the ear. Cites causes of impaired hearing.)

EXAMINING THE ORAL MECHANISM. 25 min. Color. State University of Iowa, Bureau of Audio-Visual Instruction, Extension Division, Iowa City, Iowa. (Shows the parts of the speaking mechanism—lips, teeth, jaw, tongue, hard palate, and velum, and the deviations which may occur in these parts.)

FUNCTIONAL STUDY OF THE TONGUE AND THE

VELO-PHARYNGEAL MUSCULATURE. 8 min. Color. University of Minnesota, Audio-Visual Extension Service, Minneapolis, Minn. (Shows the velo-pharyngeal closure and the action of the tongue.)

HOW THE RESPIRATORY SYSTEM FUNCTIONS. 11 min. black and white. Bray Studios, 729 Seventh Avenue, New York, N. Y. (Explains the mechanism of breathing and its functions.)

HOW WE HEAR. 16 min. black and white. Silent. Bray Studios, 729 Seventh Avenue, New York, N. Y. (Tells about the outer, middle, and inner ear. Shows how sound waves reach the brain.)

LARYNX AND VOICE. Part 1. FUNCTION OF THE NORMAL LARYNX. 21 min. black and white or color. Institute of Laryngology and Voice Disorders, 159 E. Chicago Ave., Chicago 11, Ill. (Gives details of vocal cord vibration in normal and in slow speed.)

LARYNX AND VOICE. Part II. PHYSIOLOGY OF THE LARYNX UNDER DAILY STRESS. 23 min. black and white. William and Harriet Gould Foundation, 39 S. LaSalle Street, Chicago 90, Ill. (Shows various types of functions of the larynx.)

THE NOSE—STRUCTURE AND FUNCTION. 11 min. black and white or color. Encyclopedia Britannica Films, Wilmette, Ill. (Gives physiology of nasal cavity and its functions.)

RESPIRATION. 12 min. black and white. United World Films, 1445 Park Avenue, New York 29, N. Y. (Shows the movement of the diaphragm and chest in breathing. Demonstrates the complete cycle of respiration.)

YOUR CHILDREN'S EARS. 15 min. black and white. British Information Service, 30 Rockefeller Plaza, New York, N. Y. (Explains the structure of the ear.)

Types of Speech Defects

INTRODUCTION OF SPEECH PROBLEMS by F. L. Darley and C. VanRiper. 20 min. Color. (Presents 12 individuals with problems of speech—sound mastery, stuttering, cleft palate, speech retardation, aphasia, dysarthria.)

SPEECH DISORDERS: PHYSICAL HANDICAPS. 29 min. black and white. Syracuse University (National Educational Television) Net Film Service, Audio-Visual Center, Indiana University, Bloomington, Ind. (Notes the various kinds of speech handicaps and their causes. Shows the need for cooperation by parents, school, and community.)

A SURVEY OF CHILDREN'S SPEECH DISORDERS. 29 min. Color. Bureau of Audio-Visual Instruction, State University of Iowa, Iowa City, Iowa. (Explains the processes of oral communication. Identifies communication problems of hearing, cleft palate, cerebral palsy, articulation, and stuttering.)

THESE UNTRAINED TONGUES. Three filmstrips. University of Denver, Denver, Colo. (Gives the nature of speech defects, how they develop, and what speech clinics do to help.)

Articulation—Auditory and Sound Discrimination

THE DOWNTOWN STORY by Helen Gene Purdy. 10 in. 33⅓. Folkway Records and Service Company, 117 West 46th Street, New York 36, N. Y. Number FC70-70. (Designed to train auditory perception of the young child. Contains sound effects of the department store and supermarket.)

FILM STRIPS FOR PRACTICE IN PHONETIC SKILLS. Black and white. Scott, Foresman and Co., Chicago, Ill. (Gives practice in auditory perception of rhyme and of consonants.)

LET'S LISTEN. M. Marie Bresnahan and Wilbert L. Pronovost. Three records. Ginn and Company, Boston, Mass., 1955. (Provides for auditory stimulation, auditory discrimination, vocabulary development, speech practice and enrichment. Includes speaking and listening activities to develop speech sound awareness, correct sounds, and a desire for speech improvement.)

THE SPEECH INITIATION BABBLE RECORD. Children's Music Center, 2858 W. Pico Boulevard, Los Angeles 6, Calif. (Presents beginning speech sounds through simple rhythmic songs. Follows normal developmental sequence of sounds. Using familiar situations, provides stimulation of early speech development.)

SOUNDS AROUND US. 78 rpm. 3 records. Scott, Foresman and Co., Chicago, Ill. (Includes sounds of the house, the farm, and the town. Used to help teach children to listen and to discriminate between meaningful sounds.)

Voice

A STUDY OF VOCAL CORD ABNORMALITIES. 14 min. Color. Audio-Visual Educational Service, Westbrook Hall, University of Minnesota, Minneapolis, Minn.

Stuttering

SPEECH DISORDERS: STUTTERING. 29 min. black and white. (National Educational Television) Syracuse University Net Film Service, Audio-Visual Center, Indiana University, Bloomington, Ind. (Depicts the problems faced by the child who stutters. Suggests causes of stuttering, problems of the stutterer. Gives goals of therapy.)

SPEECH OF STUTTERERS BEFORE AND AFTER TREATMENT. 30 min. black and white. Audio-Visual Educational Service, Westbrook Hall, University of Minnesota, Minneapolis, Minn. (Presents a group of stutterers over an eight-year period.)

Organic Speech Difficulties

CLEFT PALATE. CHILDREN WITH CLEFT PALATES. 20 min. black and white. Audio-Visual Center, University of Michigan, Ann Arbor, Mich. (Outlines program of speech development for children with cleft palate.)

THE UNMASKED PALATAL CLEFT. 20 min. Color. Newington Hospital for Crippled Children, Newington, Conn. (Contrasts the physical structures and speech of a child with normal palatal structure and two with undetected submucous clefts.)

THE WISCONSIN CLEFT PALATE STORY. 30 min. black and white. Bureau of Visual Instruction, University of Wisconsin, Madison, Wis. (Shows the team approach to rehabilitation of child with cleft palate.)

CEREBRAL PALSY. OUT OF THE SHADOWS. 20 min. black and white. Audio-Visual Department, University of Southern California, Los Angeles, Calif. (Shows diagnosis and treatment of the cerebral palsied.)

Hearing Problems

BASIC AUDIOMETRIC TESTING. 30 min. black and white. Bureau of Audio-Visual Instruction, University of Wisconsin, Madison, Wis. (Demonstrates the administration of basic audiometric tests—pure tone air conduction, pure tone bone conduction, spondee, and PB.)

LISTENING EYES. 19 min. Color. John Tracy Clinic, 937 West 37th Street, Los Angeles, California. (Explains the facilities and work with pre-school deaf children and their parents.)

PAY ATTENTION. 30 min. Child Study Department, Vassar, Poughkeepsie, New York. (Gives the educational and personality problems faced by the child who is hard-of-hearing but not deaf. Shows treatment from pre-school through high school.)

THE RIGHT TO HEAR. 33 min. Color. Bureau of Visual Instruction, Extension Division, State University of Iowa, Iowa City, Iowa. (Explains the need for the conservation of hearing. Shows public school hearing testing procedures and the follow-up for those children who need help.)

THAT THE DEAF MAY SPEAK. 42 min. Black and white or color. Ideal Pictures Corporation, 58 East South Water Street, Chicago 15, Ill. (Explains how the deaf learn to handle language at the Lexington School for the Deaf. Shows preschool training, elementary and high school training, and young adulthood of a deaf girl.)

Index

Subject Index

Abdominal cavity, 82
Acceptable speech, 41-42
Acquisition of sounds, norms for, 179
American College Dictionary, 52, 53
American-English speech sounds, 90-102
The American Language, 62
American Pronunciation, 62
Ammons Full Range Picture Vocabulary Test, 365
Anatomy and Physiology of Speech, 86
And So We Speak: Voice and Articulation, 61
Anxiety reaction and stuttering, 312
Articulation, 88-102
    defects of, *see* Articulatory difficulties.
    manner of, 94-95
    place of, 95-96
    testing for errors, 181-188
        in final position, 181
        in initial position, 181
        in medial position, 181
        through pictures, 182
        sentences for, 187-188
        story for, 185-186
        words for, 182-184
    tests of, 208
Articulatory activity and vocal disturbances, 289-290
Articulatory difficulties, 172-267
    categories of, 173-175
        distortion of sounds, 175
        omission of sounds, 175
        substitution of sounds, 173-175
    causes of, 210-212
    correction of, 215-250
        in everyday speech, 247-248
        in games, 245
        recognition of error in, 216-221

Articulatory difficulties, correction of
    —Continued
    teaching acceptable sound in, 221-225
    in words, 225-247
    definition of, 4-6, 172-175
    diagnosis of, 172-198
    difficulties related to, 176-177
    factors associated with, 189-198
        auditory discrimination, 196-197
        auditory memory, 196-197
        emotional difficulty, 190-191
        faulty learning, 197-198
        hearing loss, 190
        intelligence, 189-190
        motor ability, 195-196
        structural abnormalities, 192-195
        tongue thrust, 194
    history of child with, 250-260
    and maturation, 177-180
    and parental help, 248-251
    and prognosis for improvement, 179-180
    and referral for therapy, 178-179
    and relationship to language ability, 201
    and relationship to reading and spelling disabilities, 198-201
    severity of, 175-176
    and the teacher, 180
    testing for, 180-194
        by correctionist, 189
        interpretation of, 212-214
    treatment of, 210-260
        finding the cause, 210-212
        interpreting test, 212-214
        motivation for correction in, 214-215
        steps in correction of, 215-248
Articulatory pantomiming, 330-331
Arytenoid cartilage, 80-81

Author Index